MAN
WHO - WHENCE - WHITHER

MAN

WHO-WHENCE-WHITHER

A LAYMAN'S ATTEMPT AT A
LOGICAL SYNTHESIS

by

Victor E. Larson

PHILOSOPHICAL LIBRARY, INC.

New York

In Grateful Memory of
MY PARENTS
and
TO MY WIFE

The question of questions to mankind—the problem which underlies all others, and is more deeply interesting than any other—is the ascertainment of the place which man occupies in nature, and of his relations to the universe of things.

Thomas Henry Huxley (1825-1895)

CONTENTS

PREFACE

The majority of thoughtful men today will undoubtedly agree that the world is in a dangerous state of confusion and chaos, and this amid the spectre of the atomic bomb. The individual man is seriously beginning to doubt whether existence has any substantial significance for him. The platitudes of religious leaders no longer have any life or conviction in them for him. One reason for this is that he has seen no signs of integration between the theories of science, the systems of philosophy, and the dogmas of the various religions, all of which reflect certain aspects of truth.

This state cannot be charged to the lack of activity on the part of the logical analysts, for they are working energetically in all fields—in science, in philosophy, and in religious criticism.

It appears that what may be needed today is a serious attempt at a logical synthesis of the principal phenomena of nature, for if we admit a futility of attempting such a synthesis, we concede causal chaos. If a qualified scientist, philosopher, or theologian were to attempt such a synthesis, he would undoubtedly jeopardize his professional standing among his colleagues. So it appears that if such a synthesis is to be attempted it must come from the ranks of laymen with no professional standing at stake.

The author has been a consistently curious observer of the various phenomena of nature regardless of their source. Furthermore, he has brought with him into the task not only an active imagination but a faith in an inherent rationality of nature and its laws, and in the universal coherence of all observed phenomena. With this faith he could come to only one logical conclusion—the world must be the creation of but one mind, an obvious bias which comes out repeatedly in the development of his thesis.

For the initial natural history portions of the attempt to find a solution to the problem, the author has of course relied on various sources for data. For the synthesis itself, however, the author alone assumes responsibility.

It is hoped that this initial attempt at a logical synthesis will lead to contributions of others with differing biases. Such contributions should enable some fascinating and fruitfully enlightening comparisons.

One gets the impression that the best minds of this world are currently allergic to logical syntheses. It is felt that this allergy should be brought under control for mankind's future welfare.

V. E. L.

MAN
WHO - WHENCE - WHITHER

INTRODUCTION

STATEMENT OF THE PROBLEM
AND
PROPOSED STEPS IN ITS ATTEMPTED SOLUTION

There is a story of a railroad man and his function which we shall take the privilege of repeating. It appears that an occasional traveler on a Boston-New York Express had his curiosity aroused in observing a railroad worker at the New Haven Station walk along the platform tapping with a hammer the wheels of the express coaches. Finally the traveler determined to find out what it was all about; so on the next trip he went out on the platform and asked the railroad man why he did it. The railroad man simply responded, "It's my job." "I appreciate it must be your job, but why do you tap the wheels with your hammer?" He shrugged his shoulders and simply answered, "I don't know," and continued with his work.

Now we will no doubt superiorly remark, "How can a man be that stupid?" First, in fairness to the railroad man, our guess would be that he left an interesting pinochle game to report on a cold night for his night shift, and that his reply to the questioner was just his polite form of saying, "Why don't you mind your own business!"

Here is another incident—this one apparently true, for it was related by Dr. S. Parkes Cadman, a Congregationalist minister in Brooklyn, New York, during the twenties. He possessed an encyclopaedic memory and was a popular question-and-answer man during that period, running a column in a daily newspaper. He told of being awakened one night by the persistent ringing of the front-door bell. He put on his robe and hurried to open the door, to be confronted by a man who ap-

1

peared to have some difficulty in maintaining his equilibrium. "Are you Dr. Cadman?" "Yes, I am Dr. Cadman." "Are you the one who answers all kinds of questions?" "Well, I try to answer some questions." "Okay—what is the difference between modernism and fundamentalism?" "My dear man, you are intoxicated—if you will go home and sober up and return tomorrow, I shall be very glad to try to answer your question."—"When I'm 'shober' I don't give-a-damn."

But can a man be that stupid or indifferent? When we stop to consider how a man may spend his "three-score-and-ten-years" in aimless meandering on the surface of this planet, daily eating, working, sleeping, and "rootin and tootin" around, without having any idea why he is existing, many times not even being curious enough to raise the question—let alone trying to find a reasonable answer to it, then one must reluctantly conclude that it is really possible for a man to be that stupid or indifferent.

Many so-called "intellectuals" or the "tough-minded" will dogmatically assert that the anticipated 70-year period of existence of the individual man on this planet is absolutely meaningless—that he is simply a puppet of chance traveling down a "dead-end street." Others, the simple or "tenderminded" so-called, will assert, timidly perhaps, that there must be something beyond this life to give it meaning and that we do bear responsibility for our actions.

That the final surveys and conclusions of two such serious and brilliant researchers as Charles Darwin and Alfred R. Wallace for an explanation of the mysteries of life should prove so utterly demoralizing to man's conception of his own significance in the universe is indeed ironical. This demoralization was further aggravated by the supporting observations of the geologists of fossilized remains of organisms in various rock strata separated by vast periods of geological time.

Surprising as it may seem to some, Wallace was actually the first discoverer of the principle of natural selection. The concept "natural selection" itself, however, was of Darwin's coinage; and the principle too was independently arrived at by Darwin; Wallace, an amiable person, with rare self-abnegation made no claim for the discovery of the principle of natural selection, and Darwin and he remained good friends for life. Even so, they differed in one important respect; Wallace disagreed with Darwin that man's moral and spiritual nature, like his physical being, had been evolved by a natural process. Darwin's earlier publication of his Origin of Species, however, resulted in the views of Wallace being more or less ignored and forgotten. Otherwise Wallace's thoughts on the psychic nature of man would have shed a ray of light and hope in the direction of man's real significance, producing thereby a more hopeful picture.

Be that as it may, Charles Darwin is quoted as having said, "How odd it is that anyone should not see that all observation must be for or against some view if it is to be of any service." The wisdom of Darwin's remark leads us to formulate briefly our problem, the importance of which Thomas Henry Huxley expresses in the following words: "The question of questions to mankind—the problem which underlies all others, and is more deeply interesting than any other—is the ascertainment of the place which man occupies in nature, and of his relations to the universe of things." This problem we shall condense and state in the following form:

WHAT MEANINGFUL SIGNIFICANCE, IF ANY, DOES EXISTENCE HAVE FOR MAN?

In short, we must determine whether man is related to the infinite or to nothing.

As recently as 1952, the late Dag Hammarskjöld made the following entry in his diary:

What I ask for is absurd: that life shall have a meaning.—
What I strive for is impossible: that life shall acquire a meaning.
I dare not believe, I do not see how I shall ever be able to believe that I am not alone.

To the lonely man who echoes these sentiments, do not despair, but join us in the search for meaning. It may be that we shall discover a factual basis for hope—a hope not only that our life possesses meaning, but moreover that we are not alone.

The task imposed by the problem is obviously a most ambitious one, but the attempt itself at its solution should prove interesting to say the least even if not especially fruitful. So, let us proceed as "innocents abroad," but first venture a brief outline of our proposed "itinerary":

PART ONE—An analysis of man as a personality—the initial formulator of the problem;

PART TWO—A review of man's progressive attempts at ascribing meanings to natural phenomena—both by philosophers and scientists, including the present-day hypotheses of mathematical physicists, astronomers, and biologists, as to the origin of the universe and the evolutionary background leading up to man;

PART THREE—A review of the various current religions of man, which reflect the source of his overall value-determining beliefs;

PART FOUR—Summations and certain abstractions, interpretations, and conclusions drawn from our total data, followed by a concise answer to the problem based upon such data.

PART ONE

WHO IS MAN?

I.

CERTAIN ILLUSTRATIVE DEFINITIONS

So God created man in his own image, in the image of God created he him; male and female created he them. (Gen. 1:27)

What is man, that thou art mindful of him? and the son of man, that thou visitest him? For thou hast made him a little lower than the angels, and hast crowned him with glory and honor. Thou madest him to have dominion over the works of thy hands; thou hast put all things under his feet. (Psa. 8:4-6)

Oh come down to earth, you plead. Very well, the following definition of man may be considered a composite of the inductive reasoning by physicists, biologists, and social scientists:

Man is an organic bipolar entity who in his strategic midway position twixt an atom and a star has learned to study one in the light of the other.

He is considered by himself to be on the lead branch of the evolutionary tree, which tree, by a process of mutation and natural selection, took two billion years to grow.

Furthermore, he has the unique capabilities, among other self-conscious organisms, of conceptual thought, imagination, and symbolic language, and most significantly of creating a culture.

Then, of course, we must not ignore some of the contributions by philosophers as regards man:

7

> Man (as an individual) is the measure of all things.—
> (Protagoras)

Socrates subsequently advocated as the beginning of wisdom to the Athenian youth during a generation of sceptics, "Know thyself!" While he entertained doubts as to whether it is possible for man to really know the outside world, he did feel certain it was possible for man to know something about himself.

Let us now bring this subject down to more recent times and see what Josh Billings had to say about the matter of knowing oneself:

> It is not only the most difficult thing to know oneself
> but the most inconvenient one, too.

Inconvenient yes, for witness man's proneness to run away from his own shadow. However, our problem of its very nature necessitates the pinning down of our own shadow, so let us jump off the deep end and proceed to analyze it. Man fortunately can do this, for he appears to be the only living entity who can observe himself, being both subject and object in one person.

II.

ANALYSIS OF MAN'S PERSONALITY

The Logical Subject

The logical subject of the personality is an empirical fact. It hovers over the stream of consciousness, sometimes with its attention focused on a particular interest or problem—at times day-dreaming and letting its imagination free to roam as it will —all the while dimly aware of sensations emanating from bodily sense organs of moving images, sounds, and odors in the external world. It is also dimly aware of feelings arising from kinaesthetic sensations from bodily muscles, and general feelings of either well-being or discomfort. It communicates with the brain via psychic energy and magnetic waves which it can itself initiate. Whereas the personality as a whole is the real subject so far as the external world is concerned, it is the object of the logical subject. Ontologically, it is a "speck" of absolute being, functioning independently as the origin within a finite being.

When attending to an immediate problem, it will gather from the stream of consciousness pertinent material, and at the same time call upon memory to furnish additional data. When the data are sufficient for a decision, it decides, and what's more, initiates via magnetic waves that which it considers an appropriate action or response, either via speech, or more overt physical action, or even inaction.

It transmutes quantities into qualities—the supreme miracle of the mind. It is a free agent and hence assumes responsibility, to itself at least, and it very definitely holds its neighbor responsible for any action directed toward it. It is quite a rationalizer, if not a reasoner, to justify its own course of action.

We shall henceforth call this invisible entity, this logical subject of all our propositions, this free agent,—the "Responsible I," or "RI" as its abbreviation. Here, before our minds, we have captured that most elusive unsuspected subject of the personality of man—not without a struggle however.

The personality is both body and mind, and the living soul of man. That the RI is the functioning head, the logical subject, of the personality (its object) will be brought out and emphasized as we review the significance of some of its functions and actions as follows:

> It decides whether to get up in the morning or remain in bed; what shirt, suit, or dress to wear; whether to have bacon and eggs for breakfast or just toast and coffee.

There is no great significance to the foregoing, you interpose. Very well, let us proceed:

> It is, in the words of Lloyd Morgan, "the center of active causality"; it is the reasoner, via mental trial and error, a mental explorer so to speak; and it interprets sense-data;
> It decides what vocation to choose for a life-time activity, and the appropriate effective steps to prepare for such work;
> It directs its imaginative faculty, as excited by the instinct of curiosity, toward discovering the laws of nature and thus freeing itself from the limitations of its instincts;
> It decides, as in the case of an artist, what its next subject shall be and goes about creating it, first in its mind before giving it overt expression;
> It thinks up new and easier ways of transportation, as in the case of the many joint inventors of transportation vehicles, beginning with the wheel, the cart, the horse-drawn carriage, the automobile, the jet plane, and for the present the space vehicle;
> It thinks up electronic computers, and programs what they are to compute;

10

It decides before going to the polls on election day who to vote for, whether in his own selfish interests and/or the interests of his immediate party, of the country, or of all mankind;

It decides, as a totalitarian leader what tactic to follow next in the "lukewarm war" to test the character of the new leader of a so-called democratic country;

It decides, as a leader of such democratic country, whether to risk war to meet a challenge, even to risk starting a nuclear holocaust. To be or not to be, that is the question the RI must decide.

Yes, you concede, these are matters of more importance. But the choice to be made by the RI on another matter is even more significant, both to himself and to mankind as a whole. That choice will be named at the close of our treatise.

From the foregoing it has become apparent that the RI is the very nucleus of the soul—the personality as a whole. We shall now proceed with an exposition on man as its own object—the personality.

The Physiological Scaffold of the Logical Subject (RI)

Kant once made the significant statement that: "It is, indeed, the common fate of human reason in speculation, to finish the imposing edifice of thought as rapidly as possible, and then for the first time to begin to examine whether the foundation is a solid one or no."

This we hasten to do, that is, to analyze the foundation for our concept of the RI. For present purposes we shall not go back further than to the brain.

Strangely, the location of the thinking organ has not always been considered to be in the brain. At one time the heart was considered to be its location; in ancient Babylon it was considered to be in the liver; Aristotle, incidentally, considered the brain as an air-conditioning unit for warm blood. Pythagoras and Alemaeon of Aston were the first men who placed the location of the thinking organ in the head. Pythagoras drew this conclusion from observation, particularly after

11

noticing in Egypt that the priests after intensive deep thinking would hold their hands on their heads and complain of a headache. Alemaeon arrived at this same conclusion from dissection, a more scientific approach.

Anatomists, after years of intensive research and careful examination of the brains of men of all types, from idiots to geniuses, could find no basis in the structure of the brain to account for the variance in mental capacities of individuals. They found some idiots with larger brains than certain geniuses; in fact, some geniuses possessed smaller brains than the normal. In 1870 Dr. Rudolph Wagner was given the brains of three geniuses, one of which being that of Karl Friedrich Gauss, one of the most brilliant mathematicians of modern times; Dr. Wagner made a most careful examination of his brain and compared it with that of one Krebs, an ordinary day laborer. He found the two brains practically identical, in size, number of convolutions, and so on. Others have made like studies and come up with the same negative results. Finally, when researchers had reached the point of giving up hope of ever finding a physical basis for differences in mental capacities, they hit upon the factor of blood supply. Heretofore, all researchers had taken off and discarded the outer covering of the brain which contained the arteries and veins furnishing nourishment to the brain. Yet here was the answer—the differences in size and complexities, especially of the arteries, correlated consistently with the differences in mental capacities of the individuals concerned. In other words, the greater the blood supply to the brain, the greater the mental capacity.

More recently studies have been made as to the composition of the blood itself before entering and after leaving the brain. Such studies have revealed that the brain uses up blood sugar more than any other element. If the supply is too little, it results in reduced mentation, but if the sugar metabolism is too great, it results in insanity.

Lime is another food element extracted from the blood stream passing through the brain. Briefly, the chemical process involved in brain activity is the breaking down of blood sugar in the presence of oxygen into lactic acid, from which form it is still further broken down. The elements iron, manganese, and copper, found in considerable quantity in the brain, are also required to catalyze the chemical reaction.

12

Let us now briefly outline the general structural components of the brain. First, we have the brain stem, a continuation of the spinal cord up along the base of the skull cavity; secondly, the first outgrowth of the brain stem known as the cerebellum; and thirdly, the cerebrum. The spinal cord and brain stem contain the lower or so-called reflex centers, while the cerebellum and cerebrum contain the so-called higher centers. According to Prof. J. Z. Young in his book, "Doubt and Certainty in Science," the number of cells in the cerebral cortex alone is about seven times the total population of the world, and their organization of scarcely conceivable complexity.

The lower centers are directly connected by nerves with the sense organs, body glands, and muscles. The higher centers have no direct connection to the body proper except through the lower nerve centers. The dynamic, inter-relating functions of the body are carried out not only by chemical-electrical processes of the nerves, but also by the chemical processes initiated by the various glands of the body, with their hormone secretions.

The cerebellum, also called the small brain, is connected by a cable of nerves running back from the brain stem. Though it has no known sensory or intellectual functions, it is closely connected with the cerebrum by a large bundle of nerves from different parts of the cerebrum by way of the brain stem, which nerves are possibly related to motor activity. It is known, however, that the cerebellum has much to do with maintaining the equilibrium of the body.

The brain stem separates into two branches, forming the so-called thalamus at the end of each branch. The thalamus, of which there are two, one for each hemisphere of the brain, is a large intermediate sensory center. The function of this center still remains pretty much of a mystery. It is thought, however, to have something to do with feeling and emotion.

Anterior to the thalamus is the cerebrum, whose convolutions fold down over the brain stem. The cerebrum is the higher nerve center of the brain. The right and left hemispheres of the cerebrum are each divided into various lobes. The parietal lobe, which is located on the top portion of the head, is considered to be the seat of the sensory areas. The frontal lobe, located in the front portion of the head, is the seat of the motor

13

area, and is also considered to be the area where thought processes take place. The temporal lobe, one located on each side of the head, is the seat of the auditory center. In the rear of the head is the occipital lobe, the seat of the visual center.

General Characteristics of Nerve Action

Considerable research has been done by nerve physiologists and biochemists to determine how the electrical impulses in the nerve fibers are generated. In 1963 the Nobel prize for Medicine was awarded to Alan Lloyd Hodgkin and Andrew Fielding Huxley of Cambridge University, and Sir John C. Eccles of the Australian National University, for work in this field. These three scientists discovered how electricity is generated in nerve fiber and how it travels along the nerve cables and is transferred from one nerve cell to another.

They worked on the nerve fiber of the squid, a single strand of which is only 1/25th of an inch in thickness. They found that the mechanism of nerve conduction could be called an ion pump. Negatively charged ions of potassium inside the nerve cell and the negatively charged ions of sodium outside the cell are kept apart until the nerve is stimulated. Then the sodium ions enter through the cell walls. During this process an electrical impulse is generated. In short, the process is one of polarity, depolarity, and repolarity.

Magnetic Waves

Today electrodes have been developed so sensitive that when attached to the head and connected with wires to an oscillograph, brain wave tracings may be obtained. These waves have been found to differ in frequency and amplitude as between those obtained during problem-solving, during rest or relaxation, and during sleep. Dreaming can be detected by means of these waves, even though the subject may maintain he never dreams.

Dr. Edmund M. Dewan, an experimenter of brain waves, discovered he could influence the shape of his alpha waves by thought alone, without muscular movement. This observation would suggest that man can influence or even create magnetic waves with his mind.

14

A biochemistry professor at the University of Cincinnati, Dr. Albert P. Mathews, has speculated on the chemistry of thought in the following manner:

Are our thoughts also at the bottom electrical? Whenever a nerve impulse sweeps over, it is accompanied by an electrical disturbance, and this disturbance is the surest sign of life. When the nerve impulses play back and forth over the commissure of the brain they are accompanied by this pale lightning of the negative variation. Is that pale lightning what we recognize as consciousness in ourselves? It would seem that there must be some psychic element in every electron if the atoms are made of electrons. There must be some psychic disturbance in every union of hydrogen and oxygen to make water and in every pulse of light and of wireless telegraphy. When an electron moves it generates a magnetic field; does it also generate a psychic field?

The Psychological Scaffold of the Logical Subject—
The Mind Tree

With this rather sketchy physical background, we shall now venture a logical construction based upon man's overt behavior, augmented by introspection, to explain mental activity and personality itself. We take our cue from Dr. Mathews' speculation, that electrical impulses generated in the nerves, accompanied with its magnetic field, also generates a psychic field. Reversed, a change of psychic field would create a magnetic field, followed by the triggering of an electrical impulse in the nerve fiber. Here we have a possible bridge over the gap between the physical and the mental areas and from the mental to the physical, via the field concept—electrical energy in a magnetic field out of which body organs are created, and psychic energy within a magnetic field out of which the personality itself is patterned.

We shall place the stream of consciousness, over which the RI hovers, at the point of the "pale lightning of the negative variation." This places a physical structure under the RI.

However, we have now reached a stage in our speculative search where we must change our terminology from physical to psychological concepts. Hence, it is both desirable and appropriate at this point to define some of the terms which will be used in our mental structure. The following definitions were taken from Harriman's New Dictionary of Psychology:

> *Instinct*: A complex pattern of unconditioned reflexes or as an unlearned, inner drive to biologically purposeful action.
>
> *Emotion*: A wide pattern of sensations within the body—in psychoanalysis, the term subsumes the expression of instinctual drives (conscious or unconscious).
>
> *Trait*: A distinctive pattern of behavior which is more or less permanent; hence a group of habits, such as persistence, introversion, accuracy, and the like.
>
> *Habit*: A learned response, in which the muscular coordination, association, or emotional element has, through training, become fairly well established, rapid, and almost automatic.
>
> *Sentiment*: McDougall's term (1923) for an organized, more or less permanent tendency to experience certain emotions and desires with reference to some particular situation. Hatred, contempt, love, respect and self-regard, are examples of sentiments (in McDougall's psychology.)
>
> *Attitude*: A mental set to respond to a situation with a prepared reaction. Whereas sets may be temporary matters, attitudes are more or less stable.—Attitudes denote bias, preconceptions, feelings and emotions, hopes and fears; opinions are the verbal formulations of attitudes.

The essential difference, then, between a sentiment and an attitude is that a sentiment has a predominantly emotional element connected with it, whereas an attitude contains a predominantly cognitive or intellectual element.

Now to proceed with our logical construction. As we have provided for a physiological structure under our RI, we must now provide for the psychological structure. As man is prone to be eye-minded and even in his imagination is inclined to resort to physical symbolism an appropriate physical analogy must be chosen for the structure of the mind and its phenomena. Such a dynamic analogy we find in the tree—it has roots, it grows, it has branches, and it has a so-called "lead" branch. The

16

roots of the tree pick up its sustenance from the soil, the water and minerals needed for growth; and it depends on the radiation of the sun for the very important chemical conversion process known as photosynthesis. Incidentally, it has been observed that an incredibly small percentage of the weight of the tree is made up of matter taken from the soil through its roots; the larger percentage is taken from the atmosphere.

The next step in the development of our hypothesis is to determine where in the brain to place the roots of the mind tree and where the so-called "lead" branch shall be located. We have dogmatically placed the roots in the vicinity of the thalami, the assumed center of the emotions, and the "lead" branch at the loci where "the nerve impulses play back and forth over the commissure of the brain" accompanied "by pale lightning of the negative variation." This is the point where we placed the stream of consciousness over which the RI hovers.

Roots of the Mind Tree

In the vicinity of the thalami the roots of the mind tree pick up psychic waves, transmuted from magnetic waves coincident with electrical nerve impulses within the thalami. These psychic impulses constitute the instincts, innate direction tendencies, and general feelings from the body. Our instinctual urges will find immediate expression within reflex action initiated within the mind tree in the presence of so-called "releasers," be they visual or otherwise.

The Trunk of the Mind Tree—and Its Branches

Man is possessed of a number of instincts. These serve as initial channels for the expression of psychic energy. Only to enumerate a few, there is the instinct of sex, play, curiosity, fear, self-assertion, self-submission, gregariousness, and the mating and parental instincts. Some authorities will name more, while the early behaviorists recognized only the fear of loss of physical support and of loud noises as innate in the newly born baby. But even psychologists have sentiments and attitudes which influence their opinions. It should be borne in mind that just because certain instincts become observable later in the life of a child, it does not necessarily mean that they are acquired

17

traits. For instance, a data processing unit does not react with everything in its coded data at the time it first begins to operate, but only at the pre-scheduled time during its operation.

Instincts make up the trunk of our mind tree. Of the various instincts heretofore mentioned, the two more incessantly dynamic ones are the instincts of self-assertion and self-submission. They constitute the give and take, the pulsating factor of the personality tree. In fact, it is the very core of that master sentiment of the personality—the "sentiment of self-regard" (McDougall). This sentiment is the most intimate creation of the RI, its very sentimental self, its solar plexus so to speak. It is this sentiment around which Alfred Adler constructed his Individual Psychology, with its concepts of superiority and inferiority. Failing the realization of the goal of superiority, a person tends to compensate for the resultant feeling of inferiority by so-called compensatory reactions and goals. The individual "pattern of life" (Adler) is thereby formed. It will often be initiated by an organ inferiority according to Adler. Incidentally, Adler's psychology is teleological—goal seeking and goal striving, and is centered around the self-preservative instincts.

The master sentiment of self-regard arises out of the "self" instincts, so to speak, of self-assertion and self-submission. The other sentiments, as well as attitudes, opinions and beliefs appear to be largely the by-products of the RI's choice of love objects, together with its other choices. They all branch out from the master sentiment. To enumerate a few such sentiments, along with the attitudes which in turn branch out from them, we shall mention the patriotic sentiment, with its particular attitude toward any subject involving the nation and its well-being; the political sentiment, with its attitudes toward a specific theory of government, particular politicians, and the like; the mother and/or father sentiment, with positive or negative attitudes toward anything touching upon the parents' welfare, and so on. This last sentiment, the parental sentiment, incidentally is the one emphasized in the psychology of Freud in his concept of the oedipus complex, which complex results from an abnormal attachment or fixation on either of the parents. This complex is centered around the sex instinct as motivator. Freud's psychology is deterministic with its root in the sex or reproductive instincts.

Carl G. Jung, who along with Adler was a former disciple

of Freud, created a system of psychology known as Analytical or Depth Psychology. He deemphasized the Freudian stress on sex, and stressed rather the collective unconscious, revelations or symptoms which appear when the personality regresses within itself in the face of frustration or so-called persistent non-adjustive reactions (Hamilton). He emphasized also the individuation process, that is, the integration of the unconscious elements of the psyche with consciousness. Such unconscious elements, which Jung calls archetypes, include among other elements, the mandala symbol, and the anima (feminine in man) and the animus (the masculine in woman), all being psychic forms like instincts which are inherited from our ancestors, race, and species. He terms the unconscious man's "shadow."

There are some instincts which will develop an independent branch near the bottom of the mind tree, free of any sentimental attachments. Such an instinct is the instinct of curiosity which fires in the mind the imaginative faculty and the notion of cause and effect. Around this instinct we like to think the scientists receive their motivation, free of emotional influences except that of the intellectual love of truth. Some scientists, however, are quite frank to concede that they find it rather difficult to divorce themselves from the influences of the sentiment of self-regard.

The Russian author Sholokhov, the recipient of the 1965 Nobel prize for literature, in a speech answering the claim of certain foreign critics that communist writing "has a bias," made the following significant psychological observation:

Well, how would they have it?
Let's say I am writing about a soldier of ours, a man who is infinitely near and dear to me. How can I write ill of him? He's mine, all mine, from his garrison cap to his puttees, and I try not to notice the pock marks on his face, say, or certain flaws in his character.
And if I do notice them, I shall try to write so that the reader comes to love him, taking him with these endearing pock marks and little flaws in his character. . . .
I want to see a writer's hot blood boil when he writes, his face whiten with restrained hatred of the enemy when he writes about him; I want to see the writer laugh and cry with the hero he loves and holds dear.

The foregoing reaction is true more or less of all men. Yes, true of even some scientists as heretofore mentioned. Thus a man's choice of love objects represents an important, if not the most important, function in his search for truth.

There is another instinct which branches out at the bottom of the mind tree, namely, the play instinct. Its function apparently is to serve as motivation along with curiosity, for the initial learning process, involving the physical manipulation of the various objects in the child's external environmental world, and of the observation of their inter-relationships. Subsequently the imaginative faculty largely assumes the function of objective manipulation, replacing it with introspective manipulation and observation.

In the case of certain abnormal personalities, this instinct of play will at times lead an independent existence. An interesting illustration of a personality centered around this instinct is Sally, one of the co-conscious personalities in the famous case of Miss Beauchamp, cited by Morton Prince. This easygoing, co-conscious personality apparently possessed no sentimental attachments to anyone, and experienced no aversions and no pain, but only a desire to play and have fun.

The Functioning of the RI

Now we can ask the very logical question: How does the RI function? First, we must concede that it cannot attend to all sensations or sense-data swirling before it. It must choose for consideration only those sensations or sense-data pertinent to its immediate situation or problem. Then, are the other sensations overlooked or totally lost? No, at least not entirely. It has been determined by Morton Prince and other investigators by means of controlled tests via the technique of hypnosis that the so-called unconscious aspects of the personality have observed fringe activity, the consciousness or awareness of which the RI was completely oblivious.

The RI, then, directs its attention to those portions of the stream of consciousness having direct bearing on its immediate problem or interests; it reasons, it rationalizes, it determines and institutes appropriate action if any.

Now to give one illustration of the actual functioning of the RI: Richard Hillary was one of the Spitfire pilots of whom Winston Churchill made his famous statement: "Never was so much owed by so many to so few." In Hillary's book "The Last Enemy" he makes this revealing introspection while floating, helpless from burns, in the English Channel, inviting death to relieve him of his pain:

> I began to feel a terrible loneliness and sought for some means to take my mind off my plight. I took it for granted that I must soon become delirious, and I attempted to hasten the process. I encouraged my mind to wander vaguely and aimlessly, with the result that I did experience a certain peace. But when I forced myself to think of something concrete, I found that I was still only too lucid.

This passage is particularly cited to show the control asserted by the RI amid all emotional and physical sensations.

Prism of Logic

The most meaningful and significant function of the RI, however, is to reflect sense-data against its prism of logic. The RI is the intellectual factor in the personality, and its prism of logic is an a priori inheritance, an innate awareness of a sense of logic, cause and effect, and of time and space (the receptacles according to Kant in which we place all our sense-data). It corresponds roughly to the light prism used in breaking down light rays.

Imagination

Besides the prism of logic, the RI is possessed of the faculty of imagination, the faculty of the mind which, according to Dr. Einstein, is most essential for the scientists. It is to the adult individual the invisible bridge between the old and the new, as the play instinct is the bridge of learning to the child.

Instinctual Drives

The instinctual drives are the primitive foils against which the RI's decisions are formulated. The instincts themselves are an invisible fence which unwittingly serves as limits to the activity of the RI. Sentiments and attitudes thereby take form within the trunk of the mind tree, as well as on the branches of its sentiment of self-regard. Out of the accumulation of its decisions are born the traits and habits of the personality. In other words, the RI by its decisions and actions, pretty largely progressively creates its own ever-evolving personality, limited by its inner instinctual forces as well as by its external environment.

The Will—What Is It? Is it Free?

What about the will? Just where in this schematic set-up is it located? And most important, is it free?

The so-called will is the tendency to action in a certain direction and manner, determined by the innate reaction tendencies of the instincts as modified by the sentiments and attitudes created by the RI. Thus the will is the composite of our primitive innate tendencies as progressively modified by the choices of the RI. It is, so to speak, an RI-created instinctive mechanism which reveals itself to the world in our personality. It is a pre-determined reaction pattern relieving the RI of attending to each individual situation in which it finds itself. The will is the created servant of the RI and not its master, at least in a normally functioning personality.

Thus we see that the will is not free; it is a slave to its conflicting emotions and instincts. It is the RI that is free—it alone is free to choose, free to modify, free to negotiate. However, as the RI is largely responsible for the will it has itself created, it does not appear an injustice for a court of law to hold a person responsible for disobeying the established laws. The RI alone holds the reins to the instincts and its created will—it alone is the directing entity.

At times it must be conceded from practical experience, the sentiment of self-regard reacts so violently to a situation that the RI temporarily loses control of its action. A person undergoing this experience will often say he "lost his head," or an observing person will remark that "he blew his top." Any RI who attempts to "ride bareback" on his sentiment of self-regard while it is agitated, is assured of an exciting and many times an embarrassing ride. A good night's sleep, however, usually reinstates the RI again in its normal function. "Go sleep on it" is good advice. A free will as man is presently constituted

22

is both dangerous to himself and to society as well. When an RI chronically abdicates to its will, mental illness and even insanity results.

If the RI persists in day-dreaming within its will, it will be "sucked" back, so to speak. It will at first carelessly feel that it has hold of the reins of his "horse" but eventually his horse will insist on returning to its stable, leaving the rider helplessly holding on. The stable of his horse is far back, far beyond the lifetime of the RI.

The RI, therefore, should not attempt delving into its unconscious except for an immediate purpose and then only for a short time, except of course under the direction and guidance of a competent psychologist or psychiatrist.

In brief, the RI should not establish its domicile within its unconscious, which is actually its unbridled will, that is, if it wishes to remain a free agent and sane. If the RI insists on becoming an equestrian, he should preferably mount periodically his imagination and seek answers to some of the many problems of man's environment. But here again he should maintain a firm hold on the reins of his mount. However, if the RI resolutely maintains its prerogative, its proper and rightful function, no vicissitudes of life can unseat it or prevent it from making progressive intelligent adjustments.

The foregoing interpretation of the will enables us to appreciate better the oft-quoted words "A man convinced against his will is of the same opinion still."

Furthermore we can now readily appreciate that this interpretation places enormous responsibility on the individual. It makes him responsible for interpreting the environment in which he finds himself and for initiating appropriate adjustments thereto. It places upon him the task of discovering the laws of nature, and the responsibility for adjustments to those laws. This conclusion becomes particularly significant in the light of Bertrand Russell's statement in his book "Human Knowledge" that: "Individual percepts are the basis of all our knowledge, and no methods exist by which we can begin with data which are public to many observers." . . . "all the raw material of our knowledge consists of mental events in the lives of separate people. In this region, therefore, psychology is supreme."

Ignorance of the laws of nature is no excuse—that we have learned from sorrowful experience, however much we may cry about it. Yet, it is the very existence of the laws of nature that gives significance to our freedom of choice. Without such laws there would be no meaning to choices.

From the foregoing observation we may conclude that the more general knowledge the RI has, especially of the laws of nature, the more intelligent his adjustment to his environment becomes, or should become. Yes, knowledge of the laws of nature, in fact all knowledge, gives us more freedom—both as to a greater range of possible choices and of possible appropriate activity. Let us reiterate, without natural laws, the concept of causality would become meaningless and the RI would soon be forced to abdicate, in fact become non-existent.

Normally, then, the will is not free but largely determined by our RI—but the RI is free to select, free to choose, free to act, and hence the responsible directing entity of the individual.

Looking down at the personality tree from above, we now see the RI firmly installed as its center, with the instincts and the master sentiment of self-regard, with the varied sentiments and attitudes branching out as vectors therefrom, forming a radiating pattern.

Evidence of this Conception of the RI

What are some mental phenomena which seem to support the conception of the RI? In this connection we shall cite certain observations by Morton Prince and other investigators.

In the Miss Beauchamp case, the instincts of self-assertion and self-submission split within the sentiment of self-regard. This split resulted from a combination of a physical and a mental illness suffered by Miss Beauchamp. Emotional conflicts had developed between sentiments having the instinct of self-assertion as its motivator, and sentiments having the instinct of self-submission as its motivator. Confusing emotional feelings appeared in consciousness which frustrated the RI. These feelings it tried to repress when it could not decide on appropriate action. This error of judgment proved to be its undoing, for the repression of the problem simply aggravated matters. In the face of physical illness and in its emotional frustration, the RI withdrew, abdicated so to speak. The sub-RI which had meanwhile incubated within the instinct of self-assertion, thereupon assumed the functions of the abdicated RI. Its personality proved to be aggressive and worldly, totally inconsiderate of the rights of others. However, it too found it could not take the

24

stress of certain shocks and it too withdrew into the unconscious. A submissive, saintly personality thereupon appeared, with the instinct of self-submission as its motivator. This saintly personality found it embarrassing to have to correct the faux pas committed by the former worldly personality, and it too finally had to withdraw.

Dr. Prince, through the technique of hypnosis, was finally able to resolve the conflict between the bifurcated personalities, and integrate them into the main personality trunk. The principal RI was thus reinstated to its proper function and with greater knowledge of the error of not facing up to situations.

All very interesting but incredible you say. But let us cite some further observations by Dr. Prince. He has found, along with other investigators, that a sub-RI can be co-conscious with the principal RI; for instance it can read simultaneously the same book, but not necessarily at the same speed, as the principal RI. Hence, apparently, it becomes a co-observer at the stream of consciousness unbeknown to the principal RI. A sub-RI, if sufficiently developed, can even influence the principal RI to do certain things against its own judgment. However, fortunately the muscular or effective organization of the individual can be under the control of only the presently functioning RI. All this would seem to suggest that a person, in this case Miss Beauchamp, was not really responsible for her actions. However, it should be kept in mind that the principal RI originally created the conflict within its sentiment of self-regard by its own day-dreaming, its indecisions, and inactions, by refusing to face up to the actual problem situation.

A further interesting case, the Hanna case, reported by another investigator, will now also be briefly summarized. A Rev. Hanna was involved in a severe accident, losing entirely his memory of his past. He became like a baby; he would evacuate uncontrolledly as a baby; his eyes would follow very curiously any moving object as a baby does; and so on. He had to be taught how to speak, learn the meaning of words, and the like. However, it was noted that he learned very quickly. This ability to learn quickly would tend to support the contention that the RI is a separate entity, and furthermore that it learns from experience. However, it is dependent on materials in its memory for making decisions. With this memory source temporarily cut off, Hanna became a new personality but apparently with the same RI. Eventually, however, memory of his life prior to the accident suddenly returned, and the two personalities became fused into the original personality.

We shall now review the phenomena of sleep and hypnotism, suggestion and auto-suggestion in the light of our hypothesis. The motivator of the phenomenon of sleep appears to be a definite instinct inherited by man. The same phenomenon registers in all animals. The basic motivating forces in hypnosis, however, apparently involves two instincts, the sleep instinct and the instinct of self-submission. In the case of sleep, the RI can resist operation of the instinct by drinking coffee, by means of physical activity, and other means, but only up to a certain point—eventually, it must succumb to the force of the instinct.

In the case of hypnosis, the RI receives spoken suggestions and instructions from his external environment via his hearing sense and not via mental telepathy. The RI can either resist or submit to becoming hypnotized as it chooses. If the RI chooses to submit, the RI of the hypnotizer appears to take over control of the person hypnotized, whose RI loses its memory and apparently ceases to reflect given instructions against its prism of logic. The hypnotizer can create the various stigmata of hysteria— localized paralysis which curiously does not follow nerve centers, as well as create other mental phenomena. (Does this suggest the possibility that the mind can create an arbitrary magnetic pattern?)

Suggestions or rather instructions, technically called "post-hypnotic suggestions," can be given by the hypnotizer to the hypnotized person to perform some act or to make some statement upon awakening from hypnosis. For instance, a hypnotized person will be given the instruction by the hypnotizer to stand up five minutes after awakening from hypnosis and shout in the presence of observers the word "doughnuts" three times and then sit down. This post-hypnotic suggestion the hypnotized person will proceed to carry out five minutes after being awakened from the hypnotic state. When asked or challenged to explain why he did it, he will embarrassingly try to rationalize his action without being aware of the real reason.

The immediately foregoing phenomena can be appreciated by a programmer of a data-processing set-up. The instructions are put in the data-processing unit and the machine performs them in their pre-established time sequence. Likewise, it appears that once the RI of the hypnotizer has instructed the mental organization of the hypnotized person before awakening, to

26

perform a certain act subsequent to awakening, the principal RI reinstated upon awakening, will be completely ignorant of these prior instructions; furthermore it can generally do nothing to resist the subsequent impulse to action regardless of its efforts.

These mysterious phenomena appear more understandable with the conception of the directing intellectual entity which we have chosen to call the RI.

III.

THE DYNAMIC DEVELOPMENT OF THE PERSONALITY

To illustrate our conception of the mind tree, let us briefly follow the gradual creation of a personality from the very inception of life in the fertilized egg, the zygote. Biologically, the process is not one of unfoldment but very much one of pure creation; in other words, the egg possesses the raw material for development but there is no observable form. The sequence of the creative activity is contained in the so-called chromosomes, whose gene contents of dominant and recessive characters are the joint contribution of both parents. The mind tree likewise is a progressive creation and not an unfoldment, even within the womb and prior to birth. It seems reasonable to suppose that the RI assumes its position, however vaguely, during the gradual development of the brain, for at birth the RI definitely asserts its presence at the first spank. When hunger pangs are felt, the baby instinctively cries. Crying attracts the attention of the mother, and the baby is fed.

The baby apparently was quick to grasp the relation of crying to obtaining milk. By what process did it sense this relation? First, there must exist in the baby an innate "primary action-tendency" (Warden) which, reflected against its sense of logic young as it is, led it to suspect a connection between crying and the subsequent feeding. Hasty generalization, the logician will protest. But the fact remains that the baby registered its hunger urge by crying and received the desired food immediately thereafter. Subsequently it again repeats the process and with the same result. This primary action tendency, motivated by the instinct of curiosity, seems to be the core of the learning process. In the lower animals it is also innate, but unconscious.

In man the process becomes conscious, and subsequently it was formulated as the law of cause and effect, or law of causality. It is the product of the child's eternal question—Why?

Returning again to the child, eventually no amount of crying gets it food. In fact, his mother remonstrates with Johnny that he is too old to cry, for only babies cry. So he compromises and resorts to whining in his attempts to get food snacks between meals. That technique too is effective for a short while, but soon becomes an outmoded and ineffective means. So what does Johnny do now? He gets the idea while his mother is out on an errand to clamber up on a chair and reach for the cookie jar. He has time to munch a few cookies and cover up the tell-tale crumbs before his mother's return.

As his mother gradually gives her son the basic teaching in right and wrong behavior, Johnny becomes aware that stealing is very reprehensible, for only bad boys steal. As Johnny loves his mother, his practice of taking cookies during her absence troubles his conscience, so this practice is also discontinued. So conscience takes form in young Johnny, a by-product of love.

Johnny finally grows up and becomes a teenager, and furthermore now attends a secondary school. One day a school-mate facetiously makes the startling statement to him that he will die one of these days. How come? Jack naturally and curiously asks. Simply because all men are mortal; and as you are a man, therefore you are mortal. But Jack doesn't like the idea of dying, so he mockingly challenges his pal, "How do you know all men are mortal?" "Just ask any undertaker," his pal smugly returns. "Has the undertaker buried all men?" "No," his pal thoughtfully concedes. "Then how do you know I will die?" "Well, because Aristotle said so."——Yes, John has now become a reasoning entity.

John subsequently becomes a scientist, and the aspect of causality with which he will then be concerned will still basically involve predictability. As a baby he unknowingly was likewise concerned. But the attainment of predictability for John as a scientist will be a most complex process, as we shall observe later as our treatise progresses.

Now let us surreptiously watch Johnny's experiences leading toward his becoming a social being.

The RI at first is quite lacking in experience and pretty much reacts to the instinctual or innate action tendencies. As the baby gradually experiences more and more in its ever-chang-

29

ing environment, the RI becomes more and more assertive. For instance in its instinctive play activity the baby notices that it can wiggle its toes when it so desires, that it can resist, sometimes effectively, any physical position it is forced into by its mother, and where strength is insufficient, it finds that a loud bellow, or perhaps whimpering will be effective. When Johnny is finally big enough to be seated in a high-chair, he feels that he has finally arrived. His field of observation now is so much greater; he becomes the center of attention and any sound that he might emit which suggests the sound of a word, immediately causes great pleasure in his observers. Eventually he becomes the possessor of a small vocabulary, which progressively increases as his needs increase. He is fascinated and delighted by observing that when a dish is pushed off the table of his high chair, it suddenly disappears, followed by a bang on the floor below. If the dish should break, the phenomenon becomes so much more exciting for him.

When Johnny becomes old enough to crawl on the floor, he has much fun in playing with a little brown dog. He makes the mistake one day of squeezing the dog's tail. The dog lets out a bark and the emotion of fear was experienced. Thereafter, the sight of the dog, or sometimes even the sight of a furry animal, excited the same fear reaction, which is technically known as a conditioned reflex. That was when the RI discovered a reaction over which it had little or no control. When Johnny ventures out from a standing position beside a chair and falls, he is at first somewhat mystified by his fall, and one cannot resist wondering whether he associates it with the same phenomenon of the falling dish.

As time went on, Johnny found himself in the company of other children, and the self-assertive instinct began to influence little Johnny's behavior. If he found that another child possessed a toy which he wanted, he would attempt to take it away. If he discovered the other child would meekly submit to his action, he would continue the practice. Subsequently, he would try to follow the same practice with another child, but to his surprise, he found his action was not only resisted, but he became the recipient of the first slap from a playmate. His first reaction was to cry, but in future contacts with this more aggressive playmate, he assumed a more cautious, if not a submissive attitude.

As Johnny passes from childhood to his adolescent stage, and later to adulthood, he attains a certain degree of control over his natural impulses. He has ceased to react as a child—in short he has been graduated into the world where instinctual impulses have been converted to sentiments, attitudes, and habits, and where reason more or less prevails. Briefly Johnny has become a social being within a society where benefits are derived from cooperation. His responsibilities, however, have increased for he is now a man.

IV.

GENERAL CONCLUDING REMARKS TO PART ONE

Because of the complex nature of the personality, as well as the abstract nature of the RI concept, the foregoing detailed exposition was considered necessary. Furthermore, it is this intellectual entity which both poses the original problem of our treatise and functions in finding its solution. It endeavors to find its position and purpose in the universe as a whole and to determine its own ultimate goal.

The considered conclusion of Julian Huxley, the outstanding evolutionary biologist, as to the position of the personality within the evolutionary process, is here quoted from his little gem of a book "Evolution in Action":

> This primacy of personality has been, in different ways, a postulate of Christianity and of liberal democracy; but it is a fact of evolution. By whatever objective standard we choose to take, properly developed human personalities are the highest products of evolution.

As this biologist eschews the supernatural, his foregoing judgment becomes even more significant.

The personality is man's only living creation, and hence his most significant self-embodiment. Man's other creations constitute his non-living culture, and as his eager potential inheritors are well aware from past observation, these creations are left behind him upon his physical death. Yes, it is true, "you can't take it with you," in spite of what one individual blurted out when so reminded, "Well then I won't go!"

As a connecting link between Part I and Part II of our

32

treatise, we quote the appropriate mature judgment of Dr. Ralph Linton taken from his book "The Tree of Culture:"

> The individual is the irreducible variable in every social and cultural situation. He is the yeast in the cultural brew, and every new element of culture can be traced back ultimately to some individual's mind.

Furthermore, to avoid the senseless "shadow-boxing" of solipsism, let us venture forth not only with a reasonable faith in the reality of our own observations but also in the reported observations of our fellow-man. Thus we shall make this search for the meaning of existence a truly joint endeavor.

PART TWO

WHENCE
VIA SCIENCE, PHILOSOPHY
AND RELIGION

V.

INTRODUCTION TO HISTORICAL STAGE
OF OUR INQUIRY

Before man had sufficient information relatively to place himself within the created universe from the standpoint of both time and space, he nevertheless ventured out, impelled by curiosity, and immediately stimulated by practical needs, to find the answer.

Before we proceed with this intriguing review, it is well first to define three of the general aspects of knowledge, namely, science, philosophy and religion:

Science—may be defined as ordered knowledge of natural phenomena and the rational study of the relations between the concepts in which these phenomena are expressed. (W. E. D. Dampier-Whetham, M.A., F.R.S.)

Philosophy—is the search for a comprehensive view of nature, an attempt at a universal explanation of things. It is both the summary of the sciences and their completion; both general science and specialty distinguished from science proper; and, like its elder sisters, religion and poetry, forms a separate branch among the manifestations of the human mind. (Alfred Weber, Professor in the University of Strassburg)

Religion—is the endeavor of divided and incomplete human personality to attain unity and completion, usually but not necessarily by seeking the help of an ideally complete divine person or persons. (Charles Francis Potter, M.A. S.T.M., Litt.D.)

Early Babylonian, Egyptian, Chinese and Indian Contributions to Science

From early Greek historians, as augmented by the more recent discoveries of archaeologists, civilization first put in its appearance along the river valleys of the Euphrates, the Tigris, the Indus, and the Nile. Early history mentioned predominantly the peoples of Babylonia and Egypt.

The beginnings of the standardization of knowledge may be considered as a fair indication of the appearance of science, in a practical sense at least. In about 2500 B.C. the kings of Babylonia issued edicts as to standards of weight, length and capacity. An edict concerning standards of length set the finger, equal to 1/65 centimeter, as basic, and the foot as 20 fingers.

Measures of weight set the grain, equal to .046 gramme and the shekel as 8.416 grammes. Barley seems to have been the earliest media of exchange. By 3000 B.C., copper and silver also were used. The proportionate value of silver and gold varied at different periods from six to twelve.

Tablets unearthed by archaeologists indicate that the Babylonians possessed a knowledge of the multiplication table, tables of squares and cubes. They also had built up a duodecimal system from the ten fingers. Problems of land surveying led to development of the beginnings of geometry. The early development of arithmetic in Babylonia might be explained because of their geographical position, the caravan routes between the east and the west either passing through and leading to it as a center of trade. Where trade is, accountants are, and they must have tools with which to work.

The cultivation of wheat and barley led to certain inventions such as the plough. The cultivation of these cereals, too, requires a knowledge of seasons, and thus necessitated the development of a calendar. The necessity of a calendar in turn led to astronomical observations, giving the day as a unit.

The physical needs of man up to this point appear to be the primary motivating force for acquiring knowledge and the invention of tools, and not primarily the instinct of curiosity.

The universe to the Babylonians was conceived of as a closed box with the earth as the floor. Accurate records from about 2000 B.C. were kept by the Babylonians of their astronomical observations, especially of the rising and setting of the planet Venus. This led to astrology, the high point of which was reached in Babylonia about 540 B.C. after the Chaldeans conquered that nation.

The first physicians were sorcerers and exorcists, who of course were ignorant of the fundamentals of medicine. Certain men had observed that when frogs croaked excessively, it rained. From this observation magic was resorted to when rain was needed—particular men would masquerade as frogs and croak, all this to bring rain. This technique is known as sympathetic magic—nature being considered animate. From this practice arose mystery and ritual cults. These later assumed the form of propitiatory rites, as the gods were considered by the Babylonians as antagonistic to man; a civilization which espoused such a depressing religion proved a discouraging environment for the development of both science and philosophy.

In Egypt, on the other hand, the gods were considered friendly to man, protecting him both in this life and in the life hereafter. Some ascribe the difference with respect to religious attitudes of the Babylonians and the Egyptians to the difference in climate and fertility of the land. In short, the gods were kinder to the Egyptians than to the Babylonians.

The Egyptians had acquired skill in tempering metal, dyeing, and in making enamel and glass. The best accomplishments in the arts in Egypt seem to have been made between 2000 to 1500 B.C., such advances having been considered by the Egyptians at that time as revelations of the gods.

The earliest document, on papyrus, covering the history of arithmetic up to that time (1800-1600 B.C.) was written by an Egyptian priest; he in turn stated that he copied it from an earlier document dating before 2200 B.C.

The Egyptians, not being as highly motivated to study astronomy as the Chaldeans, did not reach the high state of development in this science. However, the Egyptians did identify the constellations with the names of their gods.

The idea of the universe conceived by the Egyptians was comparable to that of the Babylonians. The Egyptians, however, modified the conception of the universe as a rectangular box with its greater length running north and south. The bottom was concave in shape, with Egypt in the center. Around the edge of the box ran a river on which traveled a boat bearing the disc of fire, the Sun.

The Egyptians far excelled the Babylonians in medicine. Of four early treatises on medicine, the best dates back to about

1600, an Egyptian writing. It mentions the name of the first physician, real or mythological, as Imhotep. He is supposed to have lived about 4500 B.C., and was afterwards deified as the God of medicine.

As disease was considered by the Babylonians as the action of antagonistic gods, they developed no rational school of medicine. It does appear that a nation's conception of the divinity has a definite effect on the direction of its cultural development.

Little is known as yet about the claim of an early development of science in China. We do know that in the past it was "a center for the development and diffusion of civilization." As to artifacts credited to China there are the compass, certain printing techniques, paper, and of course gun-powder. The only other country to consider of the early civilizations then is India.

Knowledge is scanty of scientific activity in India prior to the conquests of Alexander. As to ethical development, however, we have Buddha (560-580 B.C.). It is known that schools of medicine existed at that time. A history of medicine in sanskrit, apparently written by Susruta, an Indian surgeon, during this approximate period, mentions operations for cataract and hernia. Susruta also wrote on anatomy, physiology, and pathology, and mentions over 700 medicinal plants. Because of the uncertainty of dates, it is not known definitely whether Hindu or Greek medicine is the older.

The dearth of contributions of the Indians to the other sciences may be accounted for by the Hindu religion. Whereas Buddha founded his system on a respect for reason and truth as well as love and knowledge, he apparently nullified these favorable factors by stressing the transitoriness of man's existence and the loss of his individuality as the ultimate attainment in spiritual completion. However, the healing art was encouraged as it was consistent with the teachings of Buddha.

The Buddhistic philosophy did lead to ideas foreshadowing the atomic theory. This philosophy maintained that everything exists but for a moment and is immediately replaced by a facsimile. In other words, a thing is a series of momentary forms of existences, and perpetual change in things is explained as a continual creative process.

As early as 300 B.C., the Indians used a system of notation which replaced the Roman numerals, and which finally developed into the system of numerals in use today. It is misnamed Arabic whereas its actual derivation is from India.

VI.

EARLY GREEK CONTRIBUTIONS TO THE
PHILOSOPHY OF NATURE

Prior to the Ionian philosophers—Thales, Anaximander, and Anaximenes—dating approximately from 600 to 400 B.C., Aryan naturalism predominated as previously mentioned. Like a child who, in imagination looks upon its wooden dolls as living beings, man at one time looked upon the various phenomena of nature, such as the sun, stormclouds, and thunderbolts, as gods who must be propitiated. Later, however, these natural phenomena were considered as manifestations of invisible divinities. These divinities were considered as jealous of man as potential usurpers of their exalted position, and hence made it miserable for man. Even then there were thinkers who assumed a melancholy attitude and considered that man fortunate who died young, in fact he would have been better off never to have been born. This attitude toward divinity reflected itself in Homer's Odyssey. In the treatment of diseases magic was resorted to, as well as spells and incantations.

In Homer's Iliad, strangely, simple straightforward treatment was applied in the case of physical injuries, foreshadowing the rational spirit in medicine and surgery. Early Greek medicine reached its highest development at the time of Hippocrates (420 B.C.), with a theory and practice somewhat comparable to those current today. A code of professional ethics was formulated at that time known as the Hippocratic oath.

Thales, however, broke away from Aryan naturalism and viewed the world as the product of a primordial substance. This substance, according to him, was water from which the others were generated.

41

His pupil, Anaximander, subsequently espoused the theory that this primordial substance was really infinite atmosphere. Incidentally, he was the first of the Greeks to attempt the drawing of a map of the then known world. He was also the first to observe that the heavens revolved around the pole star. Anaximenes, Anaximander's pupil, in turn considered this substance to be breath or air.

To assume that these early Ionian philosophers of Miletus were pure metaphysicians and that their philosophies were exclusively the speculative products of deductive reasoning would be unfair to them. Whereas the methods of science had at that time not been developed, yet these philosophers were undoubtedly keen observers of the phenomena of nature. Without such observation they would never have had anything about which to write or upon which to speculate. The deductive and inductive methods have never been all mutually exclusive one against the other, but it has always been a matter of relative proportion.

It should be mentioned that during this early period Anacharsis is said to have invented the potter's wheel, that Glaucus learned to solder iron, and that Theodorus conceived the lathe, the level, and the set-square.

The Problem of Becoming

Problems arise as philosophy develops. Beings persist, beings change constantly; they are born—they pass away. How can they persist and at the same time not persist? That is a philosophical problem which even today the scientists are endeavoring to solve. The consideration of this problem, the problem of becoming, produced at the time of the Ionian philosophers three systems of thought as solutions, (1) the Eleatic system, (2) the Heraclitean system, and (3) the atomistic system.

Negation of Becoming—The Eleatic System

First let us briefly review the Eleatic system. Xenophanes originally lived in Miletus at the time of Anaximander. He traveled around as a rhapsodist and philosopher, finally settling in Elea in Lucania. He violently opposed national mythology with its polytheism, and created so-called philosophical monotheism. From this came pantheism. He maintained there was only one God, all eye, all ear, all thought, both immovable and immutable. To infinitely divide the divine being and to attribute to him human form and passions was to Xenophanes so much nonsense.

Parmenides, a pupil of Xenophanes, went one step further. As there is no change in "All-One", what man calls change is an illusion. Certain doctrines put forward by him, such as the universe being composed of concentric spheres were to be considered as merely hypotheses to orient us in this illusory world. As the world was considered an illusion, he of course could embrace only the science of metaphysics with its a priori reasoning. He affirmed nothing but being, neither body nor soul, matter nor spirit. This neutralism on his part became both the off-shoot of Plato's idealism and Spinoza's concept of substance, which is a form of materialism.

Melissus of Samos went on to interpret Parmenides' term "Being" in a materialistic sense. He concludes that if becoming is impossible, there is no point in endeavoring to determine how the universe originated. He conceived of being as infinite both in time and in space.

Zeno, one of Parmenides' pupils, was the controversialist in the group. This propensity led to his becoming the initiator of dialectics and sophistry, using the method known as reductio ad absurdum. By this process he proved that Achilles could never pass the tortoise because of the infinite divisibility of a line. And if movement takes place, it must be in space. If space existed, it too must exist in space, and so on. He therefore concludes only Being exists, and this being is matter.

It took Gorgias of Leontinum, one of Zeno's pupils, to end this metaphysical nonsense. He concludes that if a Being existed, it would have to be eternal. But an eternal being is infinite and an infinite being cannot exist in time and space for it would be limited thereby. Hence, Being is nowhere, and that which is nowhere does not exist.

Deification of Becoming—The Heraclitean System

The very absurdity of Gorgias' conclusion naturally brought reactions. The principle of Heraclitus ("the Obscure"), thereupon gained favor, that is; Being is nothing; becoming is everything.

Heraclitus lived in Ephesus about 536-470 B.C. He was called "the Obscure" because of his love of the paradox. His thesis up to this point was similar to the early Indian philosophy, namely, that there was nothing abiding in the universe; everything was in a constant state of flux. Nothing is; change is the only reality. But here he differed in that he likened this continuous passing away as an everliving fire—a consuming movement which withal possessed a certain orderliness—"reason" or "destiny" as he termed it. He left a deep impression on Greek thought, and certain modern hypotheses have been formulated from his philosophy. Like the early Ionian physicists he considered all bodies as different forms of the same basic substance. However, this primordial element in his philosophy was fire or at times warm breath—or what modern chemistry calls oxygen. For example, physical solids are extinguished fire, periodically rekindled and extinguished by Fate. The universe is therefore fire in a constant state of transformation. Neither a god nor man has anything to do with the process. It has had no beginning and has no ending. It is impossible for men to enter the same stream once, let alone twice, under the Heraclitean philosophy.

Since non-being produces being and vice versa, being and non-being are the same. This perpetual flow, however, is not the easy smooth-going process that it would seem to be; for becoming is a struggle between contrary forces. Opposite currents from above endeavor to transform the celestial fire into solid matter; and the other current re-ascends and tries to change solid matter into fire. This process of the strife of opposites produces all life on earth, plant, animal, and even intellectual life. Hence, good is destroyed evil, and the reverse—both good and evil disappearing in the universal harmony. Almost Hegelian as we shall later see.

In this world of perpetual change, individual existence becomes a vanity. This makes Heraclitus the typical pessimist of antiquity, along with the Indians. Truth, he maintained, would be non-existent as everything perceived by the senses is ever changing. Knowledge based on sensation is also deceptive. Reason alone, however, reveals what is stable—the divine law according to Heraclitus is the only fixed point in the external flow of things.

Here we note for the first time the acknowledgment of the noumenon as opposed to sensible phenomenon, the latter alone having been considered heretofore by philosophers. In other words, Ionian philosophy effects a very significant breakthrough at this point.

The soul is considered an emanation of so-called celestial fire, and only by its remaining in contact with the source of life can it continue to live. Also an individual's energy depends upon this communion with "the supremely intelligent and wise soul of the world."

Briefly, then, the Heracliteans maintained that the universe is in a state of continual change, with the sole exception of the unchangeable law which governs it. This hylozoism becomes materialism only when opposed by the spiritualism of the Pythagoreans, whose philosophy we shall next review.

The atomists, which movement was initiated by Pythagoras, now carry the torch of philosophy and attempt to explain becoming.

Explanation of Becoming—The Atomistic System

Pythagoras was a brilliant mathematician and one of the great philosophers among the ancients. He was born in Samos about 572 B.C. and is said to have visited extensively in Phoenicia, Egypt, and Babylon. It is said that he had been a pupil of the Brahmans. Upon Pythagoras' return from the East, he became the founder and leader of a brotherhood known as the Pythagoreans.

Whereas the Ionian metaphysics sprang out of physics, the philosophy of Pythagoras was built around mathematics. He endeavored to explain perpetual change in the universe by the use of numbers; in other words, everything had a number. (Pythagoras, who believed in metempsychosis, must be back with us today; witness our fast growing data processing procedures with each of us being assigned clock numbers, bank numbers, prison numbers, social security numbers, ZIP numbers, and so on ad infinitum.)

Pythagoras was the first one to prove deductively that the square on the hypotenuse of a right-angled triangle is equal to the sum of the squares on the other two sides. According to Pythagoras there are two kinds of unity, the first being the unity of the whole, and the second the unity which begins the series 2, 3, 4, etc. He considered the opposition between the one and the many as producing all the rest.

45

. . It all began by the so-called "void" breaking in on the so-called "full," resulting in an infinite number of small particles. These particles were joined together again into earth, fire, air, water and ether, of which fire is the catalyzing element. Hence, all change is a change of place, i.e., mechanism.

The sun was therefore considered the hearth of the universe, and the very residence of the Supreme God. The earth was considered a sphere, possibly for the first time except in the Scriptures (see Isaiah 40:22 and Job 26:7).

By his explanation of becoming, Pythagoras was the first philosopher to unite the philosophy of Parmenides, which made Being everything, and that of Heraclitus which made Becoming everything.

Empedocles was another philosopher who attempted to explain Becoming, to reconcile the permanence of Being of the Eleatics and the perpetual change and motion of Being as conceived by Heraclitus. Empedocles maintained that the universe was the product of four elements,—Earth, water, air, and fire, and that the cause of motion was love and discord. Out of the opposition of these two forces, working with the four elements as agents, all individual things came to be. In fact, good and evil in the world resulted from conflict between these two forces. (This brought a theory of value for the first time into the explanation of nature.) Love is the principle of principles, with Discord as its accomplice, and the four elements as its agents. Life, he theorized, was the expiation of the soul's desire for a separate existence.

Empedocles performed experiments with the water clock, and made the observation that water can only enter a vessel as air escapes. Thus he proved that air was distinct from empty space.

Anaxagoras followed Empedocles. This philosopher was born in Ionia and settled in Athens about 460 B.C. There he remained for a number of years until he was forced to leave because of his contempt for the official religion. Along with his philosophical speculations, he performed dissections of animals, giving him more exact knowledge. He also observed that blood ran to and from the heart.

Anaxagoras believed that the original building blocks of the universe were infinitely small substances or particles. Their coming together produced all individual things and their separation the passing away of individual things. The quantity of these

46

infinitely small particles or "seeds" as they were called, always remained the same. (Can this be the first suggestion of the law of conservation of mass-energy?)

In order to explain the cosmos he must assume in addition to these material unintelligent elements, an element which possesses an intelligence of its own, along with the force necessary to put it into action. This so-called soul-substance was the only element which is in motion, and therefore, the only element to impart motion to the inert elements. He conceived of this special substance as eternal reason which was diffused throughout the universe. (Thus, Anaxagoras was the first philosopher to introduce the purposive principle in explaining the natural world.) His philosophy only vaguely defines the later dualistic conception of the universe, as he finds it difficult to deviate from monistic materialism. He speaks of the vous in nature as a pantheist. Yet he never mentions the questions of transcendency and immanency, conscious intelligence and unconscious intelligence, or personality and impersonality. However, he went far enough in spiritualism to cause a reaction toward strict materialism. And this is where Diogenes of Apollonia enters the scene.

Diogenes is a disciple of Anaximenes who assumes air as the only original element—the source of all life in nature and the very essence of all things. He objects to the conception of pluralism of all elements, as well as the dualism of unintelligent matter and immaterial intelligence. He argues that since the mind leaves the body when the air does, mind is derived from air and not the reverse. He contends all things are differentiations of the same thing, and hence they are the same thing. That thing is air.

Archelaus of Athens, a disciple of Anaxagoras, is loyal to his instructor's atomism, but objects to its dualistic interpretation. He contends that the "vous" is an element along with the other elements. While being material, yet it is finer and more intangible than the other elements without being a so-called simple substance. He defines a simple substance as composed of nothing, and therefore it does not exist. Hence, matter and substance are synonymous terms.

Archelaus was followed by Leucippus and his disciple, Democritus of Abdera. They were the founders (420 B.C.) of the so-called materialistic school.

Leucippus is generally credited with having first stated clearly

47

the principle of causation—"Nothing happens without a cause, but everything with a cause and by necessity."

Democritus—Vague theories of former Ionian philosophers on the nature and structure of matter were definitely formulated by Democritus. This philosopher conceives of matter as indeterminate and divided into infinitely small molecules of infinite number. These molecules alternately come together and segregate. They are extended and therefore not mathematical points; unextended molecules would be nothing, he stated. They are in perpetual motion, which is one aspect of their very essence. These atoms, moving at random through space, would strike against one another to produce lateral movements and vortices, initiating the formation of elements and eventually innumerable worlds. These worlds grow, decay, and perish, only those surviving which fit into their environment. In astronomy, however, the atomists were regressive, and pictured the world as flat.

Democritus is a strict determinist as motion to him has the character of necessity and not purposiveness. He also maintains that the reason we use the word chance is to confess we do not know the cause, which is there nevertheless.

However, Democritus is forced to accept the "void" as well as the so-called "full." How otherwise would his molecules have room to move? The void, according to him, is therefore a condition of matter and motion. The conception of the void along with matter gives the monistic philosophy of materialism a dualistic turn, as much as they try to avoid it.

According to Democritus atoms making up matter, other than the soul, are more hooked and rough than those making up the soul; for the soul, atoms are more smooth and nimble.

Sensation and perception are explained by emanations from bodies entering our sense organs, where they excite sensations; these in turn enter the brain where they produce images and ideas. Sensation, therefore, is the only source of knowledge.

As to his explanation of death, Democritus states that inasmuch as soul-atoms cause self-consciousness, the individual dies when they leave. Whereas the gods are considered by him as more powerful beings than man, they too eventually die.

Necessity is the supreme law which governs the heaven and the earth, and our happiness according to Democritus depends upon our "submitting joyously" to this law. (Sounds almost communistic.) The atomic theory of Democritus was nearer our present conceptions than any system which preceded it or replaced it. The philosophy of materialism, too, brought about a reaction, and it was forced temporarily off the stage to make room for the scepticism of Protagoras.

Philosophy of the Mind—The Appearance of Scepticism

During the fifth century philosophers were in demand as teachers of the young potential politicians of Athens and Sicily. Instead of being seekers of truth, the philosophers became teachers of the mumbo-jumbo use of words and speech to enable the young politicians not only to get elected to office, but also to enhance their position once elected. These teachers were stigmatized as sophists—rationalizers so to speak, for selfish purposes rather than seekers of truth.

Protagoras, who lived in Athens about 480-410 B.C., was a leading sophist and sceptic, and a friend of Democritus.

As the sensible world is constantly changing, a fact brought out by prior thinkers, Protagoras concluded we cannot learn the truth from the product of our senses, but must fall back on reflection and reason. However, as the data furnished by the senses are in constant flux and yet at the same time the only source of knowledge, all our knowledge must be considered as uncertain. Furthermore, as the atoms of Democritus are not perceivable by the senses, their existence is merely a doubtful hypothesis. Hence, both theoretical and practical truth are relative, a matter of temperament, taste, and education. Thus, metaphysical controversies are vain endeavors, and man should direct his attention to the only object accessible for problem study, namely himself. Therefore, the only important problem for philosophy is the necessary condition for man's happiness and the happiness of others. From this basic contention he concluded that practical ethics, dialectics, and rhetoric were the only important branches of philosophical study which would lead to man's happiness. This approach revealed and emphasized thought as being the unifying principle and the true measure of reality.

The abuses of the laws of thought by the sophists ironically made the mind conscious of the existence of such laws, and led to their analysis. This activity was the beginning of the science of logic, as well as the science of language—grammar and syntax.

Protagoras did not study the collective man but the particular man. He maintained that man as an individual is the measure of all things. As man differed one from another, so there were as many opinions as men; thus there was no universal truth applying to all men. This error in the system of Protagoras was rectified by Socrates.

Socrates (469-399 B.C.) was a sculptor for livelihood, but chose instructing and teaching the youth of Athens as his avocational activity, which subsequently took all his time. Moral man and his duties as a citizen became the center of his teachings. The object of his teaching was not to make the youth learned but to make them happy and useful citizens.

Socrates believed firmly that there is something in the world than can be known absolutely, i.e., man himself. "Know thyself" was his first principle.

Socrates' outstanding contribution to thought was his attempt, at least in morals, to separate the general from the particular. From the contemporary mass of opinions he segregates the true immutable opinion, the conscience of human beings, the law of minds. He sought the universal in man, as opposed to Protagoras who maintained the existence of only the particular. Socrates' efforts were untiring in examining and defining goodness and wickedness, wisdom and folly, justice and injustice, courage and cowardice. He applied the inductive method in the study of values. The close relationship existing between knowledge and will constituted the fundamental principle of his philosophy—that our moral values and our knowledge are directly proportional, and therefore virtue is teachable. Socrates does not attempt to suppress nature but tries to subdue it and make it the instrument of intelligence, intelligence eventually to become the absolute ruler.

Socrates' advocacy of moral law over caprice brought about a reform of philosophy along with that of morals. Detrimental to his physical well-being, however, was his contention that inasmuch as there was no exact definition of God, an individual had as much right to espouse atheism as theism. But the politicians thought otherwise, and Socrates was condemned to drink the hemlock.

Aristippus of Cyrene was a follower of Protagoras before joining the Socratics. He maintained with Protagoras that all our knowledge is subjective. His ethics, too, leaned toward the doctrine of Protagoras. He considered pleasure the ultimate aim of life, and hence became the founder of hedonism. However, he espoused mental pleasures, art and literature, parental and filial love, as opposed to the gross sensual pleasures. In the matter of moral principles, therefore, he was a follower of Socrates, with his advocacy of moderation in indulgence and intelligent control of our natural instincts. In other words, we must be masters of ourselves. Yet all our actions were motivated by a desire to be happy.

The hedonists were freethinkers and some openly espoused atheism. Euhemerus, however, believed that the gods were distinguished men which were deified after death. Strangely, but after all no more than might have been expected, hedonism changes into a pessimistic philosophy. Hegesias, a contemporary of Aristippus, maintained that inasmuch as the only purpose in life is pleasure, a purpose never realized, life has no value. In fact, he states death is preferable to life as pain ceases with death.

Antisthenes was the philosopher who espoused the motto— Virtue for Virtue's Sake. He was the founder of the Cynic school, its name having been derived from the name of the gymnasium of Kynosarges where he taught. Virtue was considered the final and only goal of all our actions and the highest good. Life has real value only to those who recognize a higher aim such as virtue for virtue's sake, and the like. The moral idealism of Antisthenes was exaggerated by some of the cynics, culminating in caricaturing it.

Euclides, the founder of the school of Megara, combined the teaching of Parmenides that being is one, and of Socrates concerning the reality of moral principles. With these two premises he concludes that mind or goodness is the only absolutely-existing being. His system, incidentally, furnished the connecting thought between the doctrines of Socrates and those of Plato, whose teachings we shall next review.

Deification of Thought—Negation of Matter

Plato, who deified thought, was born about 427 B.C. of a noble family in Athens. His later philosophy revealed the influence of his early instruction, first under Cratylus who was a disciple of Heraclitus, then as a pupil of Socrates, and finally under Euclides who gave him a background in the thinking of Parmenides. Pythagoreanism also influenced his thinking.

Some of his wealthy friends in Athens presented him with the place where he taught, a place known as the Academy.

Plato's treatises whose genuineness is unquestioned are nine in number: (1) Phaedrus, in which he criticizes the rhetoric of the Sophists; (2) Protagoras, in which he treats of the doctrine of virtue of Socrates; (3) Symposium, which concerns the various manifestations of love from the strictly sensual to love of beauty, truth, and goodness; (4) Gorgias, the true sage versus the Sophist; (5) Republic, which deals with the State embodying the idea of justice; (6) Timaeus, concerning nature; (7) Theaetetus, a treatise on knowledge and ideas; (8) Phaedo, concerning the immortality of the soul; and (9) Laws, which appears to be a modification of his ideas in Republic.

These treatises were in dialogue form, Socrates (having passed on) being the chief spokesman. It was thought by some that he used this form so he could place in the mouth of someone else his own thoughts on controversial subjects such as religion. Others felt he used the dialogue form because he had no complete philosophical system.

Out of polytheism Plato, with others, evolved the idea of a single supreme, and righteous Zeus. This gradually led to a belief in the uniformity of nature under universal laws in place of the capricious happenings dependent on the changeable will of many irresponsible gods. Plato's theology later undoubtedly influenced St. Augustine's thinking, and his dialectics no doubt influenced the thinking of Hegel. Plato's philosophy has its basis not in sense perception but is, like the science of mathematics, a product of a priori intuition and reasoning. It is a science of ideas and is called dialectics from its new rationalistic methods.

From his science of ideas, he attempts to rationalize a theory of nature. He maintains that ethics, the science of the highest good, is the ultimate in philosophical thought. Practically speaking, however, he apparently deduced his idea of the good from overt observations, such as observing the reactions of a mother to her child, and so on; the idea of the beautiful from observation of works of art, and the like. It does appear, then, that he deduced his so-called ideas from overt observation of nature; however, he disowned such sources and embraced ideas as the unsoiled products of pure thought. Ideas alone are real and the final goal of nature is the so-called highest good (the ultimate idea). Ideas which we acquire through reason are to our notions what objects of sense are to sense perception, in other words, their objective causes. He contended that the entire sensible world is only a symbol of what the ideas are in reality. The ideas form a unity and cannot be separated, and their abode is heaven. (The fallacy of his system, therefore, would seem to be his dogmatic assumption of the creator's thought prior to his creative activity, and the denial of the creator's accomplished creation as the real source of his [Plato's] ideas. After all Plato himself was the product of the creator's thought.)

Rationalizing nature from his ideas undoubtedly presented quite a problem for Plato. Yet Plato would defend his viewpoint by stating that the senses are deceptive (which is very often true) and that reasoning is the only way to truth, inspired by the love of truth, a particular form of universal love. The human body to him was constructed and organized as a house of correction and education of the soul with a view to its moral perfection. Intelligence or reason was considered by him to be immortal, and sensuality as mortal. Being-mind (thought) was considered to be being itself, the phenomena of nature as non-being. Reason, of course, could not be considered as the creator of non-being for then his system would lose its claim for monism but become dualistic.

The destructive criticism of the atomic theory by Plato to be followed later by that of Aristotle, was one of the reasons this theory was quiescent for a thousand years. Plato was, according to Whitehead, the greatest mind ever produced by Western men—but so far as encouraging experimental science is concerned, he was disastrous.

Speusippus, Plato's successor, apparently saw the necessity of correcting this blind spot by combining the One (the Idea) and the many (matter). This he accomplishes by the use of the Pythagorean notion of emanation, that perfection is to be found in the differentiated and organized unity and not in the original abstract unity. However, it fell upon Aristotle to reform the concrete spiritualistic doctrines of the Academy, and we shall next consider his contribution.

Aristotle was born in 385 at Stagira. As he came from a family of physicians, the inclinations of an experimentalist and scientist were innate within him. He was the star pupil of Plato, later becoming a rival of the old master.

He became the teacher and friend of Alexander, the son of King Philip of Macedon. This friendship proved very advantageous for him because later his friend as Alexander the Great, would during his conquests in the East collect specimens of all forms of nature life and send them to Aristotle for study. This in a large measure enabled Aristotle to become the founder of natural science.

Aristotle was a prolific writer on all subjects—mathematics, physics, theology, ethics, politics and logic. His various writings on logic, beginning with the categories, were collected under the name Organon. This work was instrumental to his being considered the real founder of deductive logic, his principal claim to fame.

Philosophy was defined by Aristotle as the science of universals. He entertained no doubt as to the possibility of a science of nature, the teachings of the Sophists and Sceptics to the contrary. He maintained that Plato erred in conceiving the Ideas as real beings subsisting apart from the individuals expressing them. The idea, he maintained, is the form inherent in the thing, and cannot be separated by abstraction.

As generative causes of real things, he postulates a material cause, a formal cause, an efficient or moving cause, and a final cause. There are for every fact the foregoing four causes.

Both Aristotle and Plato regard matter and form as eternal. To Aristotle, however, matter is the beginning of all things, and shape or form (Idea) is the goal. For Plato the Idea is the only reality. They both strive for monism, not by pure reasoning, however, but by means of rationalization. Aristotle used the inductive method in the study of nature and Plato the deductive.

Aristotle postulates the principle of causality as the necessary consequence of his so-called principle of the first mover, which is itself immovable. Aristotle maintained that a continually acting cause is needed to keep a body moving. Plato, however, maintained that a cause is necessary only in deflecting a body from a straight path.

Absolute thought is identical with its object; whereas our discursive thought must pursue an object which is different from it, and therefore requires gradual stages for its attainment. Thought begins as an empty tablet, and later experience leaves its impressions upon it.

In his science of nature, circular and rectilinear movements upward and downward, are the two basic forms in the physical world. And the mistakes of nature are chargeable to matter and not to the active idea.

His contributions in Biology are outstanding, especially in classifying animals and in ascribing function to bodily organs. (Two seemingly inexcusable errors are made by him, namely, that the heart was the seat of intelligence and the brain a cooling organ. He also maintained there was no sexuality in plants.)

Whereas Democritus had taught that the heavier atoms fell faster in a vacuum, Aristotle denied this, and stated that bodies in a vacuum would fall equally fast. However, as his own conclusion seemed inconceivable to him, he concluded that there could never be a vacuum.

The relation existing between the physical body and the soul, its vital principle, is analogous to the relation between matter and form. Without the body the soul may exist potentially but not in reality. He therefore did not believe in immortality; when the body died, the soul too ceased to exist. Aristotle further maintained that the human understanding is not the creator but only the recipient of ideas.

Morality is possible in man, according to Aristotle, as a result of the coexistence of animal and intellectual principles, and he defines virtue as the equilibrium between these two principles.

Because of the prestige of both Plato and Aristotle their erroneous conclusions were not questioned until years later, thus delaying the advancement of science until Galileo and Copernicus.

Theophrastus, born 370 B.C., was a pupil of Aristotle. He made outstanding contributions in botany, apparently using the collections made on Alexander's conquests as materials for study. During this same period, Eudoxus of Cnidos did good work in astronomy. His system later led to the elaborate systems of Hipparchus and Ptolemy, whose systems met the approval of astronomers until the time of Copernicus.

Deification of Matter—Negation of Thought-Substance

Epicurus follows Aristotle with the negation of the thought-substance of both Plato and Aristotle. He replaces it with the deification of matter, and the creation of a philosophy of pleasure.

Epicurus believed that man's fear of the gods and the hereafter constituted the chief hindrance to his happiness; that the duty of philosophy by observation and reasoning was to free man from belief in the supernatural. He was interested in theory only as related to practice; his aim was to make science practical.

Matter was the universal principle of things and the soul, mind, and thought were but accidents. Outside of matter there was only the void—to permit movement.

He assumes chance, which view makes it possible for him to recognize the freedom of indifference in ethics.

As death does not exist with the living and as the dead have no feeling, he concluded that there is no reason for man to fear it. Pleasure is the greatest good, that is, pleasures of the mind—which have greater permanence rather than sensual pleasures which are only for the moment.

Early Emphasis on Will—Stoicism

The next system of philosophy we shall consider is Stoicism, which philosophy deifies the will rather than matter. The Stoic school was founded by Zeno in Cyprus, the son of a family of Phoenician merchants. Zeno first studied under the Cynics, later under the Magarians, and finally under the Academicians. He sought the final goal of life by searching for the first cause. He rejected the Idea of Plato as having no objective existence. He maintained, too, that the soul has no innate ideas, that it was an empty tablet, with all its concepts coming from without. Sensation was recognized as the source of all our ideas.

Stoic metaphysics is concrete spiritualism, mind and body being considered as two aspects of the same reality. The theology of the Stoics is a sort of compromise between pantheism and theism. The universe is considered as a real being, a living God who governs man's destiny, and is motivated by love and a desire for man's welfare.

The physics of the Stoics is similar to that of Heraclitus. As a spark is to the flame, so is man to the God-universe.

The moral idealism previously taught by Socrates and Plato was the unifying element between different members of the Stoic school. Their motto was "virtue for virtue's sake." Their moral idealism and at the same time the thorough-going realism of their ontology were of course contradictory doctrines.

It should be kept in mind that Stoicism was not only a

system of philosophy but a religion as well; it was a substitute for polytheism. This philosophical system appears to have been embraced by a select class and did not get down to the people as a whole.

Rise of Scepticism

Pyrrho of Elis, a contemporary of Aristotle, concludes that the essence of things is incomprehensible. Therefore, he avoids the categorical affirmation of the dogmatists, as well as the absolute negation of the Sophists. He takes no part in heated disputes and suspends judgment on controversial subjects. He maintained that no two schools of philosophy agreed on the essential problems.

The doctrine of Pyrrho has been summarized by Eusebius as having three aspects: (1) that the dogmatic philosophers cannot prove their starting point; (2) that an objective knowledge of things is impossible; and (3) therefore, in order to be happy, barren speculations should be avoided and nature's laws should be obeyed.

Arcesilaus of Pitane was a sceptic of the same type as the Academicians. His main activity was devoted to teaching in the Socratic tradition. He stressed that nothing should be accepted unconditionally. Whereas Zeno made clear ideas the criterion of truth, Arcesilaus calls attention to the illusions of the senses, and exaggerates the scepticism of Socrates who maintained that the only thing he knew was that he knew nothing. Arcesilaus went one step further by stating that he was not even sure of that.

Another sceptic, Carneades, did not differ from the early Sophists. He opposed the Stoics in ethics and religion as well as in ontology. He asserted that the Stoic god was no god; that inasmuch as the Stoics maintained that god was the soul of the world, he must have feeling; that if he had sensation, he could be changed as anything else subject to sensation, even to the extent of dying.

He also considered that there was no more certainty in morals than in metaphysics. In fact, on a political trip to Rome he delivered a speech in favor of justice one day, and the next day against justice.

Aenesidemus of Cnossus was an exponent of sensationalistic as opposed to idealistic scepticism. He questioned the possibility of a certain knowledge; differences of position and distance change our perception of objects, and so on; no sensation is pure—qualities differ with quantities. He criticized the notion of causality, stating that the efficient cause of a body cannot be a body, nor can it be an immaterial entity.

The sceptics, because of their doubts, could espouse no philosophical system; and their only dogma, if they were to have one, would be to doubt their own scepticism. To doubt their own conclusions was the last straw for radical scepticism. They abdicated in favor of Academic probabilism.

Scepticism wrote the finale on further creative philosophy in Greece. The Greek scholars now devoted their time to reflecting back on the good old days, their creative force spent; they became eclectic and lived on their past. Of course, it may have been true, too, that they had exhausted all the main avenues of philosophical thought. This would appear to be true, for all later philosophical systems, as well as science itself, contain basic elements of thought suggested in the philosophies of this early period.

VII

EARLY GREEK AND ALEXANDRIAN CONTRIBUTIONS TO SCIENCE

Mathematics flourished in Egypt while barbarism existed in Greece. The Greeks later became interested in mathematics. However, they had no interest in experimental science for reasons of their own impatience and their paralyzing belief that their senses were deceptive and that reasoning was incapable of correcting this deception. The exact sciences—mathematics and mathematical physics, based on reasoning, made good headway, however, among the Greeks.

We shall now turn our attention from Greece to Alexandria (the City where east met west) and southern Italy, where a more scientific attitude of mind prevailed. Increased knowledge of natural things stimulated more and more curiosity, and analytic science gradually replaced synthetic philosophies.

Euclid, a Greek living in Alexandria about 300 B.C., collected and systematized miscellaneous data on geometry from various sources. From a few axioms he deduced by logical principles a series of propositions in a manner which remained the accepted method until recent years. This deductive method was an hypothesis of the nature of space based on observational facts of Egyptian land-surveying around the Nile Delta. Mathematical geometry, based on Euclid's principles, subsequently succeeded in verifying Newtonian three-dimensional astronomy. Hence, Greek geometry is given the highest place, along with modern experimental science, among the accomplishments of the human mind.

Now we shall mention the interesting background of the so-called Archimedes' principle. Archimedes of Syracuse (287-212

B.C.) was asked by King Hiero to check his suspicions that certain gold entrusted to artificers for a crown had been alloyed with silver. In his endeavor to solve the problem Archimedes recalled that the weight of water he displaced in his bathtub was equal to his own weight. He went on to use the principle thus revealed in solving the King's problem.

In solving other problems he discovered the theoretical principle of the lever. He also determined the ratio of the circumference to the diameter of a circle as approximately 3 1/7.

The recordings made by Archimedes of his various experiments were much sought after later by Leonardo da Vinci. Archimedes was killed when the Romans stormed Syracuse in 212 B.C.

Aristarchus of Samos (310-230 B.C.) with the use of geometry concluded that the sun was considerably larger than the earth, and further that the earth circled the sun rather than the reverse. His conclusions were too far advanced to receive general approval at that time, although Seleucus of Babylonia confidently supported his conclusions about 200 B.C.

About 130 B.C., Hipparchus, using the ideas of Eudoxus of Cnidos, developed the geocentric theory, which was expanded by Ptolemy of Alexandria about 127-151 A.D. This theory was generally accepted until the sixteenth century.

Hipparchus also invented both plane and spherical geometry. He attempted by measuring their latitude and longitude to determine the position of different places on the earth. His geocentric theory, while it explained all facts, overlooked the principle of inertia. His theory, incidentally, encouraged astrology.

The intellectual center by the beginning of the third century B.C. had moved from Athens to Alexandria. The fame of Euclid, the great geometer, and Herophilus, the anatomist and physician, helped to bring about this change of location.

As the scholars of Alexandria limited their inquiries, they made more scientific progress. Erasistratus established physiology as a separate branch of biology, and Eratosthenes was the first great physical geographer. The latter scholar estimated the circumference of the earth as 24,000 miles, as against the modern estimate of 24,800 miles. It was probably he who conjectured that the Atlantic might be divided by land running from north to south. If Columbus had followed Eratosthenes' theory instead of Poseidonius, he would not have been surprised at discovering

America. Poseidonius had rejected Eratosthenes' contributions and had greatly underestimated the circumference of the earth, and as a consequence, the distance to India via the western route.

In the second century B.C. Apollonius introduced the names parabola, ellipse, and hyperbola in the study of geometry. Sometime between the first century B.C. and the third A.D., Hero found algebraic solutions to equations of the first and second degree, and at the same time worked out formulae for computing areas and volumes. Hero also invented certain mechanical contrivances, such as siphons, forcing-air pump, and a steam engine.

During the second century A.D., Claudius Ptolemy, the distinguished Alexandrian astronomer, wrote an encyclopaedia on astronomy based on the work of Hipparchus. This encyclopaedia was considered the standard until the time of Copernicus. Claudius Ptolemy also wrote a book on Optics which is considered by some as revealing remarkable experimental research.

The oldest known works on alchemy are those of the so-called "pseudo-Democritus" around the first century A.D., and of Zosimos who lived in Egypt about the third century A.D. An industry, in making imitations of such items as dyes, pearls, and metal alloys resembling gold and silver, used early chemical processes. This industry therefore served as motivation for the development of alchemy, and alchemy in turn became the science of chemistry. Alchemists, of course, strove to transmute metals into gold, applying the method of trial and error, coupled with observation. This activity, however, came to an abrupt halt in Alexandria when Emperor Diocletian decreed that all books on alchemy be destroyed. This study was later revived with the Arabs and later in Europe.

VIII.

EARLY CONTRIBUTIONS TO GENERAL CULTURAL DEVELOPMENT

Roman Contributions

The Romans were principally concerned with the welfare and promotion of the State. This naturally involved the development of administrators and soldiers. Hence any creative work in science during the Roman Age was the work of Greek philosophers and scientists who lived in or later moved to Italy. The Romans were interested in science only from the standpoint of practical applications of it.

Diogenes of Babylonia brought the Stoic philosophy to Rome. This philosophy, with elements of Platonism, represented the main philosophy of the Romans for three hundred years. Its highest form is seen in the works of Emperor Marcus Aurelius.

Marcus Tullius Cicero (106-43 B.C.), a Roman lawyer and statesman, wrote a cosmological treatise called de Natura Deorum, in which he summarized Greek philosophy and the current scientific knowledge. He did much to put this knowledge in the Latin language. He also developed a teleological theory of the human body.

It was during this period that Titus Lucretius Carus composed his poem de Rerum Natura, in which he emphasized the principle of causation in all the phenomena of nature. In this way he discouraged the propagation of magic then current.

Gaius Julius Caesar (100-44 B.C.) was the greatest man of that century. He is remembered as the creator, with the technical assistance of Sosigenes, of the so-called Julian calendar in which the year is considered as made up of 365¼ days.

Road maps first put in their appearance during this period, necessitated of course by the many ramifications of the Roman Empire.

Vitruvius wrote a treatise on architecture. This treatise revealed that he was aware of sound as a vibration in air, for his treatise furnishes the first account of the principle of acoustics.

Sextus Julius Frontinus (40-103 A.D.), an engineer serving as Superintendent of the Aqueducts of Rome, wrote a treatise giving useful observations on hydrodynamics.

In the reign of Tiberius, Celsus wrote a treatise on medicine and surgery. This book is the chief source of our knowledge of medicine in Alexandria as well as in Rome at that time.

In the middle of the first century A.D., Dioscorides, a botanist, wrote a book on botany and pharmacy, giving an account of about 600 plants and their medicinal properties. This book was in use for fifteen centuries.

The elder Pliny (23-79 A.D.), compiled a massive encyclopaedia called Naturalis Historia, covering all the knowledge of the period, real and imaginary. He was killed while venturing too close to the erupting Vesuvius which destroyed Pompei.

Diogenes Laertius wrote the Lives of Philosophers, which together with the works of Plutarch (50-125 A.D.), served as a principal source of information on the early Greek philosophers.

As to historians, Josephus (37-120 A.D.) furnished us with a record of the Jews. Tacitus (55-120 A.D.) is the Latin authority for the early social and political history of Britain and Germany.

Galen, who after Hippocrates was the most famous physician of the Ancient world, was born in the year 129 A.D. at Pergamos, Asia Minor. He practiced medicine in Rome until about 200 A.D., and also systematized and united the various schools of medicine of his time. He engaged in dissection of animals, including man; through these dissections he learned about the operation of the heart and the nature of the spinal cord.

In philosophy he held that the structure of the body was created by God, each organ for a specific purpose. His theistic attitude appealed to both Christendom and Islam, which partly explains his general influence.

Here again is an example of where the great reputation of

a man can temporarily discourage further development. Galen's theory of animal spirits, along with his interpretation of the functions of various organs of the body, discouraged further development of physiology until Harvey discovered the circulation of the blood some 1500 years later. It seems that it is never left to any one man to proclaim all truth, but to each man a partial contribution only. The task is to sift out error.

Mention should be made before we leave the Roman Age of the culmination of Roman law, a great achievement during the first three centuries of the Empire.

In philosophy Platonism predominated over Aristotle's philosophy, although Aristotle was considered the authority on questions of scientific theory. This predominance of Plato and Aristotle was also true in Alexandria during that period.

Plato's Timaeus, on which Chalcidius wrote a Latin commentary during this period, became the only source of knowledge of nature during the centuries when Aristotle's works were forgotten.

Alexandrian Contributions

The scientific work of the Alexandrian school was carried on mostly by scholars of Greek descent. However, among the non-Greek elements the most important were Jews. In this connection it should be kept in mind that only a small proportion of the Jews in Babylon returned to Jerusalem after their captivity. The rest established themselves as traders in the various cities of Asia Minor and the Levant. Alexandria became the commercial center and Jerusalem their religious center. Hence, a school of thought arose in Alexandria influenced by not only Greek thought but also Jewish and Babylonian tradition. Alexandria became an important meeting-ground between the Hellenistic and Oriental religions, especially Judaism and Christianity. As many early Greek Fathers of the Christian Church lived in and drew their philosophy from Alexandria, the resulting synthesis shows up in the composition of Patristic theology.

Neo-Platonistic Philosophy

The system of philosophy known as neo-platonism grew up together with the Christian religion, but later parted ways as neo-platonism reverted to polytheism.

Plotinus of Lycopolis in Egypt, a disciple of Ammonius Saccas of Alexandria, went to Rome about 244 A.D., and taught philosophy there for twenty-five years. Beginning to write at the age of fifty, he turned out numerous treatises, fifty-four of which were published later by Porphyry, his disciple.

The fundamental thesis of Plotinus' works was emanatistic pantheism. He maintained that every being is made up of matter and form. God is the One (the Form). Matter suffers everything, becomes everything, and is that which is infinitely modified—the very opposite of the Absolute principle. God eludes thought; he transcends everything that can be conceived. As we abstract ideas from sensible things, so we abstract ideas in order to reach God.

Plotinus conceives three stages of being which "overflow" from God: (1) Intelligence—It is creative like the Absolute, and inasmuch as it is the first emanation from God, it is the greatest thing in the world; (2) The Soul—This is an emanation or creation of Intelligence, but it is an inferior emanation to that of Intelligence, the original emanation of the Absolute; (3) The Body—While the body is far removed from God, the Absolute, yet it bears its stamp. The Intellect has its ideas; the Soul its notions, the Body its forms.

As the soul is intermediate between the intellect and the body, it contains both elements, in a larger sense the meeting place of all cosmical powers. In the intellectual sphere, logical necessity rules, and in the world of bodies, physical necessity rules.

The seat of the free-will is in the Soul. It must choose between the attractions of the body and those of the intellect. The higher choice would be that toward the intellect or reason.

The end of human life as neo-platonism saw it, is the purification of the soul, gradually becoming one with the divinity. Its ethical system contains elements from both Platonism and Stoicism.

Both Plotinus and Porphyry speak against superstition. However, their successors, Jamblichus and Proclus, subordinate the search for truth to interests in religion and apologetics. Greek philosophy had spoken out against traditional religion, polytheism, only to witness a foreign religion, Christianity, replacing it. As these philosophers felt that the new religion was more intolerant than polytheism, they reverted to supporting polytheism, with its system of magic. The fundamental dogma of

Christianity assumed the communicability of God. This dogma led Proclus to exaggerate the transcendency of the divine, which was the chief weakness of Platonism. Proclus maintains the practice of magic as the principal element in religion. Plato, on the other hand, states that religion means the practice of justice.

The school at Athens where Proclus taught was closed in 529 by order of Emperor Justinian. By that time Christianity had been the dominant religion of the Roman Empire for two centuries.

Patristic and early mediaeval Christianity discouraged secular learning. Whereas the older Greek philosophies were based on observation of the visible world, philosophy in Rome now became subservient to theology. In such an environment natural science went into an eclipse, with the exception of medicine.

Mithraism, a Persian mystery religion, disputed with Christianity for control of the Roman Empire. Beneath the rites and legends of Mithraism primitive nature-worship appears. The legends were accepted literally by the uneducated whereas the educated class interpreted them symbolically.

At that time it was Saint Paul who preached Christianity as a world religion and prevented it from becoming just a Jewish sect.

Origen (185-254 A.D.) proclaimed the conformity of the Alexandrian science with the Christian religion. His basic tenet is the unchangeableness of God, and involved both the eternity of the Logos and of the world, and the pre-existence of souls. Origen's theology became progressively unacceptable to the Christian leaders and was condemned in 553 by the Council of Constantinople.

IX.

GENERAL CULTURAL DEVELOPMENTS DURING MIDDLE AGES

Saint Augustine — Christian-Platonic Philosophy

Saint Augustine (354-430) exerted the deepest influence on Christian thought. He was first a Manichean (another Persian mystery religion), and then a Neo-Platonist. He was finally converted to Christianity, and gave up his rather loose living.

He wrote the Confessions and the City of God, among the greatest of Christian classics. He combined Platonism with the teachings of Saint Paul's epistles, forming the first great Christian synthesis of knowledge. Both Christianity and Neo-Platonism are based on the fundamental assumption that spirit is the ultimate reality.

It appears that the attacks by philosophy against the Christian Gospel compelled the Christians to study philosophy in self-defense. As a result of the disputes, the Christian faith was reduced to dogmas, formulated and systematized.

Plato was the only philosopher to receive serious consideration by the Christian leaders. They believed Plato had gotten his basic ideas from the writings of the Old Testament.

St. Augustine's writings served as the connecting link between Greek philosophy and Scholastic speculation. He maintained, as did Plato, that science means a purer and more exalted life, that reason can comprehend God as it was given to man by Him to know all things. He maintained reason was the so-called eye of the soul, and that wisdom is the highest truth for which we should strive. To have wisdom is to have God, and therefore true philosophy and true religion are identical.

Instead of faith being opposed to reason, faith is only possible with those endowed with reason; faith precedes intelligence and is a condition of knowledge, ultimately resolving itself into knowledge. Goodness, justice and wisdom are the innermost essence of God.

St. Augustine avoids being a pantheist by his doctrine of creation ex nihilo. St. Augustine maintained the trinity as constituting one God-head, as against the Arianists who maintained each of the three aspects as three separate persons. St. Augustine disputed with them concerning this belief.

He stated that the existence of the soul is proved by thought, consciousness and memory. The soul is a substance differing from all known matter, for it contains the conceptions of the point, length and breadth, and other like notions which are incorporeal. The soul is a creature of God, with a beginning like every other creature. He maintains God's freedom; and this leads to a strictly deterministic doctrine which excludes so-called free-will.

Scientific Contributions of Rome and Its Subsequent Eclipse

Just before the so-called Dark Ages of the sixth and seventh centuries, Boethius was the last writer to show the true spirit of ancient philosophy. He was a Roman of noble birth who wrote compendiums and commentaries on Plato and Aristotle, and on the four mathematical subjects—arithmetic, geometry, music, and astronomy. His manuals were used as school textbooks in the Middle Ages, in fact practically the only knowledge of Aristotle in the early part of the Middle Ages came from Boethius' commentaries. He was a Christian and died a martyr in 524.

Many causes have been given for the beginning of the decline of Rome. Sir Archibald Alison ascribes as one of the principal causes its shortage of currency, causing an economic dislocation. The gold and silver mines of Spain and Greece began to fail, and the Empire went through a period of serious deflation. Industry and agriculture ceased to be profitable, and taxes became unbearable. Also vast tracts of land became uninhabitable because of malaria. Then, too, the population dropped among the better class and increased with the poorer mongrel class. In other words, the superior Roman and Greek population gradually died out. The barbarians from the north have been blamed for the fall of the Empire whereas in truth it was more a case of internal decay.

Paradoxically, with the collapse of the upper class who regarded work beneath their dignity and position, men became more practical in order to keep alive. The mechanical foundation of present-day culture was really laid during the Dark Ages. Ralph Linton, the anthropologist, states in his 'Tree of Culture,'—"As a matter of fact, more mechanical improvements were made during the Dark Ages than during the whole Greek and Roman Classical period."

During the period that European learning was in eclipse, a mixed culture of Greek, Roman and Jewish sources was nurtured in the Byzantine Imperial Court at Constantinople, and in the countries from Syria to the Persian Gulf.

Muhammadan and Arabian Contributions

Under the stimulus of Muhammad between 620 and 650, the Arabs conquered Arabia, Syria, Persia and Egypt. One hundred and fifty years later Harun-al-Rashid, a famous Abbasid Caliph, encouraged the translation of Greek authors, and in that way initiated the greatest period in Arab learning.

According to the Koran, Allah created and upholds the world, which has only secondary existence. This view had previously been modified by Greek philosophy to incorporate the Neo-Platonic idea of endless chain of existence with Aristotle's idea of the Cosmos. Hence, the Cosmos is God. To explain nature in orthodox Muhammadan terms, another group espoused a theory of time apparently derived from the Indian Buddhistic atomic philosophy. The world is made up of like atoms, which Allah recreates from instant to instant; even space is atomic. If Allah were to cease recreating, the Universe would disappear. Time is composed of indivisible "nows," i.e., instants in the sense used by modern mathematicians and physicists. Man is but a so-called motion-picture automaton.

It would seem that these theological speculations would discourage the study of nature in the Near East. Contrariwise, it stimulated a curiosity regarding nature, to which the Muhammadan theologians denied reality. Islamic science grew while the science of the West went into eclipse.

Since the Alexandrian alchemists of the first century, little progress was made until the Arabians took up the subject where

69

the Alexandrians left off. The Arabian alchemists set before themselves two problems, one to transmute basic metals into gold, and the other to find the elixir vitae to cure all human ills.

The chief center of alchemist activity was in Irak and later on in Spain among Arab-speaking people. They failed in solving both problems, but in the process of their search, they developed the science of chemistry. This science entered Europe through Spain during the Middle Ages. The most famous Arabian alchemist and chemist, Abu-Musa-Jabir-ibn-Haiyan, flourished about 776. He is now thought to be the original author of writings on chemistry appearing later in Latin under the name "Geber." This supposition is still uncertain however.

It was during this period that so-called Arabic numerals were observed among Arab traders in Spain. These numerals have since been found to be of Hindu origin.

Muslim astronomers were stimulated by the translation of Ptolemy's works. Among the Arabian astronomers was Muhammad-al-Baltani (850), who recalculated the procession of the equinoxes.

About the year 1000, Ibn Junis placed on record his observations on solar and lunar eclipses; these were made possible because of advances in trigonometry. This astronomer is generally considered the greatest among the Muslims.

Persian Abn Bakr al-Razix is considered to be the greatest Muslim physician, who practiced in Baghdad in the tenth century. He compiled many textbooks, one containing an article on measles and smallpox.

Ibn-al-Haitham (965-1020) was the greatest Muslim physicist, working in Egypt. He specialized in optics; the technique used by him was a great advance in the experimental method. He improved knowledge of the eye—of the process of vision. He also solved with the use of mathematics the problem in geometrical optics. The Latin translations of his works influenced the development of this science in the West by Roger Bacon and Kepler.

It was during this period that the Muslim physician and philosopher Avicenna (980-1037) is said to have sought in vain among the courts of Central Asia a place to carry on his scientific and literary labors. He wrote on all the then known sciences. "Canon," his greatest work, was a compendium of medicine, and represents one of the highest accomplishments of

Arabic culture. It afterwards became the textbook of medical study in European universities.

Living in the same period as Avicenna was al-Biruni, a geographer, philosopher and astronomer. He determined latitudes and longitudes with some degree of accuracy, made geodetic measurements, and explained the principles underlying natural springs and artesian wells.

In the eleventh century appeared an important algebraic work by Omar Khayyám, a Persian poet. During the same period al-Ghazzali synthesized philosophy with Muhammadanism, similar to the work Thomas Aquinas performed for Christianity.

By the end of the eleventh century, the decline of Arabic learning had commenced. Strangely the reasons for the decline were comparable to those of Rome. The Arabian Empire decayed as a result of internal quarrels between Muhammadan princes and generals. The gifted old-established noble Arab families gradually died out. The distant provinces, sensing the weakness of the central government, one by one pulled away from the Empire.

Arabian, Jewish, and Christian Civilizations in Spain

In Spain, the farthest province of the Muhammadan Empire, the intercourse between the Arabian, Jewish, and Christian civilizations produced fruitful results, even before the Muhammadans conquered Spain in 711. An environment of law and order conducive to learning was made possible between 418 to 711 by a West Gothic Kingdom which had established itself in Spain. Traditions of Alexandrian culture had been carried to Spain by Jews originally deported from Palestine to Spain under Titus. As we have already indicated, this favorable environment continued even after the Muhammadans conquered Spain.

Attempts were made to harmonize the sacred literature of Spain with Greek philosophy, resulting in a contest between the theologians who relied on reason and those who relied on revelation. The new Orthodox Muslim Scholasticism, founded by al-Ghazzali in Baghdad, was also prevalent in Spain.

The real fame of the Spanish-Arabian school was the result of Averroës' work. He was born in Cordova in 1126. Averroës showed a great reverence for Aristotle, and introduced a new

71

interpretation of the relations between philosophy and religion. Religion, he maintained, is not a branch of knowledge that can be reduced to propositions and dogmas, but a personal and inward power. Theology, being a mixture of both, is a source of evil to both. Religion should not be corrupted as a pseudo-science.

Maimonides (1135-1204), a Jewish philosopher, physician, mathematician, and astronomer, constructed a Jewish system of Scholasticism comparable to that of al-Ghazzali and Thomas Aquinas for their respective religions. He sought to synthesize Jewish theology with Aristotle's philosophy. Because his followers tried to press too far his views to the point of interpreting the whole of Biblical history as symbolic, great controversy on this issue arose later.

Revival of Knowledge in Constantinople, Italy and Other European Countries

While it is probable that some of the secular schools in the large towns in Italy continued during the Dark Ages, yet the rise of monasteries gave the secure and peaceful environment conducive to the new growth of learning appearing at the dawn of the new period. Medicine was the earliest science to take on new life. The Benedictines studied the works of Hippocrates and Galen, and gradually spread this knowledge. The monks were also active in farming, and thereby kept alive the art of agriculture.

The first new secular schools were in Salerno, and in the ninth century the Salernian physicians were already famous. In the eleventh century they began to read translations of Arabic works.

During the ninth and tenth century a revival of knowledge took place in Constantinople when Constantine VII ordered the compilation of certain encyclopaedic treatises. Because of this order, many Greek manuscripts were reproduced and preserved.

In Northern Europe both Charlemagne and Alfred the Great encouraged scholars, the latter translating certain Latin works into Anglo-Saxon. Gerbert, a learned French mathematician, taught at Rheims and elsewhere from 972 until 999, and later became Pope Sylvester II. In his treatises he dealt with the abacus, the astrolabe, and Hindu numerals.

In the ninth century Scotus Erigena (815-877), a disciple of Origen, founded the school of Scholasticism. St. Anselmus, Abelard, Thomas Aquinas, and Duns Scotus are its later outstanding representatives. Scholasticism proved to be modern science in embryo.

Scotus Erigena represented the first period of Scholasticism, the so-called Platonic period. It will be recalled that St. Augustine used the philosophy of Plato in adapting Christianity to philosophy in his theology.

Thomas Aquinas represented the second period, the Peripatetic or Aristotelian period. The peripatetic period, in turn, is made up of two sub-periods, one interpreting Aristotle in the realistic sense and the other in the nominalistic sense.

Among some of the teachings of Scotus Erigena is the theory that the divine is the only reality. It contained the first great synthesis of the medieval period of the Christian faith with Greek philosophy. He maintained that reason leads to a philosophical system which agrees with properly interpreted scriptures. Philosophy studies, discusses, and explains with the aid of reason, what religion worships and adores. The word Nature in its broadest sense embraces all beings, both uncreated (God) and created things. Perfection and reality are identical; hence a thing has existence to the extent of its goodness. Evil from that standpoint would have no reality. Wisdom and science are derived from reason, and reason in turn springs from life. Creation is interpreted as an harmonious progressive sequence of concentric circles. He further maintained that the aim of human science is to learn how things arise from first causes, and how they are divided into species and genera.

Scotus Erigena also taught that as everything comes from God, so everything is destined to return to Him. He further taught universal predestination for salvation.

Nominalism vs. Realism

The original dispute between Plato and Aristotle on the nature of universals or "intelligible" forms found its way to Europe through the writings of Boethius. To the medieval mind it became a problem of classification, nominalism versus realism. Are Democritus and Socrates realities, and humanity only a name? (Realism to the medievalists is comparable to our idealism; nominalism to our materialism. Likewise the subjective to the scholastics is what the modern scientists call objective; the objective to the scholastics is comparable to what modern scientists consider subjective. Both Descartes and Spinoza used these latter terms in the scholastic sense, which is a good illustration of the importance of the definition of terms.)

Platonic Viewpoint—the Original One of Catholicism

Catholicism naturally espoused the platonic view, that the idea was real and not the individual, for the Church must be real as against the individual members.

The dispute came to a head so far as the Church was concerned when Berengarius of Tours (999-1088) criticized the doctrine of transubstantiation, stating that no change of substance could take place in the bread and wine with no corresponding change in its appearance and taste. Roscellinus (1125) supported this tendency toward nominalism, stating that the individual is the sole reality. He thus reached a tritheistic conception of the Trinity. William of Champeaux and Anselm of Canterbury, being on the side of realism, both opposed this nominalistic interpretation. Anselm used the term realism in the scholastic sense in his so-called ontological argument to prove the existence of God, i.e., that we have in ourselves the idea of an absolutely perfect being; now, perfection implies existence; hence, God exists. Gaunilo, a monk of Marmoutiers, pointed out, however, that we may conceive and imagine a being, and yet that being may not exist. What Anselm aimed to prove is not the God idea of Plato and Hegel, but the existence of a personal God.

This orthodox view of realism lay dormant for several centuries, when the realistic interpretation was again reversed by Thomas Aquinas in favor of Aristotle's interpretation. (Incidentally, the old disputes between the realists and the nominalists have again come up for consideration by the logical positivists of today.)

Pierre Abelard, who was born in France 1079 and studied in Paris under William of Champeaux, tried to mediate and compromise the differences of contention between his teacher and Roscellinus. According to Abelard the universal exists in the individual; that outside the individual the universal exists only as a concept, i.e., a doctrine of conceptualism.

Hugo of Blankenburg, a monk of St. Victor at Paris (1096-1140), maintained that it is impossible to have the same notions of God as God transcends all human conception. In his "Libre didascalici" he appears to anticipate evolution and comparative psychology by tracing the successive stages of psychical life from the plant to man.

St. Thomas Aquinas and Aristotle's Nominalistic Viewpoint

The availability of translations of additional works of Aristotle than were existent at the time of Abelard and Hugo of St. Victor, enabled Alexander of Hales, William of Auvergne, and Vincent of Beauvais to make significant contributions which gradually led the Church to the nominalistic viewpoint of Aristotle in place of Platonic realism. To appreciate the extent of the change, it should be kept in mind that Aristotle's works had been previously anathemized.

Albert of Borstadt also wrote many commentaries on Aristotle's works. He had a definite taste for natural science as was evident by his anticipation of Roger Bacon's views.

St. Thomas Aquinas (1225-1274), a Dominican, and Duns Scotus, a Franciscan, completes the swing toward the Peripatetic philosophy. St. Thomas gave up a life of luxury to go to Cologne to study and there he became an enthusiastic disciple of Albert the Great, and as a consequence a profound student of Aristotle.

He synthesized Aristotle's philosophy with the Christian faith at a time when the Church had its problems proving the agreement between the dogma and natural reason. By fully incorporating the teachings of Aristotle into the Church, Thomas Aquinas brought in a philosophy which was generally accepted at the time as an authority in natural science, and which answered the problem the Church was facing at that time.

St. Thomas maintained that there is only one simple essence or pure form, God, and that all the rest are composed of matter and form. Form is what gives being to a thing. Truth is the agreement of thought with its object. As God is truth itself, it follows that he exists; and that it is not possible to deny the existence of truth. God being free, his divine will is identical with necessity. The determinism of God maintained by St. Augustine loses its offensive character in Thomas Aquinas' interpretation who states there is moral but no arbitrary predestination, for the divine will itself is subordinated to reason.

Nature is a hierarchy, each stage being the form of the lower stage, and at the same time the matter of the higher stage.

Whereas Anselm in his time feared the use of reason by the nominalists, St. Thomas regarded human reason as formed for the purpose of apprehending both God and nature. Inasmuch as Scholasticism as conceived by Thomas Aquinas also took over Aristotelian logic based on the syllogism, it naturally led on the one side to the idea of knowledge derived from intuitive axioms, and the authority of the Church on the other. This approach naturally did not furnish a satisfactory guide to experimental research of nature. In other words, the study of Democritus' "atoms and a void" could not be properly accomplished and described in terms of human sensation and human psychology; these were the terms of scholasticism, as it considered man as the center and object of creation.

Thomas Aquinas also accepted the astronomy of Ptolemy. Whereas both body and mind are realities according to Thomist philosophy, there is no sharp antithesis between them as later formulated by Descartes.

Medieval Schools

In Bologna during the twelfth century, schools of medicine and philosophy were installed in addition to that of law. The University at Bologna was governed by the so-called Students Guild. The universities of Northern Europe, however, were governed by the teachers, including those at Oxford and Cambridge.

During the Carolingian period, academic subjects were comprised of the elementary subjects of grammar, rhetoric, and dialectic, and the more advanced subjects as music, arithmetic, geometry, and astronomy. All were treated as preparatory to the study of the sacred science of theology. Philosophy, on the other hand, became an advanced science under dialectics.

Experimental Science versus Scholasticism

Scholasticism represents the highest point of the metaphysics of the Church. The spirit of experimental sciences, however, revolted against its extreme rationalism, and preferred to seek and accept bare facts whether consistent with a preconceived rational conception or not.

It fell upon Roger Bacon (1210), a Franciscan, to make the initial contribution in the direction of experimental science. He studied at Oxford under Adam Marsh, a mathematician, and Robert Grosseteste, Chancellor of Oxford. The latter appears to have been the first to invite Greeks to serve in England as instructors of their language in its ancient form. Roger Bacon thereafter wrote a book on Greek grammar.

What marked Roger Bacon from among the other philosophers of the Middle Ages was his clear appreciation that certainty in science could only be arrived at by the experimental method; that the only technique to verify statements was by observation and experiment. He anticipated his namesake, Francis Bacon, by three hundred and fifty years.

With the encouragement of Pope Clement IV, Roger Bacon wrote three books covering his views and sent them to the Pope. Pope Clement died soon after, and Jerome of Ascoli, General of the Franciscans who became Pope Nicholas IV, had Roger Bacon imprisoned for his writing.

Roger Bacon considered that the end of all science, as well as of philosophy, was to elucidate and adorn theology. He espoused the study of mathematics and optics (perspective) as not only a good mental exercise but as a good basis for the study of the other sciences.

Among other works, Roger Bacon gave lengthy descriptions of the countries of the known world of that time; he pointed out errors in the calendar; and he supported the theory of the earth's sphericity. The last contribution is said to have influenced Columbus.

Just as logic is used to test argument, so experimental science should be used to judge the contentions of magicians. Roger Bacon's ideas, however, were far ahead of the spirit of his times, and hence they did not alter the prevailing philosophical doctrines. However, the philosophic attacks on Scholasticism by Duns Scotus (1265-1308), a Franciscan, proved more damaging. He taught at Oxford and Paris. Among other ideas, he maintained that free-will was the primary attribute of man, placing it above reason. This view was the beginning of a revolt against the union of religion and philosophy for which the Scholastics strove. A revival of dualism appears; while unsatisfying, it seems necessary in order to free philosophy from theology so that it could form a union with experimental science.

The writings of William of Occam (1347) went much further than Duns Scotus and denied that any theological doctrines could be proved by reason. William of Occam's views led to a revival of nominalism, the belief in individual beings as the sole reality. In a statement called "Occam's razor" he objected to the use of abstractions upon abstractions to prove theological doctrines. (Here he anticipates the objections of modern science to unnecessary hypotheses.) Naturally Occam's writings were condemned, but it did not prevent his attacks from marking the end of the dominance of Scholasticism in the Middle Ages. The ground was prepared for the Renaissance, and the sprouting of the seeds of natural science with its practical applications, as well as other cultural developments in art, etc.

The assumption of the Scholastics that God and the world are understandable, the spirit of logical analysis, and the belief in the regularity and uniformity of nature, proved invaluable intangibles inherited from Scholasticism in the work of scientific research conducted during the Renaissance.

X.

THE RENAISSANCE AND ITS IMMEDIATE SUBSEQUENT INFLUENCE

Introduction to Renaissance and Its Influence on Science

The Black Death, an Oriental infectious disease caused by a microbe, first put in its appearance in Europe about 1342. This deadly epidemic, together with the confusion caused by the Hundred Years' War (1337-1453), discouraged cultural activity. As a consequence, after the thirteenth century there was a period of lull in intellectual development in Western Europe.

The spirit of the Renaissance first appeared in Northern Italy. There the city life of the intelligent and leisured classes furnished an ideal environment for its birth.

Petrarch (1304-1374) was one of the first harbingers of the new era. He endeavored to restore a taste for classical Latin, as well as classical thought which claimed the liberty of reason. From the early part of the fifteenth century on, interest in classical literature attracted many Greeks from the East. Also the Turks' capture of Constantinople in 1453 led to the migration of many competent teachers to Italy who brought with them valuable manuscripts. As a result a wider search for additional manuscripts became quite a popular activity. "Humane Letters" gave an impetus to study in all directions. By broadening the mental horizon, the humanists prepared the way for the revival of science.

Johann Müller (1436-1475) of Königsberg went to Italy and studied under the teachers of the New Learning. He was one of the earliest to bring to Northern Europe the influence of this learning, and probably also the first to combine science with humanism. Among other contributions, he translated Ptolemy's works into Latin, and in 1471 founded an astronomical observatory at Nürnberg. Spanish and Portuguese explorers used his book Ephemerides, an early type of nautical almanac.

The German Renaissance led, through study of the Scriptures, to the Reformation.

Desiderius Erasmus (1467-1536), a native of Rotterdam, was one of the greatest contributors to the Northern Renaissance. Erasmus endeavored to show what the Bible really said and meant and what the early Fathers taught. Humanism was to him the means of bringing the influence of knowledge to combat the evils of the day—scholastic pedantry and low standards of morality both public and private.

For a short period, to Pope Leo X (1513-1521), the Vatican was also a center for the stimulation of ancient culture.

The art of paper-making (invented in China during the first century) was introduced in Europe following the later Crusades. About a century later, movable type was invented, replacing printing with the use of fixed moulds. This, of course, gradually led to the availability of more and more books.

Under the inspiration of Prince Henry the Navigator, the Portuguese discovered the Azores in 1419, and later the western shores of Africa. The Greek theory that the earth was round now became a generally accepted belief. Christopher Columbus, born in Northern Italy, succeeded in obtaining the patronage of Ferdinand and Isabella of Spain in an attempt to find a shorter passage to India. He sailed west from Palos in Andalusia and on October 12, 1492, arrived in the Bahamas. Magellan, twenty-four years later, succeeded in circumnavigating the globe after a three years' voyage.

These great voyages of discovery naturally served to broaden the mental outlook of the time. But in addition to that, the exploitation of the New World brought in treasures of gold and silver to the fast dwindling supply in Europe. It brought about a period of inflation and a rising economic activity. The resulting wealth, with its accompanying leisure for pursuits of an intellectual nature, gave a great stimulus to learning. In fact, there seems to be a definite positive correlation between the economic health of a period with its intellectual development. This seems to have been true at the time of the crowning age of Greece, the Renaissance, and in fact the present time. However, this may be a hasty generalization—the labors of the monks in the monasteries during the Dark Ages copying manuscripts and in other ways preserving ancient learning should not be overlooked. Here, of course, we are indebted to the Church who made it possible for the monks to have the leisure time to continue their work during the Dark Ages.

Alberti (1404-1472) was one of the scholars who made a contribution in the direction of reviving science. He was a mathematician in the early period of the Renaissance, and he also performed physical experiments. He met Paolo Toscanelli, an astronomer who had encouraged the voyage of Columbus; and Amerigo Vespucci who presented him with a book on geometry. He had also been helped in anatomical research by Antonio della Torre.

The real star of the Renaissance, however, was the personality of Leonardo da Vinci. He was truly a genius in many branches of intellectual activity. He was born at Vinci near Florence in 1452. His father was a lawyer of some eminence, and he served as Leonardo's early teacher.

Leonardo was supreme as an artist, being a painter and sculptor. He was also an engineer and architect, as well as a biologist and philosopher.

If Petrarch led the literary Renaissance, Leonardo led in the other branches of intellectual activity. He maintained that the only fruitful method in the study of science was by observation of nature, coupled with experiment. Art was apparently his first love and source of income, although later on in life science held his main interest. Practical problems led him from one branch of science to another.

Fortunately for posterity he left many note books which he undoubtedly had planned to put in book form but never got around to. He apparently had no theological preconceptions, although he accepted the essential Christian doctrine for his inner spiritual life.

Leonardo apparently intuitively perceived and used the proper experimental method a hundred years before Francis Bacon philosophized about it. He foreshadowed the principle of inertia which was afterwards proved experimentally by Galileo. He ignored "perpetual motion" as a source of power; apparently this thought was a popular speculation at that time, just as the transformation of baser metals to gold was popular as a study among the Egyptians and Arabians. He regarded

81

the lever as the primary machine; all other machines being a complication and modification thereof.

He had read Archimedes' contributions to knowledge. The subject of waves in various media, such as water and air, apparently interested him. From his observation of the refraction of light, he speculated on light too being a wave phenomena.

Dissections of human bodies were made by him, originally to study muscles for the purpose of improving his artistic creations of the human form. These dissections created in him an interest for anatomy and physiology. He showed how an image was formed on the retina of the eye; he gave no attention to the prevailing belief that the eyes gave out rays in order to capture the image.

Another great star of the Renaissance was Nicolaus Koppernigk (1473-1543), Latinized to Copernicus. His father was Polish and his mother German. He traveled and studied for six years in Italy, part of the time as a pupil of Maria de Novara, a professor of mathematics and astronomy at Bologna. The young Copernicus had heard his professor criticize the Ptolemaic system of astronomy as being too complicated to satisfy the idea of mathematical harmony. This led Copernicus to study all philosophical books he could find dealing on this subject.

Copernicus finally presented an hypothesis placing the sun as the center of the solar system, with the earth as only one of the planets revolving about the sun. Tycho Brahe had previously placed the sun in the center but conceived of it circling about the earth; he also made methodical recordings of his astronomical observations.

Kepler, after considerable labor, succeeded in confirming the Copernican hypothesis. This revolutionary hypothesis could not be accepted by the Church as it did not coincide with certain portions of the Scriptures. However, in 1822, it formally accepted the Copernican hypothesis. The scientists of that period also hesitated about accepting the hypothesis as they could not understand how the "heavy" earth could be set in motion. Other celestial bodies were considered by them as relatively light in weight.

The Copernican astronomy naturally had a great effect on the minds and beliefs of men of that period; in fact, it caused an intellectual revolution.

Developments in Medicine and Chemistry

We shall now briefly review the developments in medicine and chemistry during the Renaissance.

Systematization was first made of the writings of Hippocrates and Galen, which resulted in spreading the knowledge of medicine. Physicians at first had a tendency to rely too much on the authority of these men. Eventually, however, men began again to observe and experiment for themselves, especially in relating chemistry to medicine. It came to be called iatro chemistry. The knowledge of Arabian chemistry entered Europe through Spain. It is said to have influenced the work of Roger Bacon, as well as Basil Valentine, a Dominican monk. The properties of sulphur, mercury, and salt especially interested them.

Paracelsus (1490-1541), a Swiss alchemist and quack doctor, was one of the first to break away from the orthodox school of Galen. In fact, he expressed contempt for all orthodox men of science. Before settling down in Basle, he traveled all over Europe studying the diseases and remedies used in various countries. He made a rather careful study of the accidents and diseases in the mines of the Tyrol. To the medical problems thus observed, he experimented with various chemical drugs on a trial and error procedure, doubtless killing many patients in the process. He naturally incurred the enmity of the orthodox physicians. In the course of his experiments, he discovered an "extract of vitriol" (ether) which he observed would put chickens to sleep temporarily. Surprisingly he missed the possibility of the application of the substance. Valerius Cordus (1515-1544), a medical doctor and botanist, gave a definite account of the procedure of making the so-called "extract of vitriol." He thereby made an initial crossover from alchemy to chemistry. However, he too missed the possibilities of the applications of ether.

Van Helmont, a chemist and mystic, born in Brussels in 1577, recognized different kinds of aeriform substances, such as ether and gave them the name "gas." He was the one who planted a willow in earth, carefully weighed, watered it regularly, and at the end of five years found it had gained in weight 165 pounds, whereas the earth's loss was only two ounces. From it he concluded that water alone caused the additional weight. Van Helmont also speculated with the idea that the mind and "soul" were outside the physical body.

One hundred years after Van Helmont, Ingenhousz and Priestley discovered that green plants absorb carbon from the carbon dioxide in the air.

Sanctorius (1561-1636) first used a modified form of Galileo's thermometer in taking body temperature. He also invented an apparatus for taking pulse beats, as well as investigating the changes in weight of the body, noting the loss of weight caused by perspiration. The accurate balance or weighing apparatus, incidentally, was inherited from the ancient alchemists.

Francois Dubois (Latinized Franciscus Sylvius) (1614-1672) founded a school of iatro-chemists. He held that the health of the body depended on the acid and alkaline fluids of the body, and that the two together formed a neutral substance. The study by Lemery and Macquer of the interaction of acids and bases suggested the idea of chemical attraction. The end result of the neutral compound, salt, led to the conclusion that every salt was the result of the union of acids and bases.

Developments in Anatomy and Physiology

Now we shall pass on to the subject of anatomy and physiology. The dissection of the human body at first was unpopular in Europe because of prejudice. This, of course, resulted in slow progress in the study of anatomy. Mondino, who died in 1327, was the first scientist to overcome this early prejudice. Whereas in the last part of the fifteenth century, Manfredi and Carpi wrote treatises on the subject, modern anatomy really began with Andreas Vesalius (1515-1564), Flemish by birth, who studied in Louvain and Paris. He subsequently taught in Padua, Bologna and Pisa. He published in 1543 a great book on anatomy based on his own work in dissection which he was prepared to demonstrate at his lectures. The opposition to his book caused him to become discouraged and give up further research, and he subsequently became the physician to Emperor Charles V. By the end of the sixteenth century, anatomy had succeeded in breaking away from ancient authority.

Physiology was slower to break away from the doctrines of Galen. Galen had taught that venous and arterial blood were two separate types of blood, one carried so-called "vital spirits" and the other "natural spirits" to the bodily tissues. Michael Servetus, an Aragonese doctor and theologian, discovered the circulation of the blood through the lungs, and the function of the heart. He was burned at Geneva on condemnation by Calvin for his radical opinions on doctrine, apparently theological.

However, it remained for William Harvey (1578-1657) to discover the true process of the circulation of the blood. He studied at Cambridge and later spent five years in Europe, chiefly at Padua. After he returned to England he practiced medicine, having among his patients Charles I and Francis Bacon. Charles I placed the resources of certain deer parks at his disposal for experimental purposes. Harvey observed the pulsations of the heart of a developing chick in the egg. His small book on the heart came out in 1628; it contained the substance of his years of observation on men and living animals. The physiology of Galen thereupon became obsolete. It should be noted that Harvey came to his conclusions based on a series of steps from observations on the heart through anatomical dissection. Harvey's new approach in the study of physiology made possible modern medicine and surgery.

His second work on embryology was the greatest advance in that subject since Aristotle.

The microscope was invented after Harvey had completed his work. The microscope led to the discovery of the lacteal and lymphatic vessels.

Malpighi of Bologna in 1661 made the first microscopic study of the lung. By observing the lung of a frog, he learned that capillary tubes connected the arteries and the veins. Malpighi also studied microscopically the glands and other bodily organs, and learned much of their structure and function.

A. van Leeuwenhoek (1632-1728) carried on Malpighi's work and observed capillary circulation and muscular fibres, discovering blood corpuscles, bacteria and spermatozoa in his various researches.

Borelli made a study in 1670 of the mechanics of muscular motion, while Glisson studied the irritability of muscles. Borelli incidentally clarified the mechanics of breathing.

John Mayow (1643-1679), a great chemist and physiologist, showed that a candle placed in a bottle goes out even though there is an abundance of air in the bottle. He was not aware at that time of the necessity of oxygen for the combustion process. He inferred correctly, however, that air is not a homogeneous substance, and later identified burning and breathing.

Niels Stensen (1678-1686), a Danish anatomist, physiologist and geologist, pointed out the great difficulty involved in the dissection of the brain and the lack of sound knowledge on the subject. In speaking of the white substance in the brain, he mentioned the fact that it was fibrous in nature, and felt that the arrangement of the fibres followed a definite pattern.

Developments in Botany

We now come to the subject of botany. This science grew out of the use of vegetable drugs, derived from plants, for medicinal purposes. Then, too, the wealth accumulated by certain classes during the Renaissance led to the establishment of botanical gardens. Gardens comprised entirely of herbs for medicinal purposes came into existence at this time, as were gardens established by various societies of apothecaries.

Valerious Cordus (1515-1544) was the first plant observer to give accurate descriptions of plants from nature. Thus, he brought about the first real advance in botany since Dioscorides (a Greek physician who at the time of Nero traveled extensively with the Roman armies at which time he no doubt made valuable observations of plants).

John Gerard in 1597 published in England a famous work on plants illustrated by woodcuts.

Early Development of Magnetism and Electricity

The sciences of magnetism and electricity were founded by William Gilbert of Colchester (1540-1603), a court physician under Elizabeth and James I. He collected all that was known at that time about magnetism, adding fresh observations of his own; he then published them in his book De Magnete.

The magnetic needle appears to have been first discovered by the Chinese, appearing in their literature at the end of the eleventh century. It was applied to navigation in Europe by the twelfth century, probably after first having been used by Muslim sailors.

Gilbert, as a result of experiments, concluded that the earth itself acted like a huge magnet, with its poles almost the same as the geographical poles. He examined the forces developed when bodies such as amber are rubbed, and gave the force developed the name "electricity." (Greek for amber) He used a light metallic needle balanced on a point to measure the force.

Early Practical Results of the Renaissance

Galileo Galilei (1564-1642)—We shall now pass on and review the epoch-making work of Galileo. The ideas in the minds of men of the Renaissance period now began to produce really practical results. Galileo combined the experimental and inductive methods of Gilbert along with mathematical deduction; thus he established the true method of physical science. Actually he started modern physical science on its present course.

In the field of astronomy he constructed a telescope which he applied in obtaining data confirming the Copernican system. A professor of philosophy at Padua, believe it or not, refused to look through Galileo's telescope. (Let us not judge the professor too harshly for a person's preconceptions are indeed dear to him.)

His most original work was the laying of the foundation in the experimental and mathematical science of dynamics. From Aristotle all scientists up to that time had believed that bodies were intrinsically heavy or light, and to fall or rise with a velocity proportionate to its heaviness. Repeating an experiment of Stevinus of Bruges (1586) Galileo dropped a ten-pound weight at the same time as a one-pound weight from the Leaning Tower of Pisa. To the consternation of the onlookers, both weights hit the ground simultaneously.

He next endeavored to learn the law of the progressive increase in speed of a body falling towards the ground. With the use of an inclined plane to facilitate observation and by calculation he determined that the space described increases as the square of the time. It should be recalled that up to that time every motion required a continual force to maintain it. Now Galileo's experiment revealed that it is not motion but the creation or destruction of motion, or a change in the direction of the moving object which requires the application of some external force. Galileo's experiment proved Plato's and not Aristotle's theory was the correct one.

Galileo had the greatness of being able to admit something he did not know. For instance, he confessed he knew nothing of the nature of the force or the cause of gravity. Galileo died in 1642, the year Newton was born.

XI.

INFLUENCE OF SCIENTIFIC DEVELOPMENT
ON PHILOSOPHY

Introduction

The publication of "Celestial Revolutions" by Copernicus, along with Galileo's work, proved to be the most influential factors in the philosophical and scientific history of Europe, in fact, marking the beginning of the modern world. From the philosophical aspect, it did not appear to shake the belief in the invisible. However, it substituted for the transcendentalism of the Middle Ages the principle of divine immanency.

The recognition of their own reason in universal reason resulted in philosophical reform among the so-called freethinkers. Bruno in Italy, Bacon in England, and Descartes in France, initiated bold innovations in philosophical thought.

Giordano Bruno

Giordano Bruno was born near Naples in 1548. As a young man he entered the Dominican order. Influenced by such writers as Cusanus, Lullus and Telesio, together with his great love of nature, he began roving about Europe. He first journeyed to Geneva, and from there to Paris, London and Germany. Protestantism to him was found no more satisfactory than the religion of his fathers.

Bruno accepted without reservation the heliocentric system of Copernicus. Space to him had no limits, as it contained both the visible and invisible world. He conceived of heaven as an infinite universe, a system of solar systems, our sun with its planets including the earth, presenting only one of many solar systems. He reasoned that there could not be two infinites; hence, God and the universe are one and the same being. He conceived of God as being the soul of the world rather than its creator and first mover. God is the immanent and permanent cause of things, the same view as held later by Spinoza. He governs from within outwardly; the being within the world has a beginning and an end, but the universe itself has no beginning or end. Freedom and necessity are identical, and constitute in God but one and the same fact. God produces things in nature by unfolding Himself. His absolute unity has nothing in common with numerical unity. Death itself, according to Bruno, is but a transformation of life. He credited the Stoics for having recognized the world as a living being and the Pythagoreans for having recognized the mathematical necessity and the immutable laws governing creation. He considered matter in an extraordinary sense, namely, that it is inextended, as immaterial in its essence, which does not receive its being from a positive principle (form) outside of itself. Matter alone in the foregoing sense is therefore stable and eternal.

The human soul is the highest form of cosmical life. All beings (monads) whatsoever are a combination of body and soul, reproducing in a particular form the Monad of monads, the God-universe. Corporeality is the result of the expansion of the monad whereas in thought the monad returns again to itself. This reciprocal movement is what we call life. Bruno's conceptions furnish the common source of modern ontological doctrines.

When he finally returned to Italy, he was arrested in Venice, and after two years' imprisonment was burned at the stake in Rome in 1600.

Tommaso Campanella

Tommaso Campanella was born in Calabria in Southern Italy in 1568, and died in Paris in 1639. He anticipated modern criticism as brought out later in Hume's and Kant's essays concerning human understanding.

As a disciple of the Greek sceptics, he taught that metaphysics of any significance must rest on a theory of knowledge. That knowledge he maintained must be derived from sensible experience and reasoning. He asserted that the thinking subject might be the determining cause of sensation as easily as any object. The only way to prove that sensation has its beginning in an external object is by the inner sense (reason). (Here he seems to anticipate the present school of logical analysis). Campanella goes on to say that the inner sense reveals to us both our existence and its limitations (the external world). In other words, the existence of the external world (the non-ego) is the cause of sensible perception in us. He suggested, however, that objects we sensed of the external world did not necessarily show them as they are. He encouraged the thinker to engage in metaphysical research, although our knowledge is necessarily insignificant as compared with God's knowledge.

Universal philosophy or metaphysics is the science of principles of existence. According to Campanella, to exist means to proceed from a principle and to return to it. The principles of power, knowledge and will are possessed by the relative being, whereas God possesses absolute power, absolute knowledge, and absolute will or love. Not even excepting the inorganic world, feeling, intelligence and will exist in some degree.

Religion to this philosopher is described as a universal phenomena having its source in the dependence of all things on the absolute Being. Twenty-seven of Campanella's seventy-one years were spent in a Neapolitan dungeon. This experience would seem to have given him much leisure time for cogitation and speculation in philosophy.

Francis Bacon and Thomas Hobbes

We shall now pass from Italy to England, to Francis Bacon and Thomas Hobbes. Philosophical reform in England gets the impress of the Anglo-Saxon character. It prefers the slow gradual ascent along the path of experience rather than the speculative deductions of prior independent metaphysicians. To the English school, science owes its progress to the direct contemplation of nature, to which are applied the influence of common-sense and reality. When they started from an a priori conception, they attempted to verify it by experience, as Columbus did; in other words the hypothesis was not accepted as truth until verified. Hence, they abandoned a priori speculation and the syllogistic form and made their approach to knowledge by observation and induction.

Francis Bacon

Francis Bacon (1561-1626), Lord Chancellor of England, espoused the foregoing approach in his Novum Organum Scientiarum, as well as in his other works. He cautioned against projecting our whims and our idols into nature. He stated we have a tendency to dispute about words instead of endeavoring to understand things. We confuse the objects of science with those of religion, which produces a superstitious philosophy and a heretical theology. The only hope for philosophy is to break away from the a priori systems and to start anew using the inductive method. This method necessitates the careful study of facts before the progressive formation of laws to explain them.

Whereas experimental science was originated long before the time of Bacon, he is nevertheless considered the founder of experimental philosophy, the forerunner of modern positivistic philosophy. He emphasized that true philosophy and science have common interests. Bacon was a naturalist when it involved science, and a supernaturalist in theology.

Thomas Hobbes

The exclusion of the invisible from the domain of science went one step further in the philosophy of Thomas Hobbes (1588-1679). Hobbes was the son of a clergyman and a friend of Bacon. After spending thirteen years in France, he returned to England to devote his time to literary endeavors. His fame at first was as a political writer and moralist, although he was also an ontologist and psychologist. He initiated modern materialism, criticism and positivism. Hobbes defines philosophy as the reasoned knowledge of effects from causes, and causes from effects. Philosophy has no other object than composable and decomposable things or bodies. Hence, God and pure spirits cannot be thought but are objects of faith and belong to theology. He considers physics and moral philosophy both as empirical sciences, having bodies as their objects. His wholly materialistic theory of perception considered that inner perception is our feeling of brain action. That is, to think is to feel. Knowledge is the addition of sensations, sensation being considered as a movement within the sensible body. To remember is to feel what one has felt, memory being a duration of sensation. The motion of objects in surrounding matter is communicated to the brain immediately by nerves. He maintains that in his opinion the reality of matter is an unimpeachable dogma. He defines the soul or spirit sometimes as brain action and at other times as nervous substance. According to him an incorporeal spirit does not exist.

He defines a voluntary action as one that proceeds from the will, against which reason without passion and moral principles without a material attraction exert no influence. On the other hand it is impelled by imagination, passions, and the emotions. Volitions themselves are not voluntary and we are not masters of them. However, every act has its sufficient reason, which in turn is synonymous with necessity. Man is subject to the law of necessity like all other creatures. Interest is the judge in morals, as in everything else.

In the State as in nature, might makes right. The state protects, at the cost of obedience, the life and property of individuals.

Hobbes differs from Bacon in teaching a system of materialistic metaphysics. Also his definition of philosophy places a higher value on the syllogism than Bacon's conception. Bacon had overlooked the part deduction plays in mathematics, as well as its part in the discoveries of the fifteenth century. Thus Hobbes' philosophy is in between pure empiricism and the rationalism of Descartes, whose philosophy we shall next give our attention.

René Descartes

René Descartes (1596-1650) was born in France and educated by the Jesuits. He was a contemporary of Galileo. He laid the foundation of modern rationalistic philosophy; he also developed new mathematical methods for use in physical science, applying the processes of algebra to geometry. He traveled in Europe, and for a time served as a lieutenant in the German Imperial Army. He wrote his main philosophical works in Holland, and died in Sweden in 1650 while on a visit to Queen Christina.

Descartes was primarily a geometrician with a taste for metaphysics. In fact, his philosophy aimed to be a generalization of mathematics. Applying the principle of axioms in geometry, he uses doubt to arrive at his first principle. "I doubt, that is absolutely certain. Now, to doubt is to think. Hence, it is certain that I think. To think is to exist." Up to this point he merely knows that he exists, but there is no evidence that the object of his thought exists outside of him. They may be the product of his imagination. If it were not that among his ideas was the self-evident idea of God, there would be no way of overcoming the doubt of the existence of the outside world. He uses a form of St. Anselm's ontological argument in proving the existence of God. God reveals himself to us in the innate idea of infinity. The certainty of God's existence is important for on it depends all truth, all certitude, all positive knowledge. It enables us, according to Descartes, to destroy the wall erected by doubt between thought and the external world. Hence, God, the ego, and the corporeal world exist.

Observation, reasoning, and a priori deduction are the basis of the Cartesian system. Thought constitutes the attribute "essence of the mind," and extension, the attribute "the essence of the body." Both are so-called relative substances, God alone being the real substance.

The body actually has no center, for the center is a mathematical point which is inextended.

The material world operates under the law of necessity. Minds and bodies are entirely opposed to one another; he speaks of the body as being an animal machine. Communication between the mind and the body cannot take place except through God's intervention, the body being absolutely soulless and the soul being entirely immaterial. Here we have dualistic spiritualism.

Descartes in his anthropology, however, assumes what his metaphysics denies.

Descartes developed a theory of vortices in a primary matter (aether), invisible but filling all space. Newton later showed that this theory was inconsistent with observation. Thomas Hobbes incidentally was an early critic of Descartes' system.

The Cambridge Platonists, however, tried to reconcile religion and mechanical philosophy by deifying space.

Robert Boyle

Robert Boyle (1627-1691), an English physicist, chemist, and a moderate philosopher, proved that air is a material substance, having weight. His fame rests upon his discovery that the volume of a given quantity of air is inversely proportional to the pressure; a principle now known as Boyle's Law.

He perceived the importance of the atomic theory as revived by Gassendi. He also accepted the view that so-called "secondary qualities" are only phantoms of the sensations. However, he did add that after all "there are de facto in the world certain sensible and rational beings that we call men." He, in other words, re-established man with his senses as a part of the Universe, the secondary qualities being as real as the primary.

Boyle considered man's rational soul bears the image of its Divine Maker, and is "a nobler and more valuable being than the whole corporeal world."

Boyle, among other scientific developments, improved the thermometer by sealing it; he observed the effect of atmospheric pressure on boiling point; he recognized heat as the results of molecular agitation; and he collected new facts on electricity and magnetism. Incidentally he ventured a cautious definition of an element that is still applicable: "It may likewise be granted, that those distinct Substances, which Concretes generally either afford or are made up of, may without very much Inconvenience be call'd the Elements or Principles of them."

Blaise Pascal

At this time we should mention the French experimentalist, Blaise Pascal (1623-1662). While he was widely known as a theologian, he was the founder of the mathematical theory of probability, the study of which originated from a discussion on games of chance. This theory is widely used today in science, philosophy, and in social statistics. The intellectual basis of all empirical knowledge is largely a matter of probability, in the terms of a bet. (In the innocent curve of normal probability is hidden many secrets of nature.)

Pascal had experimented with and written a treatise on the equilibrium of fluids. In this connection he directed that a barometer (invented during this period by Torricelli) be carried up a mountain, the Puy de Dome, and learned that the height of the mercury column diminished progressively as they went up the mountain, the pressure of the atmosphere being less.

Witchcraft—A Version of Magic

The practice of magic was, of course, pre-historic. However, a more modern version of magic produced horrible results during the two centuries following the Renaissance. It has been variously estimated that from 750,000 upwards were burned at the stake as so-called witches during this period. It is believed that many belonging to so-called witch-cults sought death to place themselves in a preferred position in the hereafter. Believe it or not, Dr. Harvey and Sir Thomas Browne assisted in the physical examination of witches under the direction of James I. At Würzburg, a Jesuit priest, Father Spee, is said to have accompanied in less than two years nearly two hundred victims to the stake. He revolted against it, and finally published anonymously a book in which he stated that the methods used to obtain a confession were such that even Bishops of the Church would confess to escape the tortures.

The belief in witchcraft gradually vanished with as little apparent reason as it arose. (It would be utterly fantastic to conceive of the Galilean teacher, from whom the religion of Christianity derived its name, supervising such an endeavor. [See Luke 9:54-56] Can it be that the evil endemic in man ran amuck after first justifying its action by rationalizing the scriptures?)

XII.

THE NEWTONIAN PERIOD

Scientific Contributions

Returning again to the subject of science, the miscellaneous facts discovered by the scientific methods began to fit together, and a definite pattern began to appear. It was in the formulation of Newton's laws of gravity that the first great scientific synthesis was accomplished. This subject will next be considered.

The concepts of substances and causes used by the Scholastics to explain *why* things move were replaced by time, space and force to explain *how* things move. Scientists now busied themselves with measuring actual velocities and accelerations of moving bodies. It had been proved experimentally by Galileo that no continual exertion of force was necessary to keep a body moving; that once started, a body traveled forward as a result of an innate quality associated with its weight. Galileo at this point suggested the idea of mass and inertia.

Huygens made researches which he published in 1673 dealing with such subjects as gravity, the pendulum, the center of oscillation and centrifugal forces.

The original Greek concept of inter-planetary aether was used by Kepler and Descartes for their theoretical purposes. Gilbert used it to explain magnetic attraction and Harvey to explain the transmission of heat from the sun to the heart and blood.

All men of science and nearly all philosophers in the middle of the seventeenth century were oriented toward Christianity. Thomas Hobbes was an exception, classifying religion as accepted superstition; though at the same time agreeing that religion based on the Bible should be established and enforced by the State. However, the fundamental belief in God was regarded by the thinkers of that period as one of the universally accepted data to which any theory of the Cosmos must of necessity conform.

During this period societies were established, making it possible for learned men to meet to discuss the new scientific and philosophic subjects and thus further their progress. Such a society started at Gresham College in London in 1645. The group was finally incorporated by Charles II in 1662 under the name Royal Society of London for Promoting Natural Knowledge. In 1666 a corresponding Academie des Sciences was established in France by Louis XIV. Eventually all countries in Europe founded similar societies. The oldest independent scientific periodical appears to have been the "Journal des Savants," the first issue of which came out in 1665 at Paris. The periodical "Philosophical Transactions of the Royal Society" came out three months thereafter. These societies largely facilitated the rapid growth of scientific activity which followed.

Isaac Newton and Christian Huygens

With this introduction to the Newtonian period, we shall now proceed to review the work of the main performer, Isaac Newton (1642-1727). He was the son of a small landowner at Woolsthorpe in Lincolnshire, and a child of delicate physical health. After attending the Grantham Grammar School, he went on to Trinity College, Cambridge, and attended the mathematical lectures of Isaac Barrow in 1664.

The outbreak of the plague at Cambridge led to Newton's return to his home in Woolsthorpe, where he occupied himself with planetary problems. During the two plague years he stated "he minded Mathematics and Philosophy more than any time since."

The prior researches of Galileo had brought out the need of a cause to keep the planets and their satellites in orbit; in other words, what kept them from flying off in a tangent through space? Galileo postulated a force but made no attempt to determine the nature of the force.

The clue is said to have come to Newton while idly watching an apple fall from a tree in his orchard. It appears that the idea of a force decreasing as the square of the distance had already been entertained by him.

One great difficulty in the way of formulating a theory of gravitation was that the sizes of the sun and planets are so small compared with the distances between them. Newton thereupon laid aside his planetary studies to devote his time to optics.

Christian Huygens (1629-1695) of Holland, published his work on dynamics in 1673 in which he assumed the principle of the conservation of kinetic energy in dynamical systems. He developed the theory of the center of oscillation and opened a new method in its application. He also established the relation between the length of a pendulum and its time of oscillation. He went on to prove that the acceleration produced by a force (acting towards the center) was equal to v^2/r.

Interest in the subject of gravitation must have been quite general by 1684, as Hooke, Halley, Huygens and Wren independently came up with the theory of the inverse square being the law of force. Apparently Halley had a mathematical problem involving the inverse square relation, and approached Newton for assistance on it. He found that Newton had solved it two years before.

Newton's thinking apparently was again stimulated in the gravitational problem by Halley's problem, and by 1685 he succeeded in proving that a sphere of a gravitating body attracted bodies outside of it as though all its mass were concentrated at the center. (Here we have the mathematical point again appearing as a theoretical necessity).

With this proof Newton realized he was now able to apply mathematical analysis with precision to the actual problem of astronomy. On the proven theory that each particle of matter attracted every other particle with a force proportionate to the products of the masses and inversely proportional to the square of the distance between them, the complicated movement of the solar system was thereafter ascertained by deduction.

In 1687 Newton published his Principia, the Mathematical Principles of Natural Philosophy, perhaps the greatest event in the history of science.

The phenomena of tides had been the object of considerable speculation up to Newton's time. Kepler, with his astrological bias, thought that the tides were due to the moon; this speculation apparently amused Galileo. However, Newton in his Principia gives a sound basis for tidal theory. He checked mathematically the combined gravitational effect of the moon and the sun on the waters of the earth, with certain allowances for the inertia of moving water. This procedure has been extended by mathematicians since Newton's day. The general approach by Newton, however, still holds good.

Newton approached the problem of mass from the aspect of density, influenced in that direction no doubt by Boyle's work on pressure and volume of air. Newton's definition of mass was "the quantity of matter in a body as measured by the product of its density and bulk." Force was defined as "any action on a body which changes, or tends to change, its state of rest, or of uniform motion in a straight line." He goes on to give his three laws of motion based on his observations and these definitions:

Law I. Every body perseveres in its state of rest or of uniform motion in a straight line, except in so far as it is compelled to change that state by impressed forces.

Law II. Change of motion (i.e. rate of change of momentum — ma) is proportional to the moving force impressed, and takes place in the direction of the straight line in which such force is impressed.

Law III. Reaction is always equal and opposite to action; that is to say, the actions of two bodies upon each other are always equal and directly opposite.

Newton's basic principles of dynamics sufficed for two hundred years. In 1883, however, Ernest Mach asserted that Newton's definitions of mass and force leave us in a logical circle, for we can know matter only through its effects on our senses; that we can define density only as mass per unit volume. According to Mach the dynamical work of Galileo, Huygens and Newton actually means the discovery of only one basic principle. Newton appreciated that we get the mechanical notion of force from the sensation of muscular effort. (Here physics and psychology appear to conjoin.)

Newton concluded from his astronomical results that the cause of gravity must "penetrate to the very centers of the sun and planets, without suffering the least diminution of its force."

In the field of mathematics, the development of infinitesimal calculus by Newton and Leibniz was a great achievement. This achievement, in the form given by Leibniz and Bernouilli, is the basis of modern pure and applied mathematics.

The binomial theorem and much of the theory of equations were the product of Newton's fertile mind. He created hydrodynamics, with the theory of the propagation of waves.

His work on optics alone, however, would have placed Newton in the front rank of scientists. He experimented with the phenomena of light and color with the aid of a prism; he studied refractions of light; and suggested a theory of polarization.

Descartes theorized that light was a pressure transmitted through so-called aether; Robert Hooke suggested it was a rapid vibration in a medium; while Huygens worked out an undulatory theory. Newton seemed to think that the apparent rectilinear rays of light required a corpuscular theory. He did not have an opportunity to prove his theory by experimentation but merely suggested the form of the problem for possible experimentation by others. Incidentally the corpuscular theory of Newton and the undulatory theory of Huygens is still in a vacillating state of indecision. (No one theory can apparently explain all light phenomena.)

Effect of Newton on Philosophy

The effect of Newton on philosophy will now be considered. One effect can be cited as the establishment of the validity of terrestrial mechanics in celestial spaces. Another effect was the removal of superfluous philosophic dogma from the structure of natural science. In fact, Newton consciously detached himself from metaphysical views during his scientific labors; this marked a real advance in scientific research.

Natural philosophy up to Newton's time may be generally grouped in two classes:—

1. The Aristotelian Approach—This approach had a tendency to attribute to things specific and occult qualities; hence, the general effects from their respective natures. As they made no attempt to ascertain whence these natures were derived, the work of these thinkers are largely limited to giving names to things. However, this particular contribution should not be hastily underrated.

2. The Atomistic Approach—This movement was initiated by Democritus. This group ignored the many words of the Aristotelians and devoted their energies more toward analysis. First, they regarded all matter as homogeneous, and from there they

speculated on the nature of the component particles, going from the simple things to those more complicated. Possibly due to impatience and mental laziness this activity led from conjectures of the true constitution of things to the assignment of occult qualities to them. In other words, no sound base was established for the ensuing superstructure.

Newton's approach was more sound, however, although it required great concentration and patient effort in order to establish sound bases for generalization. This change in approach initiated experimental philosophy, a twofold method of alternate analysis and synthesis.

Newton distinguished between relative space and time as measured by our senses in terms of natural bodies and motions, as against absolute space which exists immovably, and absolute time which flows equably without regard to any external thing.

Both Huygens and Leibniz criticized Newton's work as unphilosophical because of his failure to give an explanation of the ultimate cause of gravitational attraction. To this criticism Newton stated that the subject of cause was a secondary and independent problem, as yet only in a speculative stage. In the form of a query in his treaties on Optics, Newton suggested that the phenomena of gravity might be the result of pressures of a hypothetical inter-planetary aether, getting denser the farther away from matter, thus pressing bodies together. But a speculation of a man of Newton's reputation is often taken as an authoritative explanation.

Newton expressed doubt that the rest of natural phenomena could be derived from reasoning from mechanical principles, as he suspected hitherto unknown causes. He expressed a hope, however, that his principles might lead to a truer method of philosophy.

Newton's science later was taken by others as the basis of a mechanical philosophy. That was not Newton's intention, however, as he believed his discoveries strengthened a spiritual view of reality. Newton was a deeply religious man, at the same time being a scientist and philosopher. In the last seven pages of the second volume of his Principia he stated in part: "This most beautiful System of The Sun, Planets and Comets could only proceed from the counsel and dominion of an intelligent and powerful Being." In his Optics he further stated: "The main business of Natural Philosophy is to argue from Phaenomena without feigning Hypotheses, and to deduce Causes from Effects, till we come to the very first Cause, which certainly is not mechanical."

As the study of reality involves in addition to the physical aspect, the psychological, aesthetic, and religious aspects as well, all of the aspects must be considered in drawing even a sketchy view of reality.

Because of the differences in psychological bias, Newton's work was misinterpreted by both the theists and the atheists to suit their particular purposes. However, a form of intellectualism has arisen which seeks to find the truth about the Divine Nature both in the physical order of the universe and in the moral law.

XIII.

EIGHTEENTH CENTURY SCIENCE

Mathematics and Astronomy

We shall now touch upon mathematics and astronomy during the eighteenth century.

Because of the unfortunate difference in notation used by Newton and Leibniz, complicated by a dispute about priority, the English school had little part in the development of infinitesimal calculus during the eighteenth century. Development work in that field, therefore, fell to the Continental mathematicians using the system of Leibniz.

It took some time for Newton's work to be appreciated in other countries. However, it was Voltaire, who spent the years 1726-1729 in England, and made known in France in his writings the work of Newton. About 1739 Voltaire and Madame du Chatelet, a good mathematician, published a treatise on Newton's system. This treatise proved a source of inspiration to the scientific writers in the Encyclopaedie, a great French work comprising thirty-five volumes published between 1751 and 1780. Diderot was the general editor, while d'Alembert had charge of the articles dealing with mathematics. It collected and classified work done in many different branches of knowledge. Euler, Lagrange and Laplace contributed articles in the mathematical branch. Euler (1707-1783) started new departments in analysis, published treatises on optics, and on the general principles of philosophy. Joseph Louis Lagrange (1736-1813), one of the greatest mathematicians of the century, created the calculus of variations and systematized the subject of differential equations. In astronomy he advanced the method of calculating the mutual gravitational effect of three bodies. He also founded the whole of mechanics on the conservation of energy in the form of the principles of virtual velocities and least action.

Further development of the Newtonian system was accomplished by Pierre Simon de Laplace (1749-1827). He improved the treatment of problems of attraction by adapting Lagrange's method of potential. He also proved that planetary motions were stable in spite of temporary influences by such bodies as comets. This problem had disturbed Newton.

Laplace's Systems du Monde, published in 1796, gives a history of astronomy, including the Newtonian system. This book also gives an account of the nebular hypothesis which was suggested by Kant in 1755; this theory put forth the idea that the solar system was evolved from a rotating mass of incandescent gas. According to modern research the hypothesis may hold good for larger aggregates of stars but not for the comparatively small structure of our solar system. Napoleon asked Laplace why in his work "Mecanique Celeste" he did not mention the Creator even once. To this query Laplace answered "I did not need that hypothesis." When Napoleon passed this comment on to Lagrange, he is reported to have been amused, and exclaimed—"Ah, that is a good hypothesis—it explains many things." (Yes, it does.)

In physics Laplace gave an explanation of capillarity by the assumption of forces sensible to only minute distances. He also explained that the discrepancy given for the velocity of sound in air as computed by Newton's formula was caused by the heat developed by the sound wave increasing the elasticity of the air and thus increasing the speed of sound.

The system of Newton and Laplace was verified from a practical standpoint in 1846 by the work of John Couch Adams of Cambridge and Leverrier, a French mathematician. It seems that because of certain orbital deviations of the planet Uranus, the influence of a new planet was intimated. Astronomer Galle of Berlin, on hearing of this suggestion, searched the sky with his telescope in the vicinity where the new planet was supposed to be and discovered it. The new planet was given the name Neptune.

Developments in Chemistry

The work of Iatro-chemists finally succeeded in weening scientific chemistry away from alchemy. The number of known substances and their reactions was increased, and a foundation was laid for improving chemical theory. It has been suggested that Newton spent more time over alchemy and chemistry than over the physical researches which made him famous. Apparently he made no significant progress for he wrote no final treatise on the subject, although leaving note books covering his chemical experiments. His chemistry notes indicated his special interest in alloys. The most fusible alloy being reported was that of lead, tin and bismuth in the proportion of 5:7:12. His notes also revealed an insight beyond that of other chemists of his day in concluding that a flame only differed from vapour as do bodies red-hot and not red-hot. It will be recalled that the Aristotelians considered fire as one of the four elements. Newton's acceptance of the atomic theory established it as orthodox. However, Voltaire in his Dictionnaire Philosophe stated in part—"The Plenum is to-day considered a chimera . . . the void is recognized."

Wilhelm Homberg, an experimental chemist in the early eighteenth century, supplied evidence supporting the theory that a salt is formed by the union of an acid and a base, a theory previously suggested by Sylvius. In 1732 Hermann Boerhaave of Leyden published "the most complete and luminous chemical treatise of his time," according to Sir Ed. Thorpe in his History of Chemistry published in 1921.

Stephen Hales conducted experiments on such gases as hydrogen, two oxides of carbon, sulphur dioxide, and marsh gas.

G. E. Stahl (1660-1734), a physician of the King of Prussia, named the substance which escapes when bodies are burned as "phogiston," the principle of fire. Joseph Priestley (1733-1804) prepared oxygen by heating mercuric oxide. He showed that the substance supported combustion and that it was necessary to the respiration of animals. However, he described oxygen as dephlogisticated air, and did not realize the importance of his discovery. Henry Cavendish (1731-1810), a wealthy ascetic genius, demonstrated the nature of water to be a compound, and thus water ceased to be considered as an element as it was from early days. Incidentally, he also designed an ingenious experimental apparatus, consisting of two iron balls of differing

105

weights, to determine the gravitational constant. This enabled him to "weigh" the earth for the first time.

Joseph Black of Edinburgh about 1755 discovered carbon dioxide and called the gas "fixed air."

It remained for Antoine Laurence Lavoisier (1743-1794) to materialize modern chemistry. He repeated the experiments of Priestley and Cavendish and accurately weighed his reagents and products. Lavoisier, with the evidence of the balance, showed that although matter may alter its states in a series of chemical actions, it does not change in weight. Water was found to be made up of two constituents, which he named hydrogen (the water-forming constituent) and oxygen (the acid-forming element). Henceforth phlogiston with its negative weight was found superfluous. By Lavoisier's contributions the way was now open for the great developments in chemistry to follow. Incidentally, he was sent to the guillotine, as the Republic apparently had no need for savants.

Developments in Botany (Including those of the Preceding Century)

The developments in the field of Botany during the seventeenth and eighteenth centuries will next be reviewed.

The invention of the compound microscope contributed to the study of botany as well as to zoology. Heretofore no attention apparently was given to the reproductive organs of plants. It appears that Nehemiah Grew was the first botanist to describe the function of the stamens and pistils, which he did in a paper to the Royal Society on the Anatomy of Plants in 1676. He speaks of the stamens as male organs and describes their action. He assigns credit for the theory, however, to Sir Thomas Millington, an Oxford Professor. Confirmatory evidence was furnished by such botanists as Camerarius of Tübingen, by Morland, and by Geoffroy. These scientists reported that no fertilization of the ovum or formulation of seed is possible without pollen from the anthers of the stamens.

John Ray (1627-1705) published the first of a series of books on systematic botany in 1760. Up to that time the classification of both plants and animals was either on a utilitarian basis or was based on obvious external characteristics, such as classifying plants into herbs, scrubs and trees. He initiated a natural system of classification, recognizing the difference between monocotyledons and dicotyledons in plant embryos, as well as the variations in the fruit, flower, leaf, and so on. He indicated many of the plant orders, some of them still in use today. As to his classification of animals he utilized comparative anatomy, thereby arriving at a natural classification of animals into quadrupeds, birds and insects.

Linnaeus, a Swedish clergyman's son, carried on Ray's work, and founded his famous system of classification of plants on the basis of the sex organs. This system has now been replaced by the system at present in use which takes into consideration all the characters of the organism. In that respect, it has returned to John Ray's principles. Linnaeus later turned his attention to the classification of the human species. His subsequent book on the subject, System of Nature, placed man in the order of "Primates" with apes, lemurs, and bats, and subdivided man into four groups, considering such external characteristics as skin color, and the like.

Developments in Zoology

As to zoology, interest in this subject was stimulated by the establishment of various royal menageries into which came specimens from all over the world.

Buffon (1707-1788) published his encyclopaedia Natural History of Animals, which marked the close of the first stage in modern zoological science. The use of the microscope enabled Buffon to enumerate facts of nature hitherto unseen and hence unknown. Buffon had indicated that while he at first considered that Linnaeus' classification of animals had humiliated man, he rather reluctantly confessed the evidence seemed to point toward a common origin for the horse and the ass, the man and the monkey. It has been suggested that his reluctance was the result of his interpretation of the creation account given in the Scriptures.

The first one to cast doubt on the belief entertained in ancient and mediaeval times that living things might spontaneously arise from non-living matter was Francesco Redi (1626-1679). For instance, in ancient and mediaeval times they believed that frogs might be generated from mud by the action of the sun. Some even suggested that the American Indians might have by such means come into existence, because they lived such a great distance from the garden of Eden. Francesco

107

Redi showed that if flesh of an animal is protected from insects, no grubs or maggots appeared. His experiments, incidentally, were considered incompatible with Scriptures. Amusingly, in the nineteenth century the two opposing sides had reversed themselves because of the work of Schwann and Pasteur. Materialists such as Vogt, Haeckel and others upheld the theory of spontaneous generation as a naturalistic explanation of the origin of life; the orthodox theologians welcomed negative results as they indirectly supported the belief in the direct act of God in the creative process. (Here again we should not judge them too harshly for we are all prone to favor ideas which tend to support our preconceptions.)

Abbe Spallanzani (1729-1799) confirmed Redi's findings that not even minute forms of life would develop in prior living matter after boiling and protecting it from air.

Developments in Physiology

Whereas Stahl had theorized that all changes in the living body were directly governed by the so-called "sensitive soul," others laid more emphasis on chemical fermentation as causing the changes. Boerhaave in his Institutiones Medicae (1708) expressed his belief that digestion was more of the nature of solution than a process of fermentation.

Greater insight into the digestive process was contributed by the experiments conducted by deReamur and Spallanzani. During this period Stephen Hales first measured the blood pressure of horses.

In 1757 Albrecht von Haller (1708-1777) published his first volume of Elements Physiologiae. The publication of this work, in the opinion of Sir Michael Foster, marked the end of the early physiological period and the beginning of modern physiology. He not only furnished a systematic and candid summary of the current status of physiological knowledge of all parts of the body, but he also contributed his own advances in the mechanics of respiration, of the development of the embryo, and of muscular irritability. He stated that action in the muscles was initiated by a force which traveled from the brain through the nerves. He further stated that all nerves were gathered together in the medulla cerebri, where he infers sensation and impressions are presented to the mind. Both sensation and movement, according to his theory, have their source in the medulla of the brain, the seat of the soul.

Geographical Discoveries
(Including those of the Seventeenth Century)

Geographical discoveries during this period greatly increased the knowledge of the earth's surface. Steven's invention of decimal arithmetic at the close of the sixteenth century and Napier's introduction of logarithms in 1614, along with Newton's lunar theory and the perfected chronometer of John Harrison in 1761-62, all facilitated the measurement of longitude. Systematic exploration of the earth then was made possible, and actively began in the seventeenth and eighteenth centuries.

A methodical observer among the explorers was William Dampier (1653-1715). His work Discourse on Winds, a treatise on meteorology, became a classic.

The favorable and romantic reports by the various explorers excited the imagination of people. Defoe in his Robinson Crusoe set off a romantic binge. This romantic tendency is suggested by some as having stimulated the French Revolution. Exaggerated reports of the virtues of other religions such as Buddhism, Confucianism, and so on, were circulated by returning explorers. These reports were used by the anti-Christians to discomfit the Christian Church. This tendency made the views of Rousseau and Voltaire quite acceptable to the people in general. Such theories as the inevitability of progress, the perfectibility of mankind, the social contract, all under the reign of so-called reason, were glibly accepted even though fallacious.

When all is said and done, mankind has improved very little on the trial and error process of the amoeba which extends its pseudopodia now here, now there, and when it discovers an acid medium it quickly withdraws; when it strikes a choice morsel, it quickly pulls itself to it and eventually engulfs it. Man's past history reveals the identical trial and error process but of course on a mental level; the only difference being that he seems to make a more difficult task of it. However, it must be conceded that his more complicated organizational structure, his more intangible desires, and his sometimes impractical goals aggravate his problem somewhat. It has been suggested that men of the period of the French Revolution unconsciously associated the Garden of Eden as support for their desire to return to the primitive. However, there is no challenge involved in this regressive process and then too it creates inconveniences of another nature.

XIV.

CONTINUATION OF INDEPENDENT METAPHYSICS DURING THE SEVENTEENTH AND EIGHTEENTH CENTURIES

Baruch (Benedict) Spinoza

Baruch (Benedict) Spinoza was born in 1632 of Portuguese Jewish parents at Amsterdam. His father, apparently relatively wealthy, wanted his son to study theology, to become a rabbi. However, his son disappointed him and he was excommunicated by the synagogue because of his tendency to free philosophical speculation. In his later years, he declined the Heidelberg professorship of Philosophy because of his love for independence. He died in 1677 in The Hague a poor, neglected and persecuted man.

His best known philosophical treatise is his Ethics. He was considerably influenced by the works of Descartes, and being a geometrician in his own right, naturally was partial to the geometric method of Descartes. However, where Descartes' philosophical system was dualistic, Spinoza's was monistic. His concepts of substance and God were identical. He defines substance as "that which exists by itself, and is coneived by itself, i.e., that which does not need the conception of any other thing in order to be conceived." Attribute he defines as "that which the intellect perceives as constituting the essence of the substance," as his attributes of extension and thought. By mode he means "the modifications of the substance, i.e., that which exists in and is conceived by something other than itself."

Substance is absolutely free in the sense that it is determined by itself alone. He asserted that movement, i.e., infinitely modified extension, produces the infinitude of finite modes, or as we call bodies. Intellect and will produce particular and finite minds, intellects, and wills. There is only one substantive; everything else is an adjective. He states, as Heraclitus did, that motion is co-eternal with substance, and makes an infinite mode of it. The human soul is considered a modification of infinite thought, whereas the human body is treated as a modification of infinite extension. God is absolute activity, pure action. The disinterested love of nature which gives everything its value in the whole of things, leads to what he terms amor intellectualis Dei (philosophical love of nature), considered by Spinoza as the summit of virtue.

There is much of Platonism in Spinoza's philosophy contained in the Cartesian geometrical form. Spinoza's conception of substance as being one and the same thing and then at the same time assuming the attributes of extension (extended substance) and thought (inextended substance), is of course a contradiction. Leibniz, however, proved that there is nothing contradictory in this assumption, inasmuch as the one and same substance can be both the principle of thought and the principle of corporeal existence.

Wilhelm Leibniz

In contrast to the life of suffering of Spinoza, Gottfried Wilhelm Leibniz (1646-1716) experienced only the bright side of life, in fact he no doubt could truthfully say as he did that "Everything is for the best in the best of possible worlds." He had a brilliant career as a jurist, diplomat, philosopher, mathematician, and theologian.

He was born in Leipsic, where his father was a university professor; he died as Librarian and Court Counsellor of the Duke of Hanover. He eagerly accepted all titles and honors which came his way, and they were numerous. While a diplomat he visited Newton, at which time we can be safe in assuming they discussed their simultaneous invention of infinitesimal calculus. He also visited Spinoza, where undoubtedly philosophical problems rather than mathematics were discussed.

His best known philosophical work was his Monadology. The term monad he most likely discovered in the works of Bruno. His most significant contribution to philosophical thought, as well as to our modern physics, was his concept of force. His reasoning on this subject begins by considering matter as essentially resistance, conceived of as activity. Behind the extended state of matter he assumes the act which constantly produces and renews the extended state. Hence, the reason a larger body is moved with greater difficulty than a smaller body is the greater resistance of the larger body. What seems to be inertia or a lack of power, is really more intense action, a greater effort. In view of the foregoing assumption he asserts that the essence of corporeality is not extension but the force of extension or active force. The idea of force, he maintains, is a higher notion than that of extension, which is merely an abstraction.

The original forces or monads, every entity possessing one, are compared to physical or mathematical points. He calls them variously metaphysical points, points of substance, or formal points; he speaks of them as formal points as they possess the characteristics of both mathematical and physical points.

He then goes on to state that each monad is absolutely independent in action; that there is no interaction between monads; and that they are so-called "windowless." Thus no monad has any idea what goes on round about itself, nor has it any influence on neighboring monads, not even the "echo" system of bats.

With this state of events, we are naturally interested in how he explains the apparent cooperative activity among monads. He does this by postulating so-called "pre-established harmony." By this notion it appears Leibniz ignored his opportunity to rationalize Spinoza's seeming contradiction of dualism within his unitary substance. By this omission he created rather an infinite pluralism in place of monism.

Leibniz's philosophy is strictly deterministic and classified as *concrete spiritualism,* God being considered the Monad of monads. Whereas Spinoza's system was basically Platonic in tendency, Leibniz tended more toward scholasticism. This tendency Christian Wolff (1679-1754) completed by putting the Leibnizian system in scholastic form.

In answer to Locke's denial of innate ideas, Leibniz asserts that nothing is inborn in the understanding except the understanding itself, which is the germ of all our ideas. This apparent insignificant difference was really important as it represented the basic difference between the philosophy of the Middle Ages and modern philosophy; it was the difference between the speculative method which proceeds from conceptions to facts, and the positive method which proceeds from facts to conceptions.

John Locke

John Locke (1632-1704) was an English physician who later developed into a philosopher. His anti-mystical and positivistic tendencies characteristic of the English schools, initiated the so-called age of criticism in philosophy. His study of medicine and the methodical introspection of his own thought processes led him to the conclusion that the scholastic approach was barren of positive results in the field of knowledge. He concluded that if truth is innate, it is obviously useless to look for it by observation and experimentation; however, he did not believe that truth was innate.

Locke organized his ideas in his treatise Essay Concerning Human Understanding, published in 1690 at London. The aim of his treatise was to discover the origin of our ideas, the certainty of the evidence, and the extent of our knowledge; and to induce philosophy clearly to mark the limits of the capacity of human comprehension.

He concludes we have no innate knowledge. The soul, he asserts, is originally an "empty tablet." Sensation is the source of our knowledge of the external world, while reflection the source of knowledge of internal facts. In fact, he maintains we do not think before we have sensations. Though passive in the formation of simple ideas, the mind is active in the formation of complex ideas. In other words, the simple ideas come into our minds by one sense only, or by more senses than one, or from reflection only, or, finally, by all the ways of sensation and reflection. Comparison, the composition of complex ideas, and abstractions are the three great functions of the mind.

Knowledge he concludes is nothing but the perception of the connection and agreement, or disagreement and repugnancy, of any of our ideas. Extension, form, and motion exist outside of us; but colors, sounds, tastes, and smells do not exist independent of our sensations.

He maintains that man is certain of his own existence, and as he had a beginning, there must be, to account for his beginning, a First Cause, which is God the Supreme Reason. We have demonstrative knowledge of God, although our understanding cannot comprehend the immensity of His attributes.

113

He further asserts that "Will" is a power or ability, and that "freedom" is another power or ability. Thus to speak of "free-will" is like speaking of "swift sleep" or "square virtue."

Locke's criticism of the understanding leads to a new idea of great value, namely his criticism of language, which has led to modern semanticism. Likewise, the method used by Locke in the study of human understanding led to introspective psychology.

Because of continual motion and continuity in nature, the objective reality of species is denied by Locke.

Locke attempted to found a rational religion as well as a rational science, all on the basis of experience.

XV

AGE OF CRITICISM DURING THE EIGHTEENTH AND NINETEENTH CENTURIES

Bishop George Berkeley

Bishop George Berkeley sensed the danger of a mechanical and materialistic philosophy arising from the teachings of Locke along with the scientific theories of Newton. To counteract this danger Berkeley took a bold step. He maintained that since the so-called primary qualities such as extension, figure and motion are themselves only ideas existing in the mind, they are no more real than the secondary qualities of color, taste, smell, and the like. Furthermore, none of them can exist in an unperceiving substance.

Berkeley does not deny the evidence of the senses; in fact, he confines himself to such evidence in his philosophy. By effacing the distinction made by Locke between so-called primary and secondary qualities, he in effect negates matter and arrives at absolute spiritualism, and hence gives support to Leibniz.

George Berkeley was born in Ireland in 1685 of English ancestors, became Bishop of Cloyne in 1734, and died at Oxford in 1763.

One of his main works is his Treatise on the Principles of Human Knowledge. He maintained that existence consists in perceiving or being perceived; thus the object of perception does not exist apart from the subject perceiving it. Logically this argument cannot be refuted. In the Berkeleyan sense an idea is something perceived, and thus the words "sensible thing" and "idea" are synonymous. A "spirit," in the Berkeleyan sense, is one simple, undivided, active being. It is called "understanding" as it perceives ideas, and "will" as it produces or otherwise operates about ideas. He states that it is impossible to form an adequate idea of spirit, soul, or will, as it is the essentially active thing, whereas the so-called "sensible thing" or idea is the essentially passive thing. To the argument that this makes a mountain an illusion he answers that he does not in the least doubt the existence of things.

He reduces human knowledge to two classes, knowledge of ideas and knowledge of spirits. Berkeley's absolute spiritualism is a unitary, homogeneous system, and in that way satisfies the basic goal of the philosophic spirit. In this sense it possesses the advantages of radical materialism without being handicapped by its difficulties.

As to his conception of time and space, he asserts that time is nothing, as it is simply an abstraction from the successions of ideas in our minds; that space cannot exist without the mind; and that mind alone exists.

Berkeley's philosophy has certain disadvantages; for instance, the question can be asked, how does the Creative Spirit produce sensible ideas in us? His deus ex machina does not explain anything, and his theory of intervention is as ineffective as the theory of occasionalism of the Cartesian school, and the "pre-established harmony" of the Leibnizian system. Berkeley attacks materialism both as theoretical error and as the source of the most serious heresies.

Condillac and Absolute Sensationalism

Abbot Etienne B. de Condillac (1715-1780) became one of Locke's first followers—Locke's philosophy having been introduced in France by Voltaire. However, where Locke distinguishes two sources of ideas, i.e., sensation and reflection, Condillac in his Traité des sensations specifies only one, sensation, making reflection the product of sensibility. Thereby Condillac becomes the founder of *absolute sensationalism*.

He proves his thesis by assuming a statue which is organized and alive but hindered by the marble exterior from having sensations. Condillac first removes the marble covering its olfactory organs, and from there he develops a personality based solely on the sense of smell. One by one he removes the obstructions from the other sense organs, and ends with a complete personality.

In the case of the sense of smell, some odors are pleasant,

others unpleasant, according to the individual's reaction. Here, of course, he makes no provisions for the inherent variability of the individuals experiencing the sensations.

Abstraction, he states, is the highest function of the understanding, and embraces all the faculties of the soul.

The "me" or inner perception is merely the sum of past and present sensations, a prolonged and infinitely modified sensation. He rates the sense of touch as the highest sense, the guide of the other senses. He agrees that there is something other than ourselves, but what the nature of this "other thing" is we do not know. He states that external bodies may or may not possess extension; he agrees with Leibniz that bodies may really exist but yet not be extended in themselves. Thus he maintains that the negation of extension does not necessarily involve the immaterialism of Berkeley. A sensationalist of the Condillac variety may be either a materialist or an idealist. It should be kept in mind that sensationalism is only an attempted explanation of the phenomena of mind, a theory concerning the origin of ideas. Materialism or idealism, on the other hand, is an ontology or a system of metaphysics. Strict materialism in the modern sense is defined by Sir Dampier-Whetham as "a belief that dead matter, in the hard unyielding lumps pictured by common sense, or the solid impenetrable Newtonian particles, is the sole ultimate reality of the Universe; that thought and consciousness are but by-products of matter; and that there is nothing real underlying it or existing beyond it."

Materialism versus Idealism

In spite of Berkeley, philosophy continued to attribute primary qualities to bodies. In other words, extension, impenetrability, figure, motion, and the like, are inherent in a reality external to and independent of our perception.

John Toland (1670-1721), an Englishman, is a champion of materialism as revealed by his work Pantheisticon. He maintains matter is an active substance, i.e., force. Thus we do not need either a soul of the world to explain universal life, or the soul of an individual to explain the vital principle of the organic body. This interpretation, according to Toland, makes dualism unnecessary. He further maintains that there can be no thought without a brain, that thought is a function of that organ.

David Hartley (1704-1757), a physician and naturalist, agrees

117

with Toland that there can be no thought without the brain. However, the brain is not the thinking subject; the soul is. Though entirely distinct from the body, it does not necessarily follow that it is essentially different from corporeal substance.

Joseph Priestley (1733-1804), an English theologian, philosopher, naturalist, and the discoverer of oxygen, published a treatise entitled Disquisitions relating to Matter and Spirit. In this work he summarizes the views of other philosophers as to the materiality of the soul. Among the views cited by him is the argument of spiritualism, i.e., that if the soul is composed of parts (living cells of grey cortical substance as we conceive them), how can it be felt as a unity? Priestley is said to have confessed that this argument is the only serious one that spiritualism can oppose—how can the one arise from the many? He admits that he cannot explain it, and neither can spiritualism. Albert Lange in his History of Materialism holds that this argument hits the weak spot in materialism.

The French physician Julien Offroy de la Mettrie (1709-1751) is one of the first outspoken materialists in France. As a disciple of Descartes, he espouses in his L'Homme Machine the idea of *mechanical determinism* along with materialism. He naively and dogmatically accepts as real the phenomenal world. His attempt to explain consciousness, however, is unconvincing. He declares that man is a machine, but a more complicated machine than the animal (apparently he is not willing to acknowledge that man is an animal). However, man is not the work of a supernatural creator, but "owes its origin to a natural evolution which gradually evolves more and more perfect forms from the elementary organisms."

The evolutionistic and transformistic conceptions which appeared in ancient philosophy now reappeared in various forms in the works of Denis Diderot, Robinet, and Charles de Bonnet; still later to be more completely espoused by Lamarck and Darwin. The materialists assert the futility of searching for design in nature where there are only accidental facts. Look at man, the spiritualists challenge, that living proof of final causes. The materialists in answer assert that the human species consists of an aggregation of more or less deformed and unhealthy individuals. As for the supposed creator, they have nothing but apologies to offer for him.

Baron D'Holbach published at London in 1770 a treatise called Systeme de la nature. It is a complete theory of ontological and psychological materialism. Matter and motion are eternal and sum up everything. The universe is governed by immutable and necessary laws, and not by God or by chance. (Then who initiated the laws?) The universe is a republic. Thought is a brain function; matter alone is immortal, but not individuals.

Cabanis (1757-1808) in a treatise formulated the principles of psychological materialism. Among other ideas, he asserted that body and mind are most intimately connected; in fact they are one and the same thing. The soul is body endowed with feeling; that body feels, thinks, and wills; that physiology and psychology are one and the same science. However, all philosophers will agree with Cabanis when he states that "intellectual and moral phenomena are like all others, necessary consequence of the properties of matter and the laws which govern beings."

Critical and Positivistic Philosophy of the Eighteenth and Nineteenth Centuries

David Hume

We now come to David Hume (1711-1776), an English philosopher and classical historian of England; he is said to have greatly influenced Kant.

In his essay Enquiry Concerning the Human Understanding, he treats of the question, "Can the human mind solve the ontological problem?" His philosophy enters the path marked out by English empiricism; philosophy becomes both critical and positivistic. We must, he declared, substitute criticism for "that abstruse philosophy and metaphysical jargon, which, being mixed up with popular superstition, renders it in a manner impenetrable to careless reasoners, and gives it the air of science and wisdom." We must seriously inquire into the nature of human understanding; we must cultivate true metaphysics by means of exact analysis in order to eliminate the false. He does not wish to renounce philosophy but give it a different direction and different objective.

All our perceptions are divided by Hume into two groups: ideas or thoughts, and impressions. Ideas are defined by Hume as the less lively perceptions of which we are conscious upon reflecting on our sensations. By impressions he means all our more lively perceptions as when we hear, see, feel, love, will, etc. Thought is limited to compounding, transposing, augmenting or diminishing the materials made available to us by our senses and experience. In other words, "all the materials of our thinking are derived either from our outward or inward sentiment, the mixture and composition of these belong alone to the mind and will."

Our ideas succeed each other in a certain order. The principles of connection which determine this order are resemblance, contiguity in time or place, and causality. These principles are not innate according to Hume, not even causality. He argues that the notion of cause and effect is the result of custom or habit, from observing one species of event always being followed with another in an uninterrupted succession. However, the necessary connection according to him can never be perceived.

As to will, we learn its influence from experience alone. Mankind, he maintains, is pretty much the same; if we would know the sentiments, inclinations, and the course of life of the Greeks and the Romans, then study carefully the temper and actions of the French and English.

By liberty he means power of acting or not acting, according to the determinations of the will. Experience he declares, destroys the dualism of instinct and reason.

He asserted that the general tendency of man to form an idea of God, if not an original instinct, is at least "a general attendant of human nature." Positive religions to him are "anything but sick men's dreams," or "the playsome whimsies of monkeys in human shape."

Thomas Reid

Thomas Reid, the founder of the so-called Scottish school, heatedly opposes Hume in the name of common-sense. Reid as a rebuttal to Hume's conception of cause, calls attention to the fact that day and night follow one another consistently and yet no one considers day as the cause of night because it follows day.

Reid goes on to state that Hume's philosophy also is vulnerable to criticism; for instance if experience is the sole source of knowledge, how explain the exceptional character of absolute certainty which Hume himself concedes to mathematics? Also, how can we explain the ideas of cause, necessity, and necessary connection if there is nothing in the intellect that was not previously in the senses.

He also maintains that materialism is impotent to refute Berkeley's idealism. On the other hand it is vulnerable to the destructive analysis of any critical philosophy. In the eighteenth century Locke, Berkeley, and Hume showed that nature could only be apprehended through the senses, and yet materialism would not die.

Immanuel Kant

Kant now takes over and corrects certain of the weaknesses in Hume's philosophy.

Immanuel Kant was born of plain folk in Königsberg, Prussia, in 1724 and died in 1804. His paternal grandparents emigrated to Germany from Scotland.

He apparently was a good student for he became a private tutor and later a professor at the University of Königsberg. He must have been quite versatile too as he taught logic, ethics, mathematics, geography, cosmography, and of course metaphysics. It will be recalled he also suggested the nebular hypothesis. In many respects he was a fortunate individual, for he was the recipient of many honors; he enjoyed good health; he never had to leave his own province; and he was free from the cares of married life. He was a reformer of philosophy. Some have likened him to Socrates, but of course minus a Zanthippe.

Kant speaks of his period as the age of criticism. By this he means a philosophy which, before affirming, weighs, and before assuming to know, inquires into the meaning and limitations of knowledge.

He distinguishes between three different spheres of knowledge: (I) the theoretical, which manifests itself as the faculty of knowing, the sense of truth; (II) the practical, the active faculty, the sense of goodness; and (III) the aesthetical, the sense of beauty and teleological fitness. We shall briefly indicate what each sphere covers:

(I) The theoretical sphere. His Critique of Pure Reason contains his views in this sphere. He first defines knowledge as synthetic judgments, a priori. In other words knowledge must have a rational basis as well as being based on observation. He goes on to explain two phases as to the acquirement of knowledge. The first phase is under his so-called Critique of Sensibility. The sensibility receives the raw sense-data within the original intuitions of space and time, places its impression and form upon it, and which finally become so-called intuitions, sensible ideas, or phenomena.

The second phase in the acquisition of knowledge is expounded under the head of Critique of the Understanding. The understanding elaborates the intuitions or sensible ideas received from sensibility. At this point he further distinguishes between (A) the faculty of judgment, that is, the faculty of connecting the sensible ideas with each other according to certain innate laws; and (B) the faculty of arranging our judgments under a series of universal ideas, which he calls "reason."

We shall briefly indicate what these two faculties are:

(A) the Classification of the innate laws involves those of quantity, quality, relation, and modality. It is the reason that prescribes its laws to the sensible universe, and in that sense makes the cosmos. (Here, it should be observed, is the germ of Hegel's panlogism.)

(B) The faculty of arranging our judgments under certain general points of view (which he terms ideas), is considered by Kant to be the highest of all in the theoretical sphere. He enumerates the concepts of "reason" or Ideas, as: the thing-in-itself—the absolute (unknowable), the universe, the soul, and God. Hence reason, the systematic and scientific faculty, is the highest synthetic faculty. Science, then, is the product of the co-operation of sensibility, judgment, and "reason." Incidentally, Kant brings out certain antinomies involving the finite versus the infinite, and elapsed time versus eternity, such as the antinomies of quantity, quality, relation, and modality. (Some light has been shed on these antinomies by Bertrand Russell of the present period.)

(II) The practical sphere of knowledge is explained in his Critique of Practical Reason. The upshot of his Critique of Pure Reason would seem to be determinism. However, the freedom-loving Kant overcomes this obstacle by asserting that "will" and not the "reason" forms the basis of our faculties and of things. In other words "reason" is placed in a subordinate position to the "will." This idea is briefly the substance of his Critique of Practical Reason. The function of the "reason" is regulative and modifying, while the function of the "will" is creative. In so far as our acts occur in time and in space, they are determined; but in so far as the source from where they spring (our intelligible character) is independent of time and space, our acts are indetermined and free.

Kant postulates a personal God in his Critique of Practical Reason but the real God of Kant is Freedom in the service of the ideal, or the Good Will. Religion within the limits of reason is nothing more nor less than morality, which he considers is the essence of Christianity.

(III) The aesthetics sphere is covered in his Critique of Judgment. Kant's synthetic impulse leads him to bridge the gap which separates theoretical reason and the conscience. The aesthetical and teleological sense, an intermediate faculty, connects the understanding and the will. The object of the understanding is truth, and nature and natural necessity its subject-matter. The will, on the other hand, strives for the good, and deals with freedom. Judgment in the aesthetical and teleological sense is concerned with what lies between the true and the good, between nature and liberty—in other words, the beautiful and the purposive. Briefly the aesthetical sense makes the beautiful —the subjective finality, while the teleological sense constitutes the suitable, or objective finality. Thus, a flower may be the object of spontaneous aesthetical judgment on the part of the artist, as well as the object of a teleological judgment of a herb doctor for its remedial effects.

Immanent teleology identifies the ends of nature with the acting causes, and thus it is the solution of the antinomy of mechanism and purposiveness.

Kant conceives of space and time as the eyes of the mind, and at the same time being the boundaries of its knowledge. However, it is the mind which prescribes its laws to the so-called phenomenal world; and it is the mind from which the moral law proceeds. It is the mind and its judgment which makes the beautiful beautiful.

Kant compares his own work with that of Copernicus and his Celestial Revolutions.

Schulze's Scepticism

As might be expected from the experience of prior philosophers, the philosophy of Kant culminates in scepticism, as witness the work of G. E. Schulze (1761-1833). He raises the question that if the categories cannot be applied to things-in-themselves, how can we know whether these exist or do not exist? "We can have no absolutely certain and universally valid knowledge in philosophy, either of the existence or non-existence of things-in-themselves and their properties, or of the limits of human knowledge." So spake G. E. Schulze.

Fichte and His Philosophy of the Absolute

The philosophy of the absolute came from theology, and Johann Gottlieb Fichte (1765-1814) is its founder. Fichte first studied for the ministry. He later won a professorship in Jena as a result of a philosophical treatise. Because he was accused of atheism, he resigned his professorship, and for ten years he and his family suffered the trials attendant to a nomadic life. He died while a professor at the University of Berlin. His chief work was Grundlage der gesammmten Wissenschaftslehre.

Fichte's philosophy centered in an espousal of Kant's so-called Practical Reason as the creative source of all that is distinctive in personality. He affirms Kant's moral ideal and Spinoza's unity of the "two worlds." Thus the philosophy of Fichte is a synthesis of liberty and monism, the monism of the moral will. The fundamental dogma of his system is the identity of the ethical and metaphysical principles. According to Fichte the real reality is the Good, active Reason, pure Will, the moral Ego.

The universe is considered by him as the manifestation of pure Will, the symbol of the moral Idea. Fichte maintains that this is the real thing-in-itself, the real absolute. He considered true philosophizing as an endeavor to convince oneself that being is nothing and that duty is everything; that the phenomenal world is inane apart from its intelligible essence.

Knowledge is neither in whole nor in part the production of sensation but the exclusive creation of the ego. Speculative thought begins with a spontaneous act of the ego's creative energy. It follows the law of opposition and reconciliation. Apparently Fichte received from Kant's categories the idea of the threefold act of the understanding and in fact all intellectual acts in general, i.e., thesis of the ego, antithesis of the non-ego, and synthesis of the ego and non-ego, all forming a single act. Suppress the Ego, and you suppress the world. Creation is the will or pure thought, limiting, determining, or making a person of itself. He maintains freedom is the highest truth, the very

124

essence of things. Freedom realizes itself in time. He asserts that self-realization means struggle; struggle in turn involves an obstacle; and that obstacle is the world of sense and its temptations.

He further asserts that the absolute or ideal ego is nothing but an abstraction. The real God is a living God, or the God-man. He goes on to say, "I abhor all religious conceptions which personify God, and regard them as unworthy of a reasonable being." Why? Because a personal being, or a subject, does not exist without an object that limits it. God is nothing but the moral order of the world, the freedom which progressively realizes itself in it.

By his denial of the personality of God he convicts both the notion of an absolute ego as the creator of the non-ego, and the a priori construction method. Fichte's disciple, Schelling, attempts to correct this contradiction.

Friedrich W. J. Schelling

Friedrich W. J. Schelling (1775-1854) was born at Leonberg, in Würtemberg. He received his education at the University of Tübingen and at Leipsic. He was made a professor of philosophy at Jena, where he made the acquaintance of Fichte and renewed his friendship with Hegel. He later served as a professor in the Universities of Erlangen, Munich, and Berlin. He died at 79 years of age.

Schelling was considered an inconsistent thinker as he first followed Fichte, then Spinoza, later Neo-Platonism, and finally Jacob Böhme.

He classified his Spinozistic and Neo-Platonic phase as his "negative philosophy," and his final phase, showing the influence of Jacob Böhme, as his "positive philosophy." We shall touch upon some of the general characteristics of each phase:

1. His so-called "Negative philosophy." He refutes Fichte by maintaining that since the ego does not exist without the non-ego, nor conversely does the non-ego produce the ego, it cannot be said as Fichte stated, that the non-ego is the unconscious product of the ego. Furthermore, as the absolute ego cannot be limited by a non-ego, we must give up the attempt to make an absolute of the ego. His conclusion, therefore, is that the ego and the non-ego, thought and being, are both derived from a higher principle, a principle which is the cause of both. This principle is a neutral principle, the indifference and identity of

contraries. This is Spinoza's main thought but using different terminology, i.e., thought (the ego) and extension (the non-ego).

Philosophy, according to Schelling, is the science of the absolute in its double manifestation, nature and mind. By the addition of the science of nature to that of mind, Schelling bridges the gap in Fichte's system.

To think is to reproduce and not to produce. As nature is a datum or fact, the ego cannot escape partially recognizing experience and observation as the source of knowledge. Schelling also emphatically denies that the non-ego makes the ego, that sense perception constitutes thought as maintained by Locke, Hume, and Condillac. On the contrary, thought, knowledge, and science have their source and principle in that which also constitutes the source and principle of the non-ego, in the absolute. The starting-point of speculation is experience; a priori speculation continues to be the philosophical method. As the world of facts and the world of thoughts have their common source in the absolute, they of necessity cannot contradict one another. Nature is existing reason; and mind—thinking reason.

Schelling, apparently applying Fichte's idea of the threefold aspects of thought as comprising thesis, antithesis, and synthesis, speaks of nature as a three-stage evolution of matter or gravity (thesis), form or light (antithesis), and organized matter (synthesis). He maintains that the human brain is the last stage of organic evolution, the climax of universal organization. The synthesis of all forces of life is the soul of the world. Mind and nature, according to Schelling's system, will gradually be blended into an harmonious and living unity.

2. His so-called "Positive Philosophy." This final phase was first brought out in 1809 in a dissertation on human freedom, in which he accentuated the mystical element. Schelling, under the influence of Jacob Böhme, becomes a theosophist, a pantheist, and a monotheist. The divine idea, the personality of God, and the Trinity, now are considered by him as important realities. This changed his basic thought less than what one would expect. The absolute indifference or identity of contraries now is renamed "primitive will." The first principle of the divine being is not thought or reason, but will striving for being, the desire to be. Before being, every being including God, desires to be. The evil in the world originated not in God as a person but in what precedes his personality, which Schelling unhesitatingly calls the principle of divine egoism. This principle in God is

eternally merged in his love. In man, however, it becomes an independent principle which becomes the source of moral evil.

Schelling's two systems, first that thought precedes being (idealism) and second that being is the antecedent of thought (realism) are merged in a common principle, the absolute. The first phase leads to Hegel with his a priori construction of the universe, and the second to Schopenhauer and empiricism. It is the first off-shoot that we shall consider next, the philosophy of Hegel.

Georg W. F. Hegel and His A Priori Construction of the Universe

Georg W. F. Hegel (1770-1831) was born at Stuttgart, Germany. He attended, together with Schelling, the theological seminary at Tübingen; and he later both renewed and dissolved his friendship with Schelling at Jena. He died while a professor at the University of Berlin.

Hegel maintained that the common source of the ego and of nature is immanent in reality and does not transcend it. Mind and nature are the successive modes of the absolute and not its aspects. The absolute to Hegel is not immovable but active; it is successively nature and mind, in fact, the very process itself. He affirms the immanency, as well as the perfect knowableness, of the absolute. The absolute is movement, process evolution. The law governing both human thought and unconscious nature is reason; the end sought is self-conscious reason. Reason is the law which is in man as the essence and norms of his thought; and at the same time it is in the things (nature) as the essence and law of their evolution. The so-called categories are not only modes of thinking things, but the modes of being of the things themselves. In short they are the forms which mould man's thought and the stages of eternal creation. Thus, Hegel stresses the importance in metaphysics of making a more thorough study of the categories, their nature, and above all, their connection. The categories are transformations of one and the same basic category, the idea of being. According to Hegel the true philosophic method, i.e., the so-called dialectical method, is to leave thought to itself, to abandon it to its spontaneous self-activity. The genealogy of pure concepts (logic) is the science which accomplishes this task. The science of reason is considered by Hegel to be the universal science; it conceives and produces being; and hence is everything. In the light of this interpretation he would seem to be inconsistent to follow his treatise on Logic with his two treatises on the Philosophy of Nature and of Mind. We shall briefly review the highpoints of (I) his Logic, (II) his Philosophy of Nature, and finally (III) his Philosophy of Mind:

(I)—Logic, with Its Categories of Pure Concepts as follows:

1—*Quality, Quantity, Measure*

The common basis of the categories is the notion of being. All concepts are expressions of modes of being, such as quality, quantity, proportion, phenomenon, and action. Being is modified by virtue of the principle of force which it contains. The notion of becoming resolves the contradiction found in the idea of being (pure being is non-being). As being becomes, it determines itself, limits itself, defines itself. The individual is the unity of the finite with the infinite. Existence is finite being. Finite being, the individual, is infinity existing in a certain manner; limited infinity: quality becomes quantity. Number is quantity broken up, and degree is concentrated quantity. They become reconciled in the notion of proportion and measure.

2. *Essence and Appearance, Substantiality and Causality, Reciprocity*

Essence is defined by Hegel as being, unfolded or expanded so that its aspects reflect one another. Therefore, the categories come in pairs such as force and expression, matter and form, cause and effect, action and reaction. This reflection-into-itself is the phenomena. Phenomena without essence is a mere appearance. No category is independent of its neighbors. The force or agent is the generative principle of the phenomena, the phenomena being the act or expression. Activity is identical with reality. Since reason alone is real, Hegel concludes that what is real is rational.

Essence (reality), as a necessary principle of activity, becomes substance. Substance is considered to be the totality of its modes. It is united with its modes by an organic tie; it is the cause of its modes, which in turn are the effects of the substance. Hence, the cause is inseparable from its effect, and the effect connected with its efficient cause. In nature the cause series is not a straight ever-continuing line but a curved line which returns to its start-ing point, in short, a circle. The absolute is not in any part of the causal chain; it is in the sum-total of the particular and relative causes.

The two spheres into which a category is divided become united in reciprocal action and become essence or logical totality.

3. *Subjective, Objective, and Absolute Totality*

None of the ideas so far indicated have reality except totality. Nothing in nature and in thought exists of itself. This belongs only to the categories in their totality. Liberty is found in the totality alone.

The idea of totality is separated into subjective totality (the notion itself) and objective totality. The subjective notion is a form minus matter; it exists as a final cause (goal). The objecti-fied notion is the objective whole, the universe, or objects.

In summary, the categories of (1) quality, quantity, measure; (2) essence and phenomenon, substantiality and causality, re-ciprocal action; and (3) subjectivity, objectivity, absolute, are the serial stages of being. Hegel applied his principle, process, and these stages in his Philosophy of nature and Philosophy of Mind, as follows:

(II)—Philosophy of Nature:

1. *The Inorganic*

Creative thought begins with space and matter. Like being, the first notion of logic, space exists and does not exist; and matter is something and nothing. Formless matter is indeter-minate being.

Attraction is the individualizing tendency in nature, like a mighty desire. Universal gravitation is the ideal unity of this attractive force. The distribution of matter corresponds to the categories of quantity.

The cosmos of astronomy is a so-called elementary society, which anticipates human society. The cosmos, however, oper-ates merely under mechanical laws.

2. *Chemism*

The next stage leads to the qualitative differentiation of matter, using such agencies as light, electricity, and heat. Chemism is an inner transformation, a change not only of place but of essence. The chemical process returns to itself and forms living beings (organisms).

3. The Organic

Hegel maintains that the appearance of life is wholly spontaneous. From the ashes of the terrestrial organism appears the vegetable kingdom. A plant is considered an imperfect organism, that individuality proper is found only in the animal kingdom.

Animals are developed by degrees until they reach the stage of the human organism, which is considered by Hegel as the most perfect animal form. It is in the human organism where the creative idea is fully reflected. But here it stops, and the creative idea thereafter reflects its activity in the sphere of the mind.

(III)—Philosophy of Mind:

1. The Subjective Mind (The Individual)

According to Hegel man is essentially mind, that is, consciousness and freedom. Like nature, the mind is subject to the law of development. Consciousness and freedom are the products of the evolution called history. Man's individual freedom is limited by the freedom of his fellow man. Hence, the subjective mind must yield to the objective mind—Society.

2. The Objective Mind (Society)

The blind forces of nature now change their form and become regulated disciplined instincts under law, i.e., marriage and legal punishment. The objective mind manifests itself successively in the form of right, person, property with right to possess and transfer, and finally the right of contract which is the State in embryo. Hegel believed in punishment as the solemn affirmation of the violated principle and is not rightfully applied with the object of individual reform. He favored capital punishment for this reason. The impersonal will (right, justice) must become the personal will of the individual. Legality must become morality; the objective mind must become a subject. Morality is the legality of the heart.

Marriage (the family) is the fundamental moral institution,

on which rests the civil society and the State. The basis of society and the State rests on the holiness of marriage and the honor of corporations; it is the source of a people's prosperity. The kingdom of the idea, of the universe, of the objective mind, is the State. (We here recognize why Marxism embraced a part of Hegelianism). The dialectic of history consists in the passing of the civilization of one people to that of another.

The Christian and parliamentary monarchy, such as in England, appears to be favored by Hegel. He maintains that the equilibrium between the State and the individual is restored in that form of government.

3. *The Absolute Mind*

The evolution of the Idea does not stop with the State, and spiritual activity does not reach its climax in political life, because freedom is the essence of mind and independence its life. "Mind cannot unconditionally subject itself to anything but mind," in the opinion of Hegel. Not finding in political activity the ultimate satisfaction it seeks, mind seeks it in art, religion, and science. Man was first an individual (subjective mind), then he formed the State (Objective Mind) and finally he returns into himself and finds the ideal of art or the beautiful, the religious ideal or God, the philosophical ideal or truth. In the realization of these ideals, he finds the supreme independence for which he seeks; in short he becomes absolute mind.

Philosophy of Art and Religion

In art the mind of man gets pleasure by anticipation of the victory over the external world. Hegel defines art as "the anticipated triumph of mind over matter; it is the idea penetrating matter and transforming it after its image." *Architecture,* an elementary stage, is merely a symbolic art in which the form suggests the idea without its direct expression, i.e., the pyramid, the pagoda, the Greek temple, and the Gothic cathedral. *Sculpture,* while it uses the gross matter of architecture, is capable of transforming and spiritualizing it. *Painting* goes one step further in representing the soul as revealed in the eye; this the statue was incapable of revealing. The foregoing forms of art, architecture, sculpture, and painting are classified by Hegel as objective art.

Music to Hegel is a subjective form of art, a spiritualistic art which can reproduce the innermost essence of the human soul, with infinite shades of feeling. However, according to Hegel the art of arts is *poetry*, which he considered as the "synthesis of all contraries, the harmonious union of the world of music and the world of objective art." Epic poetry Hegel considered as comparable to objective art, lyric poetry to music, and dramatic poetry as the poetry of poetry.

Hegel's philosophy of art is said to be unsurpassed.

Religion reacts against the pantheism anticipated by art, and shows us the transcendent Being, God, whom man cannot reach. Christianity proclaims the unity of the finite and the infinite in Jesus Christ, and thus anticipates the mind's highest development, philosophy. Art and religious faith spring from feeling and imagination. (Science also springs from imagination according to Einstein). Science is pure reason, the deification of the mind.

In speaking of the salient features of different religions, he states that in the religions of the Orient the idea of infinity predominates. Their main feature is pantheism. God is everything; man is nothing. Brahminism is cited as the most complete expression of Asiatic pantheism.

According to Hegel Mosaic monotheism shows the same general characteristics. God is the creator, and men are his creatures. Man is to God what the earthenware is to the potter. Human liberty and spontaneity are out of the question. Both the act and the will come from God. (This conclusion does not appear consistent with the Old Testament).

Under Hellenic polytheism in early Greece, however, man is everything. The gods adored by the Greeks as Zeus, Apollo, Athene, Aphrodite, are men and their power, intelligence, and beauty. The early Greeks considered gods as relative beings, and they worshipped at the shrine of the finite.

In the Hindu, God is everything and man is nothing. With the Greeks, God is very little if anything, and man is everything. However, in Christianity the important thing is neither God considered in the abstract, the Father, nor man in the abstract, but the concrete unity of the divine and the human in Jesus Christ, a being which is both God and man. This conception is quite consistent with Hegel's basic philosophy, the unity of contraries.

In order for the mind to reach the climax of its evolution, Hegel divests the religious doctrine of its representative form and gives it the rational form, the advance which is made by philosophy. In other words, the gospel and true philosophy have the same content.

Some General Reactions to Hegelianism

Philosophy has been defined as a comprehensive view of nature, an attempt at a universal explanation of things. According to this definition, then Hegelianism fulfills the definition more fully than any other philosophy so far expounded. At first it greatly influenced many phases of intellectual life, i.e., jurisprudence, politics, ethics, theology, and aesthetics, and for a period it was considered "the philosophy." It finally lost its popularity because of the errors arising from its method. His a priori speculation cannot be the final form of science; science to be a science must be verified by experience. Knowledge of things does not come from pure thought but from thought supported by observation and experience.

Kant vigorously protested against the absolute idealism of his so-called "false disciples," (Fichte, Schelling and Hegel). He maintained that he taught an ideo-realistic form of philosophy, considering the form alone as given a priori, and the content—matter, as solely and necessarily furnished by the outer and inner sense. Whereas reason produces a priori the categories, it cannot produce a priori the ideas of iron, light, pleasure, or pain; these ideas are supplied by experience.

Johann F. Herbart

Johann F. Herbart (1776-1841) followed more closely Kant, his master, occupying a position between Hegel and Locke. Herbart served as professor at Königsberg and Göttingen. His writings are largely an expression of his opposition to the principles, method, and conclusions of Hegel. Things are not just our thoughts, but exist really and independently of reason which thinks them. The problem of philosophy then is not to construct the universe but to explain, as far as is possible, its mechanism. A philosophy without the basis of the positive data of science is hollow. In short the task of philosophy thereupon becomes the elaboration of the concepts which underlie the different sciences. He maintains that Hegel's elimination of the principle of contradiction by his form of logic is not a solution to the contradict-

133

ing ideas in our thought. Scepticism also is no solution. As a rebuttal to scepticism Herbart maintains that *it is beyond doubt that things appear to exist, although it may be doubted that they exist.* In other words, it cannot be denied that the phenomena exist. Provided it provokes philosophical thought, the doubt that things may not exist as they appear to exist is legitimate. Thus the task of philosophical thought is to free our general ideas from the contradictions contained in them by continual correction and revision.

Herbart, in his attempt to solve contraries or antinomies, maintains that the difficulty arises from asserting that one thing is many things (colored, sapid, liquid, odorous), the notion of inherence. The notion of the ego is likewise a contradiction because of its diverse faculties. The confusion of two contraries of which Hegel is guilty, gives rise to the idea of limited and relative being; this Herbart flatly rejects for being admits of neither negation nor limitation. However, he ends up with a plurality of real beings or realities. His realities, therefore, closely resemble the monads of Leibniz, except that the "monads" of Leibniz are complex unities with many properties, whereas the realities of Herbart are simple, possessing one property only. Thus real being is not what the senses show for the objects perceived which have many properties; on the other hand real being is each property alone. The sensible object, say iron, would then contain as many realities as it has properties.

The seeming contradiction in the notion of inherence then is the result of confusing real being (Kant's thing-in-itself) with phenomenal being. The phenomenal being is therefore an integration of real beings, or in the term of present-day psychology, the "gestalt."

The ideas of change and causality are similarly explained by Herbart. The real beings are not subject to change but only their mutual relations. Likewise, the relation of causality cannot exist either between two real beings (external causality) or between a real being and its supposed characteristics (immanent causality). Hence, causality can signify nothing but reality, or at the most, self-preservation. Here it would seem Herbart contradicts himself as self-preservation involves a reflective act which divides the real being into two, the subject which preserves and an object preserved.

The ego ceases to be a contradictory idea if we cease regarding it as a multiple unity. The ego has simply one function, and that is to preserve itself in its indestructible originality. The function varies under the influence of its surroundings. Its only faculty manifests itself in a number of different faculties according as the soul is solicited by similar, different, or contrary realities. The act by which the ego affirms and preserves itself in opposition to objects, is thought. Herbart defines the psychological consciousness as the sum of relations which the ego sustains to other real beings. Will is nothing but thought; feeling is a thought arrested by other more energetic thoughts; psychical life is a mechanism; and psychology proper is a true mechanism, an application of arithmetic.

The philosophy of Herbart, which attempts to free thought from its contradictions, is itself full of contradictions. Whereas his ontology asserts that real being is simple and inextended, his psychology is based on the opposite assumption. Real reality (life, activity) is excluded from the sphere of beings and becomes nothing but lifeless abstractions. His philosophy presents to us a so-called "pulverized universe," the very opposite of Hegel's monistic universe. Apparently his antipathy toward Hegelianism caused him to over-react. This weakness in Herbart's system is corrected by the philosophy of Schopenhauer, a system of a happy mean between speculation and positive knowledge.

Arthur Schopenhauer

Arthur Schopenhauer (1786-1860) was born in Danzig, Germany, the son of a banker and an authoress. He studied at the Universities of Göttingen and Berlin, and taught philosophy at the latter university as a Privatdocent for approximately eleven years. Thereafter, he retired to private life at Frankfort on the Main.

Schopenhauer's philosophy may be considered the second offshoot of Schelling's philosophy. He sat in on the lectures of Schulze at Göttingen and of Fichte at Berlin. However, he devoted his studies mainly to Kant, Plato, and Buddhism. From Kant, Fichte, and Schelling he receives the germ of his main doctrine, the conception of the will and the absolute; from Plato he gets his theory of ideas or stages of the voluntary phenomenon; and from Buddhism his conception of the negation of the will, his pessimistic tendency.

He separates the world as it is in itself and the phenomenal world as conceived by his perception, his idea, the product of his intelligence. The real world exists independently of him, but as a phenomenon it depends on the perceiving subject. As a phenomena the world is a relative thing created by the ego and the a priori conditions of thought. Yet he maintains that consciousness declares unequivocably that behind the phenomenal world there is a higher reality, an absolute, a thing-in-itself. However, the perception which we have of ourselves furnishes us with at least an image of what the things are outside of us. He asserts that he is both the subject and the object of his thought, as he is the object of the thoughts of others, as he states he is conscious of being an object among other objects. The essence of the entire objective world is what he is; its essence is analogous to his. He declares we have the right to judge things according to what we find in ourselves. Descartes, Spinoza, Leibniz, and Hegel asserted that the essential thing is thought. According to Schopenhauer, however, the essential thing is the Will, while thought is a derived phenomenon, an accident of will.

Will is our very essence. In fact, the entire universe in its essence is a will that objectifies itself, that is, gives itself a body. My body is the product of will, my desire-to-be made visible. He considers pure will as not connected with the intellect, in which case it is irritability, that mysterious force which controls our digestion, the circulation of the blood, secretions, and the like. When will is connected with our intellect, it is conscious and commonly called free-will. Will in this sense is irritability acting knowledgeably as, for example, in raising our arm. As an example of the power of conscious will he cites cases of Negroes committing suicide by arresting their respiration.

However diverse its manifestations, the will as such is one. Whereas the body and the intellect get tired and require rest, the will alone never tires, for even during sleep it causes dreams. The will exists prior to its body for it forms and organizes it according to its needs. Because the body wills to assimilate oxygen of the air, it transforms the mucous membrane of the thoracic canal into lungs, and so on. He asks us to consider the organization of animals; for example it would at first appear that a goat butts because it has horns, but that is not true according to Schopenhauer, for a goat will butt before it has horns. Thus, the will is the center of creative evolution, the very principle of its organization. The will-to-be or will-to-exist provides the motivating principle in the behavior of animals. The most efficient safeguard to existence which the will provides is intelligence, which in men supersedes all the others. He declares that in the case of lower animals the will is quite manifest, but in man the will can only be concealed by false appearances.

The same principle of will is observed, although not so apparent, in the vegetable kingdom. In this connection he cites the example of a root seeking moisture in the most roundabout way; of potatoes growing in a cellar which infallibly will turn their sprouts to the light, and so on. No essential difference exists between so-called irritability and the faculty of being determined by motives; the motive, he asserts, regularly produces an irritation which sets the will in action.

Recognition of the will is most difficult in the two extremes of creation, i.e., in man at one extreme and in the mineral kingdom at the other extreme. The character of man and in the minerals is full of mysteries. Man especially can conceal his character and disguise the tendency of his will. In spite of this we can observe in man certain marked tendencies and propensities. The mineral kingdom, too, has its constant tendencies, for instance the gravitational force, the various opposing forces observed in chemistry, and the like.

Schopenhauer regards will as the unconscious force which produces specific beings living in space and time. The various phenomena of universal will follow each other in time according to uniform laws, and according to immutable types called ideas by Plato. These ideas are independent of time and space, unchangeable and eternal, as the will itself. Individuals, however, become and never are. The so-called inferior ideas (the lower stages) of the will are weight, solidity, chemism, electricity, magnetism, and so on. The higher stages (the superior ideas) appear in the organic world, with man manifesting the highest stage (the ideas of beauty). The so-called struggle for existence results from the different stages of voluntary phenomena contending with each other for their needs of matter, space, and time.

There will be a universe as long as the will's perpetual desire-to-be continues. The will never dies; hence birth and death do not apply to it but only to its manifestations. As man has within himself a part of the universal will, he is guaranteed a certain measure of immortality. This, he declares, is a disappointment to those who want to free themselves from the pains of existence by committing suicide. The will is the origin of all evil, as it is the endless source of all life.

137

The mind of man understands only what is subject to the law of causality, in fact is fatally dependent on it.

Schopenhauer has a rather bleak conception of history; he asserts that it is just a series of murders, intrigues, lies, and robberies. He goes on to say that the only virtue worthy of the name is pity or sympathy, the Buddhistic principle of morality. In fact, sympathy is the basis of all morality. Other virtues to Schopenhauer are based upon the will-to-live-and-to-enjoy. Laughter and tears are phenomena peculiar to man alone.

As being is synonymous with suffering, positive happiness can never be had. Only negative well-being enables one to bring about a cessation of suffering, that is, by negation of the will. This is the common principle which Buddhism and Christianity shares according to Schopenhauer; both religions also agree that man enters the world as a sinner.

Schopenhauer does not presume to explain the ultimate causes of the world but confines himself to the facts of inner and outer experience. He attempts to understand only the immanent essence of the world. He does not attempt to answer why or by what cause the universe exists as the conceptions of cause and effect apply to time and space only, and there is no time and space in a transcendent sphere.

He further declares that his conception of the will is the starting fact of experience, the fact on which he grounds his philosophy. He goes on to say that his method is empirical, analytic, and inductive. Thus he gives us a system of empirical metaphysics. His philosophy reunited elements which seemed irreconcilable.

His extreme pessimism evidently reflects his own personal experiences, and therefore rests upon an imperfect knowledge of human nature. He appears to have had an antipathy especially for professors of philosophy.

Eduard von Hartmann

Eduard von Hartmann (1842-1906) is considered the most original of Schopenhauer's disciples. He attempts in his Philosophy of the Unconscious to reconcile Schopenhauer and Hegel. He declares that the will reaches its ends as though it were intelligent. The will in the form of soul communicates to the human body such movements it desires as though conscious of the means necessary to realize its purpose. Hartmann was the first to formulate clearly the distinction between intelligence and inner apperception, supporting his distinction with facts. Intelligence is conscious that it knows, whereas the inner apperception is unconscious intelligence revealed as in healing wounds and fractures.

Hartmann's philosophy, too, reflects optimism rather than the pessimism of his master, Schopenhauer; evil to Hartmann is considered reparable; redemption is universal.

He assumes a creation and an end of the world. (Hence an end of suffering?) He maintains, however, that chance has produced the present universe, and the same chance may in the future produce other worlds. He terms this "evolutionistic optimism," as against Schopenhauer's absolute pessimism.

Auguste Comte and His Positivism

In France at the beginning of the nineteenth century there was gradually formed a party of thinkers who, while having materialistic sympathies, yet were hostile to metaphysics and determined to replace it by science. These thinkers rallied around the standard of Auguste Comte.

Isidore Auguste Marie Francois Xavier Comte, Auguste Comte for short, was born in Montpellier, France, in 1789, and died in Paris in 1857. Emil Littré of France and John Stuart Mill of England were numbered among his followers.

Comte was one of the original thinkers of our age. The philosophy he espoused is known as positivism. He maintained that the human mind successively passes through three stages of philosophizing: (1) the theological stage—the elementary stage; (2) the metaphysical stage; and (3) the positive stage—the final and scientific stage.

In the theological stage, the mind travels from fetishism to polytheism, and finally to the conception of one God. In the metaphysical stage mind no longer explains phenomena by conscious wills but by abstractions considered as real beings, such as force, power or principle; this system of thought ceased at the end of the Middle Ages. The positive or scientific period came into being with Galileo, Descartes, Bacon, Hobbes, Gassendi, and Newton. As the advance of scientific research reveals an increasing number of invariable laws, so the theological and metaphysical explanations of the universe are being superseded by the scientific explanation.

Not only philosophy in general, but each science in particular, pass through these three stages.

Comte observes that the different sciences naturally fall into an order of increasing complexity and diminishing generality, each one depending on the truth of all the preceding sciences, with of course such truths as belong particularly to it. His classification briefly is as follows: (1) the science of number (arithmetic and algebra), which deals with the most fundamental and at the same time the most general phenomena; (2) geometry, which presupposes the laws of number; (3) rational mechanics, which depends on the science of number and geometry, plus the laws of equilibrium and movement. These three all constitute the science of mathematics, the universal science and the basis of all natural philosophy; (4) astronomy is directly connected with mathematics, to which is added the law of gravitation; (5) physics follows astronomy, which embraces barology (science of weight), thermology (science of heat), acoustics, optics, and electrology; (6) chemistry follows next, with its connection with electrology, and which adds its own particular data; (7) biology (physiology) which depends on the contributions of the previous sciences as well as on its own specific data; (8) and finally, at the top of the positivistic scale, comes social physics or sociology, which besides its own data depends on all the other sciences.

When social ethics reaches the stage of a true science, the totality of the sciences, philosophy, will become positive. Positive philosophy has for its object the whole of phenomena, the universe.

XVI.

SCIENCE OF THE NINETEENTH CENTURY

Introduction

The beginning of the scientific age may generally be dated as the nineteenth century. The preparatory work, which could not be escaped, was a long and laborious task, as are all trial and error procedures. To entertain the belief that the prior workers were a naive and stupid lot is to admit to an even greater naiveness, stupidity, and indeed a definite shallowness of thought processes. To say that they were unnecessarily bogged down with religious problems may be true to some extent, but it should be kept in mind that the religious problem has not yet been solved; it has simply been swept under the rug. We should be reminded that before analyses can be intelligently attempted, we should have a general conception of what we are analyzing. It is for this service that we are eternally indebted to the workers of prior centuries.

One of their most significant contributions is that man himself is a part of nature and subject to a large extent to the same physical laws and processes as the world around him. He is subject to the same scientific methods of observation, induction, deduction and experiment as the original subject matter of science.

Early Practical Applications of Pure Science

During the nineteenth century practical applications of pure science now begin to appear. This naturally leads the general public to take an interest. Examples may be here cited, such as

Faraday's electromagnetic experiments leading to the invention of the dynamo, Maxwell's investigation of the properties of electromagnetic waves leading to wireless communication; Pasteur's discovery of microscopic living organisms which led to important results in medicine and surgery; and Mendel's experiments with garden peas leading to discovery of inheritance factors and systematized plant breeding, etc. One of the greatest factors in bringing about the industrial revolution was James Watt's patent of the condenser in 1769.

Emphasis on Mathematics

The study of science, at least for a time, made great strides without the aid of philosophy. Ironically and perhaps unawaredly science found itself more and more dependent on the science of mathematics, a relatively absolute science which must rely on abstraction. In other words, science must retreat back to pure reason for support, and what is more, mathematics is an overt proof of the existence of pure reason. New branches of mathematics were discovered (more correctly, created by pure reason to solve problems arising out of sense-data) during the nineteenth century, theories of numbers, new developments in geometry and trigonometry. The application of these new developments to physical problems naturally stimulated the advances in physical science. Fourier's Theorie Analytique de la chaleur, published in 1822, along with the contributions of Poisson and Gauss, furnished techniques applicable to the study of electricity.

Riemann's work in 1854 in non-Euclidean geometry, along with the subsequent contributions of Cayley, Beltrami, Helmholtz, Klein, and Whitehead, later assisted Einstein in formulating the modern theory of relativity.

Developments in Knowledge of Heat and Electrical Phenomena

The study of imponderable fluids also made considerable progress during the nineteenth century, and the subject is still very much alive today, as for example the mystery of heat. Newton, Boyle and Cavendish all entertained the opinion that heat was due to vibratory action of particles within a body. However, a theory was at first advanced that heat was an invisible weightless fluid which passed freely between the particles of bodies. Applying this theory Joseph Black (1728-1799) discovered and investigated the change of state from ice to water, and from water to steam. He discovered that large portions of heat were absorbed without any change in temperature—was rendered latent as he put it. The change registered after definite amounts of heat were applied, and in that manner Black determined, for instance, the latent heat of evaporation, etc. His work served as authoritative until Helmholtz and Joule made their contributions between 1840 and 1850. By ingenious experimentation these two men demonstrated the equivalence between heat and work; in other words, heat was considered a mode of motion.

The scientists investigating the phenomena of electricity theorized that electricity is a substance like heat, created by friction or work. The existence of two opposite kinds of electricity was recognized in the early history of this subject. The electric charge resulting from rubbing glass with silk was found to neutralize a charge produced by rubbing ebonite with fur. There was a one-fluid and a two-fluid hypothesis. The one-fluid hypothesis conjectured that the excess or defect from the normal quantity gives rise to the so-called electrified state. The terms positive and negative electricities are still in use, terms appropriate to the one-fluid theory. At present, however, electricity is considered atomic in character rather than a fluid.

The so-called Leyden jar, a glass bottle coated with tinfoil inside and out, facilitated electrical experiments. The identity of the spark and the noise of an electric discharge with lightning and thunder was early suspected. This suspicion led Benjamin Franklin (1706-1790) to conduct his famous successful kite experiment. This experiment completely demonstrated the identity of the so-called electric matter with that of lightning. D'Alibard and others in France suggested the idea of the lightning conductor. Marli in 1752 constructed a forty-foot iron rod and observed sparks at the lower end of it when thunder clouds passed over; in fact, a Professor Richmann of St. Petersburg was killed by such a rod over his home.

The organs of electric fish were studied, and it was found that the shocks received from them were electrical manifestations.

Early Development of Field Physics

When the investigations were made at the end of the eighteenth century on electric and magnetic forces, the fluid theories of electricity and magnetism were assumed. In 1784 a French military engineer, named Coulomb, invented a torsion balance by which he found that electric and magnetic forces diminished as the square of the distance increased, being the same relation Newton had demonstrated for gravitation. As the electric force was discovered to be proportional to the amount of the electric charge, Coulomb's apparatus could be used to measure it.

Henry Cavendish proved experimentally that there is no electric force inside a closed charged conductor of any form. Newton had shown mathematically that if the inverse square law holds good, a uniform shell of gravitating matter exerts no force on a body inside it and that no other law will give this result. A similar conclusion was drawn from investigations of electric forces, namely, that there is no internal electric force. Sir Humphry Davy "advanced the hypothesis that chemical and electrical attractions were produced by the same cause, acting in the one case on particles, in the other on masses." J. J. Berzelius also developed this same idea.

As the law of forces was thereby established, the mathematicians were free to go to work. Electric force, like gravitation, appeared to act at a distance across intervening space. The physicists naturally began speculating about the nature of space which somehow could transmit two forces apparently different. These speculations eventually led to modern theories called "field physics."

Standard Weights and Measures Established

The determination of a universal terminology for units of weights and measures now became essential. A both logical and convenient decimal system was conceived by the French in 1791, which became compulsory in France in 1820. An agreement was reached in 1870 to adopt a standard system for scientific measurements. This system was based on three fundamental units of: the centimetre (the hundredth part of a metre), the gram (the thousandth part of a kilogram) and the second. This system is generally called the c.g.s. system.

144

The atomic theory finally came into its own at the start of the nineteenth century, after going through "on and off" stages since the time of Democritus.

When the theory of phlogiston was overthrown, the three phases of matter (solid, liquid, and gaseous) were brought clearly to light, for example water as liquid, frozen as ice, and gaseous as steam. These observations led eventually to the study of the laws of chemical combination. Gases, as a result, ceased to be considered half-spiritual entities. Lavoisier and others found by careful analysis that a chemical compound is always composed of the same amount of constituent parts. This observation played an important part in the development of the new chemistry. Water was found to consist of hydrogen and oxygen combined in a one to eight ratio. Thus the conception of combining weights was reached.

John Dalton (1766-1844) began to experiment on gases while holding a teaching post in Manchester, England. He found that the properties of gases are best explained by a theory of atoms. He later applied the same ideas to chemistry, suggesting that chemical combination can be represented as the combination of discrete particles with definite weights. He maintained that "chemical analysis and synthesis go no farther than to the separation of particles one from another, and to their reunion. No new creation or destruction of matter is within the reach of chemical agency. . . . Now it is one great object of this work, to show the importance and advantage of ascertaining the relative weights of the ultimate particles." At the conclusion of his enumeration of certain chemical combinations, he states—"In all these cases the weights are expressed in atoms of hydrogen, each of which is denoted by unity." His discovery brings out that the combining weights of chemical elements reveals the relative weights of the atoms. Dalton converted a scientific hypothesis into a definite theory.

Jöns J. Berzelius, a Swedish chemist, introduced our present system of the representation of the elementary atoms as letter-symbols. His chief experimental work was the determination of the equivalent combining weights, with the greatest accuracy possible with the techniques then available. He also discovered certain new elements, as well as making new advances in the study of mineralogy. He speculated on the relationship between chemical and electrical phenomena.

Gay-Lussac (1778-1850) observed that gases always combine in volumes bearing simple ratios to one another. *Amerigo Avogadro* advanced the hypothesis that equal volumes of all gases must contain numbers of atoms that bear simple ratios to each other. *Cannizzaro* in 1858 brought out that Avogadro's hypothesis should have stated "the same number of molecules" rather than "the same number of atoms." The simplest particle that can exist in a free state is sometimes a molecule rather than the atom of that substance. Thus, the assignment of true atomic weights was made possible by his correction.

The combination of an atom of oxygen with two atoms of hydrogen led to the conception of an atom of oxygen possessing a valency of two. The subject of valency was the basis for much of the chemical speculation of the succeeding years. Whereas Dalton recognized some twenty elements, the number has gradually grown to over ninety at present. New techniques, such as spectrum analysis and methods of radio-activity, have made the discovery of new elements possible.

The relationship between atomic weights of elements and their physical properties was sought by *Prout* in 1815, as well as by other chemists. In 1869 this relationship was successfully demonstrated by Lother Meyer and by Mendeléeff (1834-1907), a Russian chemist. Mendeléeff arranged the elements in the order of their ascending atomic weights, and noted that they displayed a certain periodicity. The so-called Periodic Table of Elements which he constructed, furnished a means of assigning correct atomic weights. Also, the blanks in the table indicated atoms yet to be discovered, some of which were subsequently found. The Periodic Law was regarded by Mendeléeff as a purely empirical statement of fact. This relationship of atoms brought to mind again the old idea of a common basis of matter. Many chemists, thinking that this common basis was hydrogen, sought to demonstrate that if the atomic weight of hydrogen was considered as unity, the weights of the other elements would all be whole numbers. Such elements as chlorine (35.45) refused to conform to this hypothesis in spite of the most careful determination of atomic weight by *Stas* and others. It was necessary to wait another half-century before this problem was solved.

146

We shall now take up the advances in the study of the electric current. The discovery of the galvanic or voltaic cell at the beginning of the nineteenth century opened up a new field of research. With the use of this new apparatus for storing current, it finally became clear that a galvanic current is nothing but a **flow of electricity. Since no accumulation of electricity could be** detected at any point in the circuit, it was concluded that the **current may be figuratively represented as the "flow of an incom-**prehensible fluid along rigid and inextensible pipes."

Like many other discoveries, the discovery of the voltaic cell was the result of a chance observation in 1786 by Galvani, an Italian, of a frog's leg contracting due to a discharge from an electric machine. He observed the same reaction when a nerve and a muscle were connected with two different metals. Galvani **speculated that these effects were caused by a so-called animal** electricity. *Volta,* another Italian, later showed that this phenomena was not caused by the presence of an animal substance. His experiments led to the invention of the Voltaic pile (cell), which made it possible to make significant advances in the study **of electricity. It consisted of an alternate series of discs, beginning** with zinc, copper, and paper moistened with water or brine, and finishing with a copper disc. It was really a primitive primary battery, each series of discs giving a certain difference of electrical potential, all of them together creating a considerable potential.

Nicholson and *Carlisle* observed that when two brass wires leading from the terminals of a voltaic pile were immersed near each other in water, hydrogen gas was given off by one, while the other oxidized. If platinum or gold wires were used, no oxidation resulted but gas was produced. It was also observed that the volume of hydrogen was about double that of oxygen. As this proportion is about that contained in water, they explained the phenomena as a decomposition of water. They observed that the same type of chemical reaction went on within the pile itself.

Cruickshank precipitated silver and copper from their solutions, a result leading later to electric-plating. He incidentally noticed the liquid around the positive terminal became alkaline and that around the negative terminal it became acid.

Sir Humphry Davy (1778-1829) proved in 1806 that the formation of acids and alkali by this means was caused by impurities in the water.

In 1801 *Wollaston* established Volta's contention of the identity of so-called "galvanism" and "electricity." *Erman* in 1802, with an electroscope, showed that "galvanism" gave "electricity in tension" and so-called electricity as "electricity in motion."

By convention the copper (or carbon) plate is named the positive terminal and the zinc plate the negative terminal of the battery.

Hisinger and *Berzelius* in 1804 determined that neutral salt solutions could be decomposed by electricity, the acid appearing at one pole and the metal at the other. In 1807 Davy, using this process with potash and soda (then considered as elements), was surprised to isolate potassium and sodium.

The decomposition of chemical compounds by the electrical process pointed toward a connection between electrical and chemical forces. Davy speculated on the probability of chemical and electrical attractions being produced by the same cause. Berzelius advanced this idea by regarding every compound as formed by the union of two oppositely electrified atoms or groups of atoms. In 1806 *Grotthus* advanced the idea that the reason the products of decomposition appeared only at the poles was due to successive decompositions and recombinations taking place in the substance of the liquid.

No new developments were made after these primary discoveries in electro-chemistry until *Michael Faraday* (1791-1867), a former assistant in Davy's laboratory. In 1833 he introduced a new terminology for the observed electrical phenomena. For the word "pole" he substituted "electrode" (way, path). For the "positive plate," the anode; for the "negative plate", the cathode; for the parts of the compound which traveled in opposite directions, the "ions" (I go). The ions going toward the "cathode" he named "cations", and those going toward the anode, the "anions." "Electrolysis" (I dissolve) is the term given by him for the whole process.

From a series of experiments, Faraday reduced the phenomena to two statements, known as Faraday's laws: (1) the mass of the substance liberated is proportional to the total amount of electricity which has passed through the liquid; (2) the mass of a substance liberated by a given quantity of electricity is proportional to the chemical equivalent weight of the substance, to the combining weight and not to the atomic weights. When a current of one ampere, one-tenth of a c.g.s. unit, flows for one second through a solution of a silver salt, 0.00118 gram of silver is deposited. This has been adopted for a definition of the ampere as a practical unit of current.

Von Helmholtz later concluded from Faraday's laws that electricity, like elementary substance (atoms), is composed of definite elementary portions which behave like atoms of electricity. Faraday's ideas, formulated from his experiments, served as the basis for the whole structure of modern atomic and electronic science.

The early experiments observed that electric current in passing through a conductor evolved heat, the amount depending on the nature of the conductor. This observation eventually led to electric lighting, heating, and the like.

A discovery by *Oersted* of Copenhagen in 1820, of the power a current has of deflecting a magnetic needle, created a still wider interest. He observed that this effect "passes to the needle through glass, metals" and other *non-magnetic* substances. He further reported that what his translators called "the electric conflict" "performs circles." We today would say that there are circular lines of magnetic force around a long straight current.

André M. Ampère (1775-1836) recognized the importance of Oersted's observations; he showed that not only were magnets acted on by forces in the vicinity of electrical currents, but that currents exerted forces on one another. He determined by experiments and geometry that the forces caused by electric currents were reducible to a law of inverse squares, thereby bringing these phenomena in line with that of gravitation, and with the forces between magnetic poles and between electric charges. Another step in the direction of "field physics."

After Ampère had provided the mathematical formula for the application of his electromagnetic results, the invention of the telegraph became a possibility.

About 1827 Georg S. Ohm (1781-1854) replaced the vague ideas of "quantity" and "tension" by the terms "current strength" and "electromotive force," corresponding with the term "potential" used in electrostatics. Hence, the difference of electromotive force is defined as the work done against the electric forces in carrying a unit quantity of electricity from one point to another.

The researches of *Fourier* on the conduction of heat served as a basis for Ohm's work on electricity. Ohm simply substituted potential for temperature, and electricity for heat, and then proceeded to work out experiments therefrom. From them he determined that the current "c" is proportional to the electromotive force "E."

Wave Theory of Light Reinstated

The wave-theory of light was another old idea resuscitated and established in the nineteenth century. Huygens had put it in more definite form than that by Hooke and others. Newton, however, had rejected it for the two reasons: (1) it did not seem to explain shadows, and (2) the phenomena of double-refraction in Iceland spar indicated that rays of light were different on different sides. However, *Thomas Young* (1773-1829) and *Augustin J. Fresnel* (1788-1827) overcame these objections and put the wave-theory in its modern form.

Young, in one of his experiments, passed a very narrow beam of white light through two pin holes in a screen, placing another screen beyond the first. He observed a series of brilliantly colored bands where the rays from the two pin holes overlapped on the second screen. If on the other hand instead of composite white light a simple colored light is used, the bands are alternately bright and dark instead of colored. A colored light is just one wave-length, which explains the difference. With this technique the wave-lengths of the different colored lights can be calculated; they were found to be of the order of one two-thousandth part of a millimeter. It was determined that light travels almost solely in straight lines; the bending around obstacles is confined to the minute effect known as diffraction.

The second objection of Newton to the wave-theory was overcome by Fresnel. Following Hooke's casual suggestion, Fresnel too considered the possibility of light vibrations being transverse to the direction of the rays. In that case, looking at an advancing wave-front of light, linear vibrations may be either up and down or right and left. Thus if a crystal in one position lets one vibration through but not the other, a second crystal turned around its axis through a right angle will stop the light from emerging from the first crystal. This is just the phenomena Newton observed with Iceland spar. Fresnel worked out his wave-theory mathematically. Although certain difficulties remained, his wave-theory of light held for almost a century. However, if light waves were transverse, the medium through which they pass necessarily must possess properties similar to those of a solid. This initiated a series of elastic solid theories of ether. Einstein called attention to the fact that the success of the wave-theory was an initial breach in Newtonian physics. When light began to be regarded as wave-motion, it no longer was possible to believe that everything real was made of particles moving in space. The ether was invented to maintain the mechanical outlook. Faraday, however, revealed that space had electric and magnetic properties. When later *Clerk Maxwell* proved that light was an electromagnetic wave, the ether ceased to be mechanical.

The first phase of field physics came into being with the wave-theory of light; the second phase initiated by Faraday and Maxwell, connected light with electromagnetism; and the third phase was later initiated by Einstein when he explained gravitation in geometric terms, and hoped to have connected it with light and electromagnetism in a still broader synthesis.

Faraday discovered electromagnetic induction by winding two helices of insulated wire on the same wooden cylinders. One of the wires was connected with a voltaic battery and the other wire to a galvanometer. When contact was first made, a slight effect registered on the needle of the galvanometer but in one direction only. When the contact with the battery was broken, there was another slight effect on the needle, but in the opposite direction. By this technique he was able to make magnets, and to change their poles by withdrawing them either before or after the contact was made with the battery.

All electric machinery of practical importance in industrial development was founded on the discovery by Faraday of electromagnetic induction. Ampère, a mathematician, was content to discover the laws of electromagnetic force in mathematical form, but Faraday, who was not a mathematician, was interested primarily in observing the physical properties and state of the intervening space, or electromagnetic field of force. He laid a card on a bar-magnet and scattered iron filings over the card; he then observed that the iron filings clung together in chains. Faraday imagined lines or tubes of force connecting magnetic poles or electric charges as having a real existence in a magnetic or an electric field, possibly as a chain of polarized particles.

While Faraday's ideas were in unfamiliar language and in

advance of his time, yet he laid the foundations of electro-chemistry, electromagnetic induction, and electromagnetic waves.

C. F. Gauss (1777-1855) and *W. E. Weber* (1804-1891), both German mathematical physicists, invented the scientific system of magnetic and electric units. Gauss in 1839 published his "General theory of forces attracting according to the inverse square of the distance," raising an imposing structure of mathematical deduction.

Ampère and Weber experimentally demonstrated that coils of wire carrying electric currents acted in the same way as magnets of the same size and shape. Hence, unit current may be defined as that current which is equivalent to a magnetic disc of unit magnetic strength, leading to the formula 2 pi c/r, where c is the strength of the current and r the radius of the circle; this agreed with an expression deduced from Ampère's formula.

Experiments Involving Heat Phenomena

Now we shall return to the subject of heat. Boyle and Newton, it will be recalled, favored the theory of molecular agitation rather than the caloric theory, which considered heat as a so-called imponderable fluid. In 1738 *Daniel Bernouilli* had shown the plausibility of the theory of molecular agitation by an idealized experiment conceiving gas as composed of molecular particles. By the application of pressure temperature was increased.

The supporters of the caloric theory had assumed that the development of heat by friction was explained on the supposition that the filings or abrasions possessed a smaller specific heat than the original substance; in other words, heat was squeezed out so to speak. However, Count Rumford in 1798 showed by experiments on the boring of cannon that the heat evolved was roughly proportional to the work done and had no relation to the amount of shavings. This result was further confirmed by Davy in 1799 who melted two lumps of ice by rubbing them together; he noted that the water formed possessed a higher specific heat than the ice.

It had become apparent that at least some of the powers of nature were mutually convertible. *J. R. Mayer* in 1842 maintained the possibility of the conversion of work into heat and heat into work. He assumed that when air was compressed, all the work would appear as heat, and calculated a numerical value for its mechanical equivalent. *Sir W. R. Grove,* an English judge and scientist, elaborated the inter-relation of natural powers in a book published in 1846, entitled The Correlation of Physical Forces. An independent study in 1847 by H. H. F. von Helmholtz (1827-1894) contained the earliest general account of the principle of "persistence of force," now known as the "conservation of energy."

From 1840 to 1850 *J. R. Joule* (1818-1889) measured by certain ingenious experiments, the amount of heat liberated by the expenditure of electrical and mechanical work. He found that regardless of how the work was done, the expenditure of the same amount of work produced the same quantity of heat. From this principle of equivalence, he concluded that heat was a form of energy. Joule determined that to warm one pound of water through 1° Fahrenheit, at any temperature between 55° and 60°, about 772 foot-pounds of work were needed. This figure was later adjusted to 778.

Energy may be defined as the power of doing work and, if the conversion is complete, may be measured by the amount of work done. The use of the word "energy" in this sense was initiated by *Rankine* and *William Thomson.* Until recent years, all known facts supported the theory that the total energy of an isolated system is constant in amount. This older principle, supported by Newton, was called "conservation of mass."

There was no known process in nineteenth century physics by which matter or energy could be created or destroyed. Until recent years, matter and energy were carefully distinguished.

The principle of the conservation of energy is regarded as one of the great achievements of the mind of man, having great importance in the history of both physical science and scientific philosophy. From safe guides for the empirical advance in knowledge, the principles of the conservation of mass and energy passed into philosophic dogmas of doubtful validity. Today we have Einstein's law of the conservation of mass-energy.

Kinetic Theory of Gases

The kinetic theory of gases will next be briefly reviewed. *J. J. Waterston* in 1845, in a manuscript at first forgotten in the archives of the Royal Society, further developed the kinetic theory of gases. Joule in 1848 worked on the same subject. These two investigators calculated independently the average velocity of movement of the molecules. However, the first adequate kinetic theory of matter was published by *Clausius* in 1857. Boyle had discovered experimentally that the pressure of a gas is proportional to its density or inversely proportional to its volume; now known as *Boyle's Law*. If the temperatures vary, since pressure is proportional to volume squared, the pressure must increase with the temperature; now known as the *Law of Charles*. Hence, if we have two gases of the same pressure and temperature, it follows that the number of molecules in unit volume is equal for the two gases. This is the law obtained from chemical facts developed by Avogadro. *Thomas Graham* about 1830 discovered the law that for two gases of equal pressure and density the molecular velocity must be inversely proportional to the square root of the density, a relation that explains the rate at which gases diffuse through porous partitions. Thus the kinetic theory enables one to calculate approximately the molecular velocities. This theory was further developed later by Maxwell, Boltzmann, and others, using more accurate mathematical methods made possible from the theory of probability and curves of error.

Andrews in 1869 and Van der Waals in 1873, contributed further refinements to the kinetic theory of gases.

Thermodynamics

Thermodynamics will be our next topic for review.

A botanist, *Robert Brown,* in 1827 observed through his microscope the irregular movements of very small molecules in plants, later known as Brownian movement. *William Ramsay* in 1879 explained these movements as caused by the bombardment of the particles by the molecules of the liquid in which suspended. *Crookes* with the use of light vanes blackened on one side and polished on the other, and pivoted in a near vacuum, observed the vanes to rotate in the direction of the polished surfaces when placed in sunlight. This rotating movement was explained by Maxwell as caused by the additional heat absorbed by the blackened sides.

Sadi Carnot in 1824 called attention to the fact that every so-called heat engine requires a hot body or source of heat, and a cold body or condenser, the engine working upon the passage of heat from the hot to the cold body. Incidentally he considered heat as a fluid. Carnot realized that in order to study the laws of heat engines, it was necessary to imagine an idealized case of the simplest nature—that of a frictionless engine with no heat loss by conduction. It also must imaginatively observe the engine through a complete cycle so that the working substance, say steam, is brought back to its initial state. Carnot's conceptions were first put in modern form by Clausius, followed by William Thomson (later Lord Kelvin). These experimenters found that Carnot's ideas are equally important with heat regarded as molecular energy.

Joule determined that although it is always possible to transform the whole of a given quantity of work into heat, it generally is impossible to completely reverse the change. It was found in the case of steam engines that only a fraction of the original heat was transformed into mechanical energy; the remainder passed from the hotter to the colder parts of the system. The difference between the original quantity of heat and the heat lost in the condenser equals the amount of the heat available for work. The ratio of the actual work done to the heat absorbed may be taken as the efficiency of the engine.

William Thomson devised a thermodynamic temperature scale which is absolute, as it does not depend on the form of the apparatus or the nature of the substance in it. No engine can produce more work than the mechanical equivalent of the heat it absorbs; hence there can be no greater efficiency than unity. As it is impossible to make a perfect engine, it is necessary to translate into more practical terms the thermodynamic scale.

Joule found that when air was allowed to expand without doing work, no appreciable temperature change occurred. From this it was concluded that there is no alteration in the molecular state of a gas on expansion or contraction; all the work done in compressing the gas appears as heat. Thomson and Joule proved by an ingenious experiment that when gases were forced through a porous plug and allowed to expand freely beyond it, the change in temperature was very small, air being slightly cooled and hydrogen being even more slightly heated. By the application of mathematics to this experiment, it follows that an air or hydrogen thermometer furnished indications very nearly those of the absolute or thermodynamic scale.

The results of thermodynamic reasoning have enabled the engineer to place on a solid basis the theory of the heat engine; they have also greatly aided the progress of modern physics and chemistry. The consequences of this research has also completed the proof of the continuity of all types of matter in its three states, the solid, the liquid, and the gaseous. By the cumulative effect of the porous plug process, gases can be cooled below their critical point and liquified.

Useful work can be obtained from a supply of heat when a temperature inequality exists. However, in nature temperature inequalities are being constantly used up by conduction of heat and in other ways. Therefore, in an isolated system with irreversible changes occurring, the heat energy tends gradually to become less and less available for the performance of useful work. Thus, the mathematical function which Clausius called entropy, tends to increase. When energy is no longer available, no work can be done, and then the necessary conditions of the system's equilibrium can be ascertained. Likewise in an isothermal system (one at constant temperature), equilibrium is reached when the thermodynamic potential (a mathematical function) is at a minimum. Consideration of these principles enabled Clausius, Lord Kelvin, von Helmholtz and Willard Gibbs to build up the theory of chemical and physical equilibrium. Modern physical chemistry is simply a series of experimental examples of the thermodynamic equations of Gibbs.

These conceptions were extended to the whole Universe, and physicists have been led to the belief that cosmical energy is continually wasting into heat by friction, and heat energy is continually becoming less available by the reduction of inequalities of temperature. When such temperature equilibrium is reached, all further change will forever become impossible. This conclusion was arrived at on the unproved supposition that the stellar Universe was an isolated system, with no energy entering.

Maxwell imagined another idealized experiment, in which a minute being (daemon) with faculties to follow the individual molecules, was placed in charge of a frictionless sliding door in a wall separating two compartments of a vessel filled with gas. On the approach of a fast-moving molecule the daemon would open the door; on the approach of a slow-moving molecule, he would close the door. Thus the fast-moving molecules would accumulate in the right-hand compartment, with the slow-moving ones in the left. As a consequence the gas in the right-hand compartment would grow hot, and the one at the left would grow cold. Thus this technique would enable the reconcentration of diffused energy. As the existence of such small daemons was a figment of the imagination, the principle of the dissipation of energy held good as long as molecules could only be treated statistically. How far this conclusion has been modified or confirmed by recent knowledge will be indicated later. Thermodynamics are linked to the known laws of probability and to the kinetic theory of matter.

Spectrum Analysis and Spectroscopic Astronomy

We shall now pass on to the subject of spectrum analysis. Galileo and Newton established by experiment, observation, and mathematics that the classical distinction between the terrestrial and celestial spheres was no longer tenable. However, to complete the identity it was necessary to prove the familiar chemical elements of which the earth is composed, exist also in the substance of the Sun, planets and stars. The solution to this apparently unsolvable problem was found in the middle of the nineteenth century by means of so-called spectrum analysis.

Newton had succeeded in decomposing composite white light into its constituent components by passing the white light through a glass prism. Wollaston in 1802 observed that this luminous spectrum of sunlight was crossed by a number of dark lines. In 1814 *Joseph Fraunhofer* again observed these dark lines, and by the use of more than one prism he carefully mapped them. It was further observed that light from flames tinged with metals or salts produced spectra showing on a dark ground characteristic colored lines. *Sir John Herschel* in 1823 considered the possibility of using these lines as a test for the presence of the metals. The observed spectral lines were thereupon carefully mapped and recorded.

Foucault in 1849 observed the spectrum of the light from a voltaic arc between carbon poles; he noticed a bright double line between the yellow and the orange which coincided with the dark double lines called "D" by Fraunhofer. By the alternate passing of sunlight and the light from a voltaic arc between carbon poles, he concluded: "Thus the arc presents us with a medium which emits the rays 'D' on its own account, and which at the same time absorbs them when they come from another quarter."

Sir George G. Stokes (1819-1903) in his lectures at Cambridge made clear the theory of Fraunhofer's lines. Any mechanical system, he explained, will absorb energy which falls on it in rhythmic unison with its normal vibrations. Thus the molecules of the vapors in the outer layers of the Sun will absorb the energy of those particular rays coming from the hotter interior of which the oscillatory periods are the same as with their own. The light which passes on will be lacking of light waves of the particular vibratory frequency, resulting in a black line in the solar spectrum.

From 1855 to 1863 *von Bunsen,* along with Roscoe, and in 1859 joined by *Kirchhoff,* devised the first exact methods of spectrum analysis—methods whereby chemical elements could be detected by their spectra even if in small quantity. By the use of this technique Bunsen and Kirchhoff determined that sodium is present in the atmosphere of the Sun and that lithium is absent.

Huggins, Janssen and *Lockyer* produced further great advances in *spectroscopic astronomy.* In 1878 Lockyer observed a dark line in the green of the spectrum of the Sun's chromosphere heretofore unobserved in terrestrial spectra. He, along with *Frankland,* predicted the existence of an element in the Sun and called it helium. In 1895 the element was discovered by Ramsay in the mineral eleveite.

In 1842 *Doppler* reported that when a source of waves and an observer are in relative motion, the frequency of the waves as observed is altered. This phenomena can be observed from the changing sound from the whistle of an express train as it passes a station. This is known as the "Doppler effect." The same phenomena was also found to apply to light. In other words, if a star is approaching the Earth, its spectral lines will be displaced towards the violet, and if away from the Earth, then towards the red.

In 1820 Sir William Herschel showed that a thermometer placed in the solar spectrum indicated heat effects that went beyond the lowest visible red light. *Ritter* soon afterwards found rays beyond the visible violet which would blacken nitrate of silver. *Thus the identity of light and radiant heat was demonstrated. Melloni* during the years between 1830 and 1840 demonstrated that invisible heat showed properties similar to those of light as regards reflection, refraction, polarization, and interference. A black body, which absorbs all radiation, was found when hot to emit complete radiation of all wave-lengths.

Maxwell theoretically demonstrated that radiation should exert a pressure on a surface on which it falls. This pressure, though small, has been experimentally demonstrated in recent years.

Bartoli in 1875 pointed out that the existence of this pressure enables one to imagine that a space filled with radiation might act as the cylinder of a theoretical thermodynamic engine. In 1884 Boltzmann showed that it must follow that the full radiation of a black body increases as the fourth power of the absolute temperature—a law which had been previously discovered by observation in 1879 by Stefan.

Electric Waves

Now we shall divert our thinking to the subject of electric waves. When a current deflects a magnetic needle or induces another current in an apparently unconnected circuit, we either must assume an unexplained "action at a distance," or to conceive the intervening space to be bridged by something through which the effect is transmitted. Faraday chose the second assumption, and imagined lines of force or chains of particles in "dielectric polarization."

James Maxwell (1831-1879) put Faraday's ideas into mathematical form. As the electric current creates a magnetic field, the magnetic force being at right angles to the current, and as a change in a magnetic field produces an electromotive force, the reciprocal relationship between the magnetic and electric forces becomes apparent.

Maxwell's studies led to a series of differential equations which demonstrated that the velocity of such waves depended only on the electric and magnetic properties of the medium. As the electric force between two charges is inversely proportional to the dielectric constant (k) and the magnetic force between two poles is inversely proportional to the magnetic permeability (u) of the medium, the electric and magnetic units which are defined in terms of those forces must involve the k and u. The velocity of an electromagnetic wave can be determined by comparing experimentally two such units. Thus Maxwell, along with others, determined the velocity of an electric current was about the same as that of light. He, therefore, concluded that light is an electromagnetic phenomenon, and thus it was unnecessary to conceive another kind of ether.

The big dilemma now was whether to conceive of electromagnetic waves as mechanical waves in a so-called elastic solid, or as in terms of electricity and magnetism, the meaning of which is unknown.

Maxwell, along with *H. Hertz* in 1887, using alternating current given by the spark of an induction coil, produced detectible electric waves in space, thus proving experimentally the similarity of properties between electric and light phenomena. Wireless waves have thus been placed in the so-called ether. It became apparent that the energy wave of an electric current passes through the insulated electric wire, whereas the current itself is but the line of dissipation of that energy into heat. Maxwell's theory failed to give a definite account of those discrete atomic electric charges suggested by Faraday's electrolysis experiments. Preliminary to discovery of this explanation we shall now consider the phenomena of chemical action.

Chemical Action

Newton was greatly interested in the cause of chemical action. *C. F. Wenzel* in 1777 determined that the rate of reaction between acids and metals was proportional to the concentration of his acids. *Berthollet* independently arrived at the same result. *Wilhelmy* in 1850 observed the "inversion" of cane-sugar in the presence of an acid, and found that the rate of change diminished proportionately in geometrical progression with the time. He concluded from the results that the number of molecules dissociating is proportional to the number present at any instant. Whenever such a relation was noted, the inference may be drawn that the molecules act singly, known as a mono-molecular reaction. If two molecules react with each other—di-molecular process—the rate of change would become dependent on the frequency with which collisions occurred, a frequency proportional to the product of the concentration of the two reacting molecules.

From speculation and experiments along this line, *A. W. Williamson* in 1850 first formulated the conception of a dynamical equilibrium. *Guldberg, Waage, Jellet,* and lastly *Van't Hoff* in 1877, formulated full statements of the mass-law of chemical action. It was found that it could be deduced also by thermodynamic principles from the energy relations of a dilute system.

Certain chemical reactions were observed to be speeded up on the presence of certain substances or agents. Berzelius called such actions "catalysis," and assigned "catalytic power" to such agents. He suggested that the many chemical compounds formed in living organisms from common raw material may be produced by catalysts of some sort. Kühne in 1878 called such organic catalysts "enzymes."

In 1862 Berthelot and others by experiments determined that the acid works as a catalyst, to hasten a chemical reaction in any direction. The catalytic action of acids was coordinated by Arrhenius in 1887 with their electrical conductivity. In 1902 Brereton Baker's experiments, along with those of Armstrong, suggest that the presence of complex mixtures appears necessary for catalytic action, that pure chemical substances, such as pure water, are ineffective.

Chemical Solutions

The theory of solution is our next subject. Solutions are the product of the dissolution of substances in water or other liquids. Some liquids will not mix in solution, such as oil and water. Certain solutes and solvents give off heat, while in others heat is absorbed. Acids and alkalies generally evolve heat. In some cases the end volume of the two combined will be less. Not until the nineteenth century did the phenomena of solution become a separate problem.

Thomas Graham (1805-1869) is credited for having performed the first systematic research on the diffusion of dissolved substances. Graham learned that crystalline bodies, such as most salts, when dissolved in water pass freely through membranes and diffuse fairly quickly from one part of the liquid to another. These substances he called crystalloids. Substances like glue or gelatine, however, diffuse very slowly when dissolved. These he named colloids.

In 1833 Faraday demonstrated that the passage of a definite quantity of electricity through an electrolyte was accompanied by an equal separation of ions at the electrodes. If we assume the current as carried by the movement of ions, this would mean that every ion of the same chemical valency would carry the same charge. On that supposition the charge on a univalent ion would be a natural unit or atom of electricity.

In 1859 *Hittorf* conjectured that the unequal dilution of a solution in the regions near two insoluble electrodes furnished a means of comparing experimentally the velocities with which the opposite ions move. This later furnished a means of measuring the ratio of the opposite ionic velocities.

161

Kohlrausch in 1879 discovered a successful way of measuring the electric resistance of electrolytes by using alternating currents and so-called spongy electrodes. With polarization eliminated he found that electrolytes conform to Ohm's law, namely, that the current was proportional to the electromotive force. Thus Kohlrausch measured the conductivity of electrolytes. This furnished a means, along with Hittorf's determination of their ratios, of calculating the velocities of the individual ions.

Pfeffer, a botanist, measured the osmotic pressure set up by the passage of water into a vegetable cell through a membrane. Van't Hoff, a physicist, as a consequence called attention to the fact that osmotic pressure was comparable to gas pressure in its relations, namely, that it is inversely proportional to the volume, and increasing with the absolute temperature. He proved, both theoretically and experimentally, that the absolute value of the osmotic pressure of a dilute solution must be the same as the pressure of a gas at the same concentration. The cause of osmotic pressure, at least from the standpoint of thermodynamics, remains undetermined.

Arrhenius, a Swedish chemist, in 1887 demonstrated that osmotic pressure was connected with the electrical properties of solutions. He found that the osmotic pressure of a solution of potassium chloride was twice that of a sugar solution of the same molecular concentration. Arrhenius found that this excess pressure was connected with chemical activity as well as with electrolytic conductivity.

The combined work of these scientists on the problem of solutions has proved to be a foundation of a vast structure of physical chemistry, both of theoretical as well as of practical industrial application.

Organic Chemistry

The chemistry involving the remarkable "sociable" element carbon is the chemistry of the complicated substances found in plants and animals. One reason carbon is called a "sociable" element is that this atom possesses the unique property of combining with its own, as well as with other atoms, to form complex molecules.

The old theory of a distinct vital principle at one time was used to explain the formation of the complicated substances found in animal and vegetable tissues. However, in 1828,

Friedrich Wöhler demonstrated that urea (heretofore found only in living tissues), could be prepared in the laboratory. The artificial production of other natural products followed, and in 1887 *Emil Fischer* built up in the laboratory fruit-sugar and grape-sugar from their elements. Although the distinction between organic and inorganic was thereby broken down, it has still been convenient to separate organic chemistry from inorganic and physical chemistry.

The basic problem of organic chemistry is to determine the elements present in a complex molecule, and the estimation of its relative proportions. Lavoisier, Berzelius, Gay-Lussac and Thenard invented methods of analysis involving the burning of the compound in the oxygen given off from the copper oxide, and the measurements of the end products. *Justus Liebig* by 1830 had perfected methods of analysis to the point where the composition of carbon compounds could be fairly accurately determined.

One surprising result in this work was the discovery of isomerism—that certain compounds, different in chemical and physical properties, possessed the same percentage composition. It was Lavoisier who proved that charcoal and the diamond have the same chemical identity. Berzelius explained this phenomena as caused by a different arrangement and connection between the atoms in molecules of the two isomeric compounds. This explanation was developed further by *Frankland* (1852), by Couper, and by Kekule (1858) with the conception of chemical valency; this conception made possible structural formulae for different carbon molecules. The theory of structural formula has also enabled the application of deductive methods to chemistry.

In 1844 *Mitscherlich* and in 1848 *Louis Pasteur* (1822-1895) observed the relation between atomic constitution and crystalline form. Pasteur noticed that two kinds of crystals were related to each other as an object is to its image in a mirror. In 1863 *Wislicenus* speculated that this phenomena was due to different arrangements of the atoms in space. *Le Bel* and Van't Hoff in 1874 inferred that all optically active carbon compounds contained an unsymmetrical atomic structure.

Liebig and Wöhler in 1832 observed that in many instances a complex group of atoms (a radical) was held together during chemical reactions through a series of compounds, behaving like a single atom. The group OH (hydroxyl) is an example.

163

The idea of radicals led to the theory of types, work on which was performed between 1850 and 1852 by *Williamson*. Thus the conceptions of radicals and types replaced as the basic idea of chemical constitution the electrical dualism of Berzelius.

The organic substances making up living matter were placed in three main classes, i.e., proteins, fats, and carbohydrates. Proteins were found to possess the most complex chemical structure, based mainly on nitrogen. Proteins, in turn, could easily be broken down to amino-acids, combined in different proportions and possessing the properties of both acids and bases.

Curtius in 1883 and *Fischer* by the end of the century had made some progress towards determining the nature of the constituents of living organisms, and even towards their synthesis.

Biology With Emphasis on Physiology

The assumptions on which the whole theory of Divine revelation had been built had been undermined by Copernicus and Newton. However, popular beliefs apparently remained unchanged. But in the advances in the field of biology and in geology during the nineteenth century, the general public gave definite attention, especially in the Darwinian evolutionary hypothesis. Darwin's theory of natural selection may not alone be able to explain the many facts which have since been discovered, yet in the opinion of biologists the theory of evolution rests on a broad firm foundation.

Physics, physical chemistry and organic chemistry have heretofore been briefly reviewed. We shall now review physiology.

Physiology

Bichat (1771-1802) suggested an early conception in nineteenth century physiology—the idea that the life of the body is the product of the combined lives of the constituent tissues. There is a conflict, he maintained, between vital forces and those of physics and chemistry. After death the forces of physics and chemistry destroy the body.

F. J. Gall (1758-1828) disproved by dissection Galen's theory of "animal spirits" and the Aristotelian sensorium commune, and demonstrated the real structure of the brain. He taught "that the grey matter was the active and essential instrument of the nervous system and the white matter the connecting links"; Gall's habit of mixing solid facts with erroneous theory results in the follies of "phrenology." However, the solid facts of Gall's research founded *modern neurology.*

Majendie's work from 1870 on, proved that the anterior and posterior roots of spinal nerves have different functions—a discovery of fundamental importance.

Marshall Hall (1790-1857) established the difference between so-called volitional and unconscious reflex action. Coughing, sneezing, and breathing are cited as examples of unconscious reflex action. *Johannes Müller,* a German physiologist in the early years of the nineteenth century, collected and published in his Outlines of Physiology all available knowledge on that subject. He made the discovery that the kind of sensation we experience depends upon the sense organ and not on the particular stimulation of the nerves. For instance, we "see stars" as a result of a blow on the back of the head, etc. Hence, man's unaided senses give him no real knowledge of the external world.

Claude Bernard (1813-1878), a disciple of Majendie, did research in connection with the action of the nervous system on nutrition and secretion. His findings foreshadowed the results of *modern biochemistry.*

Boussingault and *Dumas* taught that there was a complete contrast in function as between animals and plants. Animals live by breaking down the organic substances built up by plants. Bernard demonstrated, however, that animals in certain cases could themselves build up certain organic substances.

Bernard by experiments on animals, made a further discovery that the function of the so-called vaso-motor nerves which are put in motion involuntarily by sensory impulses, is to control the blood vessels. This led to the discovery that the "animal heat" developed by a nerve section was due to the dilation of the blood vessels.

The investigations of *E. H. and E. F. Weber* led to the discovery that the heart's beat can be stopped by stimulation of the vagus nerve. Bernard also found that the poisonous action of carbon monoxide was the result of the irreversible displacement of oxygen from the hemoglobin in the red blood corpuscles.

Casper F. Wolff (1733-1794) was the originator of the modern science of *observational embryology.* With the use of a microscope he observed the progressive formation and differentiation of the various organs from a germ, originally homogeneous in character. This embryonic development is now known to proceed along identical lines through the whole animal creation.

Von Baer, about 1820, demonstrated that the pre-natal growth of man resembles that of other animals. Thus his work forged a link in the chain of evidence that binds man to the rest of animal creation. His contention that the history of the individual recapitulates the history of the species resulted towards the end of the century in embryology becoming the favorite method of studying evolution.

Schleiden in 1838 formulated the *cell theory* from observing the embryo of a plant arising from a single cell containing a nucleus. *Theodor Schwann* (1810-1882), Professor of Anatomy in the University of Louvain, founded modern histology by tracing different kinds of animal tissues to their origins in nucleated cells. He worked towards a *physico-chemical theory of life.*

Hugo von Mohl of Tübingen originated the term *protoplasm* for the plastic substance within the cell wall. *Karl von Nägeli* discovered the substance to be nitrogenous, while *Max Schultz* held that the "mass of nucleated protoplasm" was the physical basis of life.

Rudolf Virchow (1821-1892) applied the cell theory to the study of diseased tissues, a new chapter in medicine. It is anticipated that the cure of cancer will be based on bringing under control the pathological growth of cells characteristic of that disease.

The use by *Karl Ludwig* of physical apparatus in laboratory research in physiology, supplemented by the work of Mayer and von Helmholtz, suggested that the principle of the conservation of energy must also apply to the living organism. Liebig taught that animal heat is the result of combustion. In 1885 *Rubner,* and in 1899 *Atwater* and *Bryant* determined the heat values of proteins and carbohydrates.

The results of experiments by Atwater, Rosa and Benedict indicated a general agreement with the principle of the conservation of energy, that the physical activities of the body could be traced ultimately to the chemical and thermal energy of the food consumed. Nervous action was found during this period to be accompanied by electrical changes.

Schiff in 1884 discovered that the cretinistic effects of the removal of the thyroid gland from animals could be overcome by feeding the animal with an extract from the gland.

These discoveries led to the belief that physiology was only a special case of colloidal physics and protein chemistry, conclusions which naturally were stimulating to the mechanistic philosophers. It became clear to the researchers that for the progress of science it is necessary to assume that physiological processes in detail are comprehensible. Hence, natural principles find their best ultimate statement in the fundamental concepts and laws of physics and chemistry. Whether the synthetic problem of the animal organism as a whole can be solved by analytic methods constitutes a more profound question. *Here the nature of the mind of man is the crux of the problem.*

The study of catalytic action during the third quarter of the century was carried to living organisms. Kühne, we will recall, gave them the name "enzymes." They seem to be colloids, and to carry electrical charges which may play a part in their actions. The most important enzymes are amylase (decomposes starch), pepsin (decomposes proteins in an acid medium), trypsin (decomposes proteins in an alkaline medium), and lipase (decomposes esters). Enzymes appear to assist and hasten chemical action; however, they do not determine its direction.

Microbic Diseases

The knowledge of origins and causes of microbic diseases in plants, animals and man was greatly increased during the nineteenth century. This knowledge has not only given man greater control of his environment but also has influenced his ideas of the relative positions of man and so-called "nature."

Cagniard de La Tour and *Schwann* about the year 1838 discovered that the yeasts present in fermentation are minute living vegetable cells, and that the chemical changes in fermenting liquor is the result of the action of these cells. From further experimentation they concluded that both fermentation and putrefaction is caused by the action of living micro-organisms.

Pasteur about 1855 disproved every known case of supposed *spontaneous generation.* He demonstrated that such diseases as anthrax, chicken-cholera and silk-worm disease were caused by specific microbes.

Koch in 1882 discovered the micro-organism which caused tuberculosis. He also developed the technique of *bacteriology* to the point where it became a science essential in the problems of public health. By isolating and permitting the specific micro-organism to reproduce itself as a pure culture in a suitable medium such as gelatine, its pathogenic effects could then be observed by experimenting with their injection into animals.

In 1897 *Buchner* extracted from yeast cells their characteristic enzyme and demonstrated that the enzyme could produce the same fermentation as living yeast cells. Hence, it was concluded that microbic cells possessed a definite enzyme which produced their characteristic effect.

Jenner at the close of the eighteenth century had introduced the process of vaccination, by which inoculation with the small-pox virus produced by a calf, resulted in immunity to the disease.

About 1888 diphtheria-causing bacteria were injected in a horse to produce so-called anti-toxins; these injected into man would create immunity against the disease.

Pasteur was successful in producing an anti-toxin against rabies or hydrophobia. By the use of this anti-toxin, the mortality of this previously incurable disease was reduced to about one per cent of the cases treated.

Laveran, a French army surgeon, about 1880 discovered the malaria germ. Certain Italian observers five years later discovered that the infection reached man from mosquito bites. Between the years 1894-1897, *Manson* and *Ross* were successful in proving that the anopheles (mosquito) was the carrier of the parasitic culprits.

Likewise the germ for Mediterranean or Maltese fever was found to be carried by goats, and passed on to man by goats' milk.

Bubonic plague was found to be carried by rats, with fleas as intermediate carriers of the germ to man.

Lord Lister in 1867 applied Pasteur's results to surgery. This, along with the previous discovery of anesthetics by Sir John Davy, W. T. G. Morton and Sir J. Y. Simpson, made possible certain surgical operations heretofore impossible.

Löffler and *Frosch* in 1893 made a thorough study of so-called ultra-microscopic virus, and discovered the virus causing the foot-and-mouth disease of animals. They concluded that they were dealing not with an inanimate poison but with a reproducing micro-organism, a possible new type of non-cellular living matter.

Carbon and Nitrogen Cycle

The cycles of change through which carbon and nitrogen pass from the ground and air in plants and animals were subjected to study. *Priestley, Ingenhousz* and *Senebier* performed early experimental work which pointed towards the mutual reciprocal exchange of oxygen and carbon dioxide between plant and animals. *Saussure's* quantitative investigations of the process resulted in Liebig's researches and eventually to the formulation of a general theory covering the phenomena. The plant pigment chlorophyll was found to be the active substance in the building up of plants. It uses the energy of sunlight to decompose the carbon dioxide of the air, liberate the oxygen and use the carbon as building blocks for the complex molecules of plant tissues. Certain animals live on plants, some on each other, which makes them all dependent on the Sun's energy made available by chlorophyll. By breathing, animals oxidize carbon molecules into useful derivatives, others are excreted, and the remainder of the energy liberated by oxidation maintains bodily heat. Plants, too, emit carbon dioxide but more slowly; in sunlight, however, this process is reversed.

Besides giving back to the air the carbon dioxide, the waste products of plants and animals return to the ground. There teeming bacteria decompose it into innocuous inorganic bodies, with more carbon dioxide given off into the air. The process is then ready for another cycle.

The nitrogen cycle is a more recent discovery. In 1888 *Hellriegel* and *Wilforth* discovered the reason for the beneficial effect cited by Vergil in his Georgics of taking a crop of beans before wheat. These investigators observed that the nodules on the roots of leguminous plants contain bacteria which are able to take nitrogen from the air and convert it by an unknown chemical reaction into protein and pass it on to the plant. *Vinogradsky* in 1895 discovered a certain bacteria in the soil which took nitrogen from the air. In both ways plants get protein; waste products containing nitrogen go back into the soil.

Gilbert and *Lawes* at Rothamsted investigated the apparent indispensable need for nitrogen for agriculture. Their work was the basic foundation for modern use of fertilizer. Phosphorus and potassium were also found necessary for this same purpose.

Physical geography and scientific exploration is our next topic. The French cartographer d'Anville was enabled to make accurate maps following the trigonometrical surveys begun in England in 1784. Such maps were important in the coming period of explorations.

Baron von Humboldt (1769-1869), a distinguished Prussian naturalist and traveller, spent five years in exploring South America. His observations made on this expedition were used to support his claims that physical geography and meteorology should be considered as accurate sciences. Von Humboldt was the first one to map the earth's surface in lines of equal temperature—so-called isothermal lines. He considered the origin of tropical storms, and noticed the position of zones of volcanic activity. He also invented the term "magnetic storm" to describe a phenomenon which he was the first to record. The variations of intensity of the magnetic forces of the earth also came under his study. After he settled in Paris in 1808 he published the results of his explorations in his Kosmos.

Humboldt's writings excited interest in scientific exploration among the European nations. England in 1831 despatched the "Beagle" to complete the survey of South America, "and to carry a chain of chronological measurements around the world." The voyage of the "Beagle" was to be for scientific purposes only. Incidentally, the official "naturalist" aboard the Beagle was none other than young Charles Darwin.

In 1839 Joseph Hooker (1817-1911) joined Sir James Ross in his Antarctic expedition, spending three years studying plant life in that region. He later proceeded to the northern frontiers of India.

T. H. Huxley in 1846 sailed as surgeon on the "Rattlesnake," which devoted several years surveying and charting waters around Australia.

The expedition of the "Challenger" in 1872 was the culminating point of organized discovery for scientific purposes during the nineteenth century. This ship cruised for several years in the Atlantic and Pacific oceans, to take records pertaining to oceanography, meteorology and natural history.

Geology

Geology is our next topic. Some knowledge of rocks, metals and minerals was obtained as a normal by-product of mining.

Leonardo da Vinci and Bernard Palissy had recognized in fossils the remains of animals and plants. Even in the middle of the nineteenth century there were those who severely questioned this conclusion as it was considered to be contrary to the Book of Genesis.

The possibility of using fossil rocks in tracing the history of the Earth was recognized as early as 1669, when Niels Stensen suggested the possibility. John Woodward (1665-1728) made a large collection of fossils, which he subsequently bequeathed to the University of Cambridge. The study of this collection did much to establish fossils as of animal and vegetable origin.

James Hutton (1726-1797) in his book, Theory of the Earth, published in 1785, contended that fossils were of plant and animal origin. His book was incidentally the result of study of agricultural methods in Holland, Belgium and Northern France. After pondering for fourteen years over the observation of ditches, pits and river beds, he established the early basis for the modern science of geology. He concluded that the stratification of rocks and the embedding of fossils were an active current process in seas, rivers and lakes.

William Smith later assigned the relative ages to rocks by noting their fossilized contents, thus leading to the acceptance of Hutton's "uniformitarian theory."

Georges Cuvier (1769-1832), a Frenchman, reconstructed extinct mammals by noting their fossilized remains as well as the bones found near Paris. *Jean B. deLamarck* later made a classification and comparison of recent and fossil shells. *Sir Charles Lyell* published between 1830 and 1833 his Principles of Geology, which contained the materials and all available evidence bearing on the manner and extent to which the Earth is still being moulded into new forms.

Of special interest to man is the problem of the age of the human race. Lyell in 1863, from a study of flint instruments and the like which lay with the remains of now extinct animals, concluded man's existence on the Earth must have extended over periods considerably greater than that indicated in Biblical chronology. It now seems to be the consensus of scientists that whereas civilization is only some five or six thousand years old, it now appears probable that our ancestors emerged from a more primitive state, and that in a real sense became men somewhere between a hundred thousand and a million years ago.

After *Buffon* (1707-1788), published his Natural History of Animals, Georges Cuvier carried on the subject of classification of animals and placed it on a sound basis. His book, LeRégne Animals, distribué d'après son Organization, compares systematically the structure of existing animals with the remains of extinct fossils. He demonstrated that the past, as well as the present, must be given consideration in any study of living creatures.

Gradual Development of the Evolutionary Idea

It appears that scientists had maintained no close connections with the practical gardeners and farmers who were active by means of hybridization and selection in producing new varieties of plants and animals. At the close of the eighteenth century, improvements in old longhorn type of cattle and a new improved variety of Leicester sheep had been established by *Bakewell* and the *Colling brothers*. New varieties of flowers and fruits were developed by gardeners using cuttings or grafts of sudden sports of superior quality. Certain hybrids, however, turned out to be sterile.

Even in the days of the Greek philosophers the idea of an evolutionary process in nature had been suggested. However, it took two thousand years of labor by physiologists and naturalists to collect enough evidence to make the idea worthy of consideration by scientists. The philosophers Bacon, Descartes, Leibniz and Kant had all suggested the theory. The scientists as a group did not favor the theory of evolution and had left the idea pretty much up to the philosophers, that is, until Darwin and Wallace had published their simultaneous treatises on the subject.

Harvey's embryology and the system of classification by Ray had pointed to the evolutionary idea. *Herbert Spencer,* primarily a philosopher, had preached the evolutionary doctrine during the years immediately preceding the publication of Darwin's Origin of Species in 1859. *Godron,* a botanist, on the other hand, rejected the idea of evolution up to 1859, although he had collected much data on variation.

172

Lamarck (1744-1829) put forth the first connected theory of evolution, a theory based on the cumulative inheritance of modification induced by environmental action, i.e., the progressive inheritance of so-called "acquired characters."

Etienne G. Saint-Hilaire and *Robert Chambers* published a book "Vestiges of Creation" which also indicated a theory of environmental action. However, it remained for Reverend *Thomas R. Malthus* (1766-1834) in his book, Essay on Population, in 1798, to suggest to both Darwin and Wallace a theory of the means of the evolutionary process.

Charles R. Darwin (1809-1882) was educated at Edinburgh, intending a medical career, and later at Christ's College, Cambridge, with the intentions of taking "Holy Orders," in which he was encouraged by his father. However, he finally chose to accept the post of official "naturalist" on the "Beagle," on its five-year voyage around the waters of South America to make scientific studies.

After his return and while compiling his first note-book on the facts collected on the voyage, he read by chance Malthus' book on the problem created by the increase of population versus the diminishing food supply. Up to that time Darwin had no opinion as to the cause of variations. However, Malthus' book gave him the ideas of "survival value" and "natural selection." If variations possessed improved qualities with greater "survival value," the individual having them had a better chance of survival. With this hypothesis he spent twenty years collecting further facts, as well as making experiments such as crossing tame pigeons, etc. In 1856 Lyell urged him to publish the results of his research, but he was not yet ready. However, in June he received a paper written by *Alfred R. Wallace* in which Wallace had put forth a theory similar to his own. Darwin immediately called the matter to the attention of his friends Lyell and Hooker. They arranged with the Linnaean Society to communicate on July 1, 1858, the paper by Wallace, together with a letter from Darwin to Asa Gray, an American botanist, which letter was dated in 1857, with an abstract of his theory composed in 1844. Darwin thereupon wrote out in condensed form his results, followed by the publication of his book, The Origin of Species, in November of 1859.

Although the idea of natural selection led to the acceptance of the theory of organic evolution, it appears that Darwin and his later disciples underrated the complexity of the process. Even today the problem of the details of the origin of species is still a matter of active research and experiment.

The effect of his theory was at first devastating to philosophy and religion. The theory appeared incredulous even to many naturalists, who appreciated the gap between one specie and another. Any attempted crossing of species had only resulted in the sterility of the off-spring. *Thomas H. Huxley,* a fighting supporter of Darwin and his theory, had stated, "My reflection when I first made myself master of the central idea of the Origin, was, 'How extremely stupid not to have thought of that!'" Huxley, however, did point out the defect in the evidence, namely, that the summation of variations ignored the fact that the offspring of crossing different though allied species, are frequently in some degree sterile.

Certain excerpts from William Bateson's address in Toronto in 1922 indicate certain problems still to be solved in connection with the evolutionary theory. He stated in part, "The Darwinian philosophy convinced us that every species must 'make good' in nature if it is to survive, but no one could tell how the differences—often very sharply fixed—which we recognize as specific, do in fact enable the species to make good."

In Germany Haeckel and other naturalists, became ardent Darwinians, in fact as one scientist expressed it, "more Darwinian than Darwin."

Darwinism became a philosophy, in fact almost a religion, and ceased to be considered as a tentative scientific theory. Experimental biology turned rather to morphology and especially to embryology. Von Baer's theory that the development of the individual in the embryo follows and illustrates the history of the race, also turned the attention of biologists to the study of embryology.

To the naturalist and breeder, species remained distinct, and new varieties appeared not by insensible gradation but by sudden, and many times large, mutations; such mutations bred true thereafter. The evolutionists in the eighties, according to Bateson, considered that species were just a figment in the systematist's mind—in other words did not exist. Bateson and deVries, however, believed otherwise, based upon their further study of variation and heredity in the laboratory. The evidence still points to the existence of definite species.

While Darwin did not rule out the Lamarckian doctrine as

a contributing cause of variation, August Weismann demonstrated otherwise. He stated that a sharp distinction must be made between the somatic cells and the germ cells which it contains. He maintained that germ cells descend from germ cells in a pure line of germ plasm. The main inheritance mechanism is that of the germ plasm, which follows an unbroken sequence from cell to cell. In view of this apparent fact, the products of germ cells are not likely to be affected by changes impressed on the body by environmental factors. Weismann examined critically the evidence of inheritance of acquired characters and in every case found it inadequate evidence. His announced results caused some consternation among biologists who had relied on "use and disuse" as the explanation of unsolved problems of adaptations. Herbert Spencer fought Weismann's contention to the last as he had consistently maintained that the inheritance of acquired characters was the chief factor in racial development. Hence, it would appear from Weismann's results that heredity is of greater significance than environment; yet it cannot be disputed that a good environment can be of benefit to the individual if not the race. Weismann's work naturally turned the attention of researchers in biology to the study of germ cells.

Weissmann himself was a firm believer in the sufficiency of Darwin's theory of natural selection. Bateson and deVries both disputed the contention that the accumulation of minute variations produced new varieties and new species. They had first collected data from breeders, fanciers and horticulturalists that pointed toward variations occurring in sudden jumps.

The forgotten experiments and results of Mendel on garden peas were finally dug up in 1900; this gave an answer to these sudden mutations.

Anthropology

The Origin of Species stimulated the comparative study of mankind. In fact, it can be said that modern anthropology arose from the influence of that book.

The comparative study of the human skull by Huxley was motivated by the Darwinian controversy; it marked the beginning of the exact measurement of physical characters on which so much of the science of today depends. It was Huxley who maintained that man in body and brain differed from some apes less than the apes differed among themselves. Consequently, he

175

returned to the Linnaean classification, placing man as the first family in the Order of Primates. Wallace, however, did not agree with Huxley's classification and held that man "is in some degree a new and distinct order of being."

The races of mankind had heretofore been classified according to stature and coloration of skin. They now also classified mankind according to shape of skull. The method of Retsius was used, by which method the longer diameter of the skull from front to back is taken as 100. On this scale the cross diameter gives what is known as the cephalic index. If the index of the skull is less than 80 it is classed as long, and if 80 or over it is considered broad.

The population of Europe showed the Northern race as tall in stature, fair-haired and long-headed. The Southern race, along the Mediterranean, was found to be short, dark and also long-headed. The Alpine race of the mountains of Central Europe was found to be intermediate in stature and coloration, but broad-headed.

The walls of certain caves in Europe were found decorated with likenesses of bison and wild boar. The drawings were considered to be the decorations of a race of prehistoric men tens of thousands of years ago. Prehistoric men were found at Neanderthal in 1866, and at Spy in 1886. In the late Pliocene deposits in Java, Du Bois in 1893 discovered bones which most authorities held to be of a being possessing a physical structure between that of the anthropoid apes and the earliest known forms of man. It has been determined that man cannot be descended from any species of apes now in existence, although a distant cousin. In fact, the evolutionary process turned out to be more complicated than at first considered.

The Belgian astronomer *L. A. J. Quételet* (1796-1874) is generally credited as being the initiator of the statistical methods in anthropology. He showed that the theory of probability also applied to human problems. He determined that the chest measurements of Scottish soldiers or the height of French conscripts vary around the average according to the same laws as are true in the distribution of bullets around the center of a target.

Francis Galton in 1869 proved by tracing the distribution of marks among the candidates of an examination that the same laws apply for physical qualities as with molecular velocities. In other words, the statistical results from all data appear to produce the characteristic so-called "bell-shaped" curve, or the normal curve of probability.

Galton also showed that superior mental ability was inherited and was not the product of environment. He found the differences of innate ability great and that the democratic idea of all men being born equal is demonstrably an error. Weismann's work, of course, strengthened Galton's conclusion, and it became clear that environmental factors as a cause of individual differences had been heretofore exaggerated. Thus, the biological qualities of a race can be improved only by favoring the better strains.

Science as Influenced by Nationalism

The general tendencies of scientific thought shifted during the seventeenth and eighteenth centuries from the ecclesiastical univeralism of the Middle Ages to nationalism. Science developed marked national characteristics, with a consequent intellectual separation between nations. Travels of intellectual discovery by such men as Voltaire to England, Adam Smith to France, and Wordsworth and Coleridge to Germany, helped somewhat to break down these national barriers.

In the early part of the nineteenth century the scientific center of the world was Paris. However, the Revolutionary Government in 1793 guillotined such scientists as Lavoisier, Bailly and Cousin, and drove Condorcet to suicide; in fact, the government suspended the Académie des Sciences. The situation was entirely opposite from that prevailing during the greater part of the eighteenth century when science fairly permeated literature.

While in France the home of science had been in the Academie, in Germany it lay in the Universities. However, for a long time after the methods of exact science were being applied in Paris, the German universities were teaching a hybrid Naturphilosophie, with conclusions drawn from philosophical theories rather than from a patient study of natural phenomena. However, about 1830 conditions changed radically, especially after Gauss and Liebig returned from studying under Gay-Lussac at Paris, and established a laboratory at Giesen in 1826. From then on, systematic scientific research was carried further in Germany than in any other country. At present, however, the United States, Russia, England, Japan, Italy and Israel are all active in research.

At first English science was characterized by its individualistic spirit, and much brilliant work in science was accomplished by those of no academic standing and with their own homes as laboratories. Both Oxford and Cambridge were unrivalled as places of liberal education but were not awake to the spirit of research as on the continent. In the middle of the nineteenth century, however, both Oxford and Cambridge were reformed. Under the inspiration of such men as Clerk Maxwell, Lord Rayleigh and J. J. Thomson, the world-famous experimental school of the Cavendish Laboratory came into being, featuring especially mathematical physics. The biological sciences followed, under such men as Michael Foster, Langley and Bateson.

During the second half of the nineteenth century the intellectual isolation of the nations of Europe which had existed during the first half of the century, had been broken down, and science became once more international.

On the other hand as national barriers to science were broken down, the isolation of the different branches of science increased. Concentration on specialties produces isolation. The simultaneous segregation of science into sciences was one of the factors which resulted in science and philosophy for a time losing contact with one another. The establishment of scientific laboratories at the universities to replace individual home experimental laboratories left less time for general surveys. However, a few broad generalizations appeared to survive alike in physics, chemistry and biology, such as the principle of the conservation of energy.

During the nineteenth century the change in scientific outlook was great because of revolutionary discoveries, especially in the field of biology, and particularly Darwin's theory of evolution.

The close connection between science and philosophy was loosened during the Rennaissance and the Newtonian period, by the establishment by men of science of the method of induction and experiment in the study of nature.

While Kant and Fichte included the results of physical science in their philosophic systems, the later Hegelians were principally responsible for the temporary separation between science and philosophy. Helmholtz in 1862 revealed clearly the cause of this separation. He brought out that whereas the Kantian philosophy was based on the same ground as the physical sciences, the followers of the Hegelian system had fol-

178

lowed an entirely separate path. The main object of Kant's Critical Philosophy was to examine the sources and authority of our knowledge. In the case of Hegel's Philosophy of Identity, however, Helmholtz stated: "it started with the hypothesis that not only spiritual phenomena, but even the actual world— nature, that is, and man—were the result of an act of thought on the part of a creative mind similar, it was supposed, in kind to the human mind." On that hypothesis Hegel considered that the human mind was competent without the guidance of external experience, to rediscover the thoughts of the Creator by its own inner activity. Helmholtz agreed this system may be applied in the case of the so-called "moral science." However, in the case of the facts of nature Hegel's system completely broke down. His system of nature, in the words of Helmholtz, "seemed, at least to natural philosophers, absolutely crazy." As no distinguished scientist came to his support, Hegel gave vent to his vehemence, especially on none other than Isaac Newton. This naturally led to scientific men to banish all philosophic influences from their work, and to characterize the work of philosophers as "mischievous dreaming." Helmholtz goes on to say, "Thus, it must be confessed not only were the illegitimate pretensions of the Hegelian system to subordinate to itself all other studies rejected, but no regard was paid to the rightful claims of philosophy, that is, the criticism of the source of cognition, and the definition of the functions of the intellect."

Retrospectively it is fascinating to observe the world Hegel deductively created by his system of logic. It did serve to suggest that a mind originally was involved in the world's creation.

In the first half of the nineteenth century, in Germany especially, the Hegelians despised the experimentalists and the scientists ignored the Hegelians. As an example of the Hegelian approach, Goethe held that "white light" was obviously simpler and purer than colored, and that consequently Newton's theory of color must be wrong. He would give no consideration to the facts revealed by careful experiment; in fact he proceeded to frame a theory of color in which white light was basic, a theory which would fail the simplest physical analysis.

However, science gradually again influenced the general thought. A new phase of an old controversy arose in England between Whewell, a mathematician, and John Stuart Mill, a philosopher and economist. Whewell maintained the a priori nature of mathematics. John Stuart Mill, on the other hand, held that even the Euclidean axioms, such as two parallel straight lines can never meet, were inductions from experience. Today, however, the axioms may be regarded as mere definitions of the kind of space we are going to investigate in our geometry. Axioms, other than Euclidean, may be framed when we are going to investigate non-Euclidean space. Riemann and other mathematicians have revealed that what we call space may have three, four, or more dimensions. While the space we observe is approximately three-dimensional and Euclidean, Einstein brought out by more exact measurements that Euclidean space is but one out of the many other possible kinds of space.

The Whewell-Mill controversy produced a solution containing the essence of both contentions. Thus the picture of nature we build is not only the product of our sense-data but in part determined a priori by the nature of minds, as also is the very fact that we have experiences.

Biologists especially, during the greater part of the nineteenth century accepted uncritically as ultimate reality the model of nature put together by science. Some of the physicists and philosophers, however, were more conservative. Herbert Spencer held that the ultimate concepts of physics—space, time and atoms—involve mental inconsistencies indicating that the reality underlying phenomena is unknowable.

The work of Bolyai, Gauss, Lobatchevski and Riemann brought out that what we conceive of as space is but a single case of many possible types which may have four or more dimensions.

Boole, Jevons and Clifford during the middle of the nineteenth century contributed to the philosophy of science, such as introducing symbolic language and notation into logic, etc., but they had little influence among scientists. Even the work of Ernst Mach, an Austrian physicist, which was published in 1883 and which called attention to the philosophical basis of mechanics, received very little notice from physicists. Mach in his treatise made use of the historical method, which was unusual at that time. He held that science constructs a model of what our senses reveal about nature, that mechanics is only one aspect of that model and is far from being the ultimate truth. He stated that we had no basis for assuming a knowledge of space or time since they are but sensations, space being known to us as a concept derived from experience. He defined a natural law as "a concise compendious rule" giving the result of past experience to guide us in subsequent sense-perceptions. Einstein, incidentally, was influenced by Mach's thoughts.

Lavoisier's demonstration of the persistence of matter in the midst of all chemical change produced an important effect from the philosophic viewpoint of matter. The sense of touch had early led to the metaphysical concept of matter as that which possesses extension in space and persistence in time. In fact the experience of solidity had early led to a materialistic philosophy. Thus Lavoisier's demonstrations supported the common-sense view that matter was the ultimate reality, for its persistence in time had been supported by his findings.

Dalton's atomic theory, the reduction of the phenomena of electricity and magnetism to mathematical laws, etc., resulted in confidence that eventually all natural phenomena would be interpreted and controlled. It was overlooked, however, that one mystery was cleared up only by expressing it in terms of another—that the basic problems of reality still remained a mystery. Many uncritical men believed firmly, first in matter and force, and second in matter and motion, as ultimate answers to nature's mysteries. Newton, on the other hand, had never accepted gravity as a physical explanation, and left its cause for future consideration.

During the eighteenth and the early nineteenth centuries many philosophers and some physicists conceived that the Newtonian system involved action at a distance, similar to Galileo's idea of force. French physicists Ampère and Cauchy were engaged in investigating electric forces mathematically based on Newton's law of inverse squares. In England, Faraday, William Thomson and Clerk Maxwell were engaged in the study of the intervening medium, trying to imagine a mechanism by which the electric forces could be transmitted through that medium. In an idealized experiment an atom can be infinitely divided, ultimately to a point as a center of force. Such reasoning brought Boscovitch, an eighteenth century Jesuit, to regard atoms as immaterial centers of force. In the nineteenth century both Ampère and Cauchy logically analyzed the atom of their day as an unextended bearer of forces. The atom today has been proved to contain more minute structures, and the electron has become a "disembodied wave-system."

Helmholtz and other physicists in his day regarded as an

adequate solution the reduction of matter to mass and force. It was a mathematical solution, but not a physical explanation. Some considered it the ultimate explanation.

Philosophic materialism arose again in the nineteenth century. Moleschott, Büchner and Vögt based their philosophy on the results of science, especially on physiology and psychology. Büchner's book Kraft and Stoff (1855) demonstrated that the ideas of matter and force as ultimate realities constituted an essential part of the new philosophic movement. Thus the reaction against Hegelianism in Germany became quite definite.

The principle of the conservation of energy served as evidence for the theory of philosophic mechanics and determinism. First it created doubt of so-called biological vitalism, a speculative mechanism by which the living organism adapts itself to its environment, even to the extent of at times suspending physical and chemical laws. Now it became apparent that animals, like machines, could operate only when supplied with energy from without.

Then, too, the old conception that the Sun was slowly dissipating its heat to the point of possible cessation of its activity, was realized as inadequate. Helmholtz calculated in 1854 that a contraction of one ten-thousandth part of its radius would supply the heat radiated by the Sun for over 2000 years.

Lord Kelvin (William Thomson) estimated in 1862 that less than 200 million years ago the Earth was a molten mass. However, by new methods of calculations, both geologists and biologists require a much greater time for the earth and its inhabitants. New sources of heat from radioactivity had not been revealed which would supply stores of heat far beyond the amount available under the older theories. Thus organic evolution and cosmic historians are now given as much time as they need.

The principle of the conservation of energy seemed to point to a beginning and an end whatever be the age of the Sun and Earth. William Thomson approached the problem using the second principle of thermodynamics. According to this theory, mechanical work can only be obtained from heat when it passes from a hot body to a cold one. In an irreversible system the availability of energy is continually growing less. Conversely, the quantity called entropy by Clausius, is continually tending toward a maximum. Thus, eventually the Universe would become motionless and dead. Thomson's work was used as further evidence by the mechanical philosophers that our scientific model of nature was the ultimate reality. It was also looked upon by some as another proof for atheism and determinism. However, the application of the principles of thermodynamics to cosmic theories, based on nineteenth century evidence at least, appeared of doubtful validity. The complexity of the problem was again underestimated. The mystery of existence is not solved by the application of the results of experiments on finite isolated or isothermal systems.

Developments in Psychology

The progress in the study of psychology during the nineteenth century will now be mentioned. During the early part of the century rational psychology (deductive) was favored in Germany, whereas in England and Scotland empirical (inductive) psychology held sway. Empirical psychology can be studied from two directions, one using the introspective method, and the other the method of objective observation and experiment. The latter method is considered scientific, yet it appears naive to believe that any science can function without introspection.

In France some progress had been made in the examination of the mind in its outward expression, both as physiological and pathological manifestations.

Empirical methods gradually replaced the rational deductive approach in Germany, especially as a reaction against Hegelianism. Herbart was one of the first to break away from the rational method. Psychology (Seelenlehre) without a soul was quite a novelty to the Germans. The Germans had heretofore favored a broad theory of the Universe before examining any part of it. The English, on the other hand, were not primarily concerned with broad theory but were more interested in practical results. Hence, an all-encompassing philosophical system is yet to come from England.

In France psychology was mainly in the hands of physiologists and physicians, and therefore their approach was experimental and analytic rather than metaphysical.

As each man's mind is pretty largely accessible only to himself, the consciousness of unity which he feels is not so readily analyzed by scientific methods. Thus, the scientific psychologists must assume man as a machine in order to make progress in their analyses. Here again the English revealed their practical nature, for they were quite mentally undisturbed to consider man as a machine in the physical laboratory, as a person with free-will and responsibility when met in the ordinary affairs of life, and as an immortal soul when met in church. They were even not averse to studying two opposing theories at the same time. That, of course, is true today of physics, for they are using two apparently inconsistent theories to explain phenomena. As one professor put it, he teaches the wave-theory of light on Monday, Wednesday and Friday, and the quantum theory on Tuesday, Thursday and Saturday.

Alexander Bain (1818-1903) was one of the first to apply the empirical examination of mental processes by the introspective methods. He followed Locke's theory of tracing back the phenomena of the mind to sensation. Hence, Bain's psychology in its final form became the so-called "association psychology." At that time he was not aware of the bearing on the normal action of the mind of the French researches on abnormal psychology. Also, he had completed his principal work prior to Darwin's work involving the influence of heredity and environment.

At first the German psychologists endeavored to construct a psychological system from scientific concepts rather than by scientific methods. About the middle of the nineteenth century a sudden change in physical methods took place, influenced mainly by two sources. One was Bishop Berkeley's treatise on the New Theory of Vision which referred the awareness of space and matter ultimately to the sense of touch. The other was Galvani's discovery of the contraction of the legs of a frog when touched by two different metals.

In England Thomas Young studied the special senses from the physical side, and revised Newton's theory of color vision to dependence on three primary color sensations.

Helmholtz made a study of physiological acoustics, at the same time elucidating the physiological basis of music and speech. He also used the stereoscope (invented by Sir Charles Wheatstone) in analyzing our perception of space.

E. H. Weber of Leipzig made observations on the limits of sensation, and discovered the mathematical relationship of geometrical progression, that the stimulus must increase at the beginning of each step in order to be observed.

In 1860 Fechner first used the term "psychophysics." Wundt of Leipzig, along with Fechner, also made comparative measure-

184

ments of sensations. Among other contributions he introduced a tri-dimensional theory of feeling, made up of three pair—pleasantness and unpleasantness, tension and relief, and excitement and subdued feeling.

Darwin's study of the expression of emotions in animals and men initiated the first step of comparative psychology. In the latter part of the nineteenth century the theory of psychophysical parallelism was the most characteristic contribution to the problem of the relation of mind and body. Descartes, Spinoza and Leibniz may be considered the first to suggest this theory. The theory suggests that physical and psychical phenomena run parallel, simultaneous if not actually connected.

As to the unity of self-conscious life, the association psychologists supposed it was the product of the grouping together of sensations, perceptions and memories. Some considered the unity as a sort of epi-phenomena of the brain, others as a higher unity. Vögt suggested the brain secretes thought as the liver secretes bile. Psychology passes this problem of unity on to philosophy.

These contributions to the field of psychology, as well as to the field of biology, facilitated the rising tide of mechanical and materialistic philosophy. The effect of the Industrial Revolution in England and on the Continent also contributed toward increasing the tide. However, philosophic materialism fails to explain the phenomena of consciousness; in fact, it appears to have difficulty surviving critical analysis. Yet before this apparent weakness could be discovered, the theory first had to be formulated.

XVII.

REACTIONS OF RELIGION, PHILOSOPHY, SCIENCE AND POLITICS TO LAMARCKIANISM AND DARWINISM.

The diverse reactions to the Lamarckian and Darwinian hypotheses are many and intensely intriguing. Some of these reactions will be enumerated herein, though necessarily in brief form. Many of them were indicated by Dampier-Whetham in his "History of Science."

The transformistic theory of Lamarck, involving the inheritance of acquired characters, and that of Darwin, involving the origin of species via natural selection, were both opposed against the creation miracle of the Bible. Naturally, the materialists eagerly embraced them, especially Darwin's evolutionary theory, as it served as a much sought support for their philosophy. It gave them an answer to the question continually posed to them by the theologians, namely, how can they explain the purposiveness revealed both in the structure and arrangement of our organs; how did they come into being without an intelligent creative cause. In short, how can they explain finality in the absence of final causes.

Darwin's second main work "The Descent of Man" (1871) created more of a reaction than his "Origin of Species." People generally reacted against the thought of being related to apes. They preferred the Biblical account of having been created from the "dust of the ground." However, Darwin's followers preferred his evolutionary hypothesis with its infinitely short steps and infinitely long time periods; they served as two keys to open the gates to an explanation of creation heretofore accessible to miracle only. The non-Christian religions did not react as did the Christian religion; Brahminism and Buddhism placed less of a gap between animals and man, with their belief in the transmigration of souls.

It now became a positive fashion to explain all natural phenomena, even religion itself, on an evolutionary basis. Ironically, the very terminology used by the evolutionary materialists implies teleology. Does not the "struggle for existence" presuppose Schopenhauer's "will-to-live," struggle in order to live? Also, the terms selection and choice would seem to introduce an intellectual element into nature. The materialists quickly retorted to this charge that these terms were merely figures of speech.

In Germany especially, Darwin's theory created a great stir. In fact, Ernst Haeckel developed the theory into a philosophic creed, and founded a new form of monism allied to materialism.

By the middle of the nineteenth century the scientific approach was applied to other subjects, such as sociology. Helmholtz stated that the lessons from physical science led to a reverence for facts and a certain distrust of appearances; it led to an effort to detect causal relationships, even a tendency to assume their existence.

Men discovered during this period that the subject of economics was also suitable for mathematical treatment. The method of statistics was applied fruitfully to the problems of insurance and sociology. William Farr (1807-1883) successfully applied the subject of social statistics to improve medical and insurance statistics.

Evolutionary philosophy also greatly modified men's conceptions of human society and destroyed the idea of finality. It also destroyed the idea that "all men are created equal." The idea of absolute laws also became a subject of doubt, especially with an ever-changing environment.

Political institutions and economic conditions change considerably quicker than biological changes. Therefore, a knowledge of history and origin casts light on present meaning, even on future probabilities.

Francis Galton in 1869, working on the idea of variation and selection as applied to man, gave the name Eugenics to the study of the innate transmissible qualities of mankind and the application of knowledge to the welfare of the human race. Galton's contributions threw new light on social problems— that biological knowledge was applicable to sociology.

No consensus of opinion was reached on the bearing of

Darwin's conception on the theories of politics. The aristocratic ideas expressed by Vacher de Bourget, Ammon and Nietzsche were stimulated by the principle of the survival of the fittest. Yet here evil qualities may under present conditions have the upper hand, as an entrenched aristocratic position eliminates competition and consequent selection.

Socialists suggested a communistic order of society, as animals such as bees and ants apparently had found value in it. But that form of society leads to a finality of development, for the bee world has shown no signs of progress for the past two thousand years under observation by man.

Strangely, in the study of "family trees" man seems to prefer showing that he has slipped rather than risen in the social scale; in other words, that he is descended from some illustrious personage. Yet, with respect to the "evolutionary tree" he gives battle for top position. Moreover, primitive races prefer postulating a direct descent from the gods; not primitive races only, for even Disraeli is reported to have said that he was "on the side of the angels." Man appears prone to be an opportunist when he himself is involved.

As Copernicus and Galileo displaced the Earth from the center of the Universe, so Darwin took man off his pedestal as a fallen angel and placed him a step over his ape ancestors. Yet even today Darwin's hypothesis of natural selection cannot satisfactorily explain the conversion of one species into another. It has been found, too, that mutations are not necessarily improvements, but the opposite thereof leading to devolution.

Darwin's hypothesis had an even profounder effect on religion than on sociology. The evolutionary theory produced an immediate clash between the Darwinian disciples and the clergy, especially with respect to the creation story appearing in Genesis. The Protestant reformers especially had emphasized the verbal inspiration of the Bible. Actually the Bible does not state that man is a descendant of angels, but that he was created a little lower than angels. The days of creation are interpreted by some to mean twenty-four-hour days, when the evidence of nature points quite definitely to the so-called "days" of creation being epochs in length. Interpreting the "days" of creation as twenty-four-hour days, Archbishop Ussher had put the date of creation, based upon the Bible, as the year 4004 B.C. This, of course, was contrary to the estimates of geologists and biologists.

The "argument from design" of Christian apologists appeared to be weakened by the principle of natural selection. However, in a larger sense the theory created more problems for the scientists than for the Christian apologists. The progressive advances made by science because of these problems have been advantageous and enlightening to both sides of the controversy. Evolution after all is espoused as a continuous process, even in an age of quantum theory. (But is it a continuous process?) The explanation of the essential meaning and origin of Being itself, as well as the phenomena of consciousness, still await an answer.

Darwin's conception resulted in a study of comparative religion. Dr. E. B. Tylor, one of the first anthropologists in the field of religion, published his "Primitive Culture" in 1871. This was followed by J. G. Frazer's "Totemism" in 1887, and "The Golden Bough" in 1890. Religious men thereby gained a perspective of the continuous revelation of religious ideas, which led to a study of the varieties of religious experience, to which William James made a significant contribution.

The evolutionary doctrine also put forth another theory to explain ethics. Heretofore, there were the famous Ten Commandments which Moses received from God at Mount Sinai, then Kant's innate "categorical imperative," followed by Bentham's and Mill's utilitarian theory based on "the greatest happiness to the greatest number." Then came Henry Sidgwick's theory of the moral process, i.e., from momentary selfish interest to a longer and wider range of social welfare. The Germans, however, quickly adapted the Darwinian hypothesis to the ethical problem, and stated in effect that the moral instincts are chance variations resulting from the process of natural selection. In other words, moral instincts are inherited by mankind for their survival value. (At that time they were unaware that this instinct had to be individually chosen to become effective.) How morality stands any chance against self-centered instincts is somewhat difficult to see, for Huxley stated that the cosmic and moral orders are in continual conflict. In other words, while there existed complete agreement on the practical aspect of the ethics problem, confusion reigns on the theoretical aspects.

The German and the French thinkers concluded that if evolutionary philosophy is consistently interpreted, then the qualities which favor the survival of the fittest are the real moral qualities. Nietzsche taught the doctrine of the super-man, and

189

maintained that Christian morality was a slave morality. The influence of his teaching of the consistent application of the "survival of the fittest" doctrine, together with his super-man philosophy, and this coupled with the successes in the wars of 1866 and 1870, are considered by some to have resulted in the first and second world wars. The "struggle-for-life" (lebensraum) is a phrase which many use to excuse the violations of conventional morality.

James Ward and W. R. Sorley in England each made studies of the theory of the Ethics of Naturalism. Both men concluded that the supporters of naturalism have failed in their attempts to derive an ethical doctrine on the basis of evolution alone. They also concluded that an idealist conception of the Universe is as necessary for ethics as for rational metaphysics.

The history of philosophy reveals that mechanical and spiritual theories of the Universe have alternated from age to age. Each time the mechanical theory has made a breakthrough, its ardent supporters have felt that they are at last at the point of reaching a full explanation of the Universe. After the contributions of Copernicus and Newton, Laplace entertained the idea that a skillful enough mind would be able to calculate the whole of the past and future history of the Universe. However, upon the assimilation of each new contribution to knowledge, the old problems in essence are still pretty much unanswered.

The first principal result of Darwin's theory was the ever-recurrent wave of mechanical philosophy. It gave renewed confidence to those who based their theory of life on scientific ground. The contemporary tendencies in physics, now supplemented by the tendencies on the biological side, serve to indicate an eventual explanation of nature in terms of eternal, unchanging matter and a limited but constant quantity of energy.

In 1899 Haeckel's book "The Riddle of the Universe" was published. He maintained in it that Darwin's theory now could be applied to explain not only the evolution of bodies of animals, but also that the instincts of animals are subject to development under the same influence of selection, even to the mind of man. In other words, he founded a complete monist philosophy. Psychic properties, he maintained, are possessed by all living cells, and the highest faculties of the human mind are but the aggregate product of the psychic functions of the brain cells.

Haeckel espoused a single supreme law, the so-called "Law of Substance," made up of the united laws of the constancy of matter and the conservation of energy. It is doubtful whether Darwin would agree with Haeckel's optimistic conclusions, as he was very reticent and modest as to the philosophic importance of his contribution. In this connection Dampier-Whetham in his "History of Science" has this to say, "The problem of descent is more complicated than it appeared to Darwin's ardent followers. Whether a naturalistic solution of the more difficult problem of man's whole nature will ever be reached, it is impossible to say. But it is quite certain that as yet it has not been attained; nor will it be attained till many more alternations towards and away from mechanical philosophy have passed like waves over the human mind."

Contrasted with Haeckel's view was that of W. K. Clifford who maintained Berkeley's contention that mind is the ultimate reality. Clifford believed in an idealist monism in which consciousness is built up from atoms of so-called "mind-stuff."

The dogmas of German materialists and mechanists were questioned by Emil du Bois-Reymond, a Berlin physiologist, and his brother Paul du Bois-Reymond. They called attention to the fact that even if the problems of life were reduced to those of physics and chemistry, the concepts of matter and force gave no ultimate explanation for they were simply abstractions from phenomena. They maintained that some problems were beyond human knowledge. Both Huxley and Spencer had entertained a similar view. Karl Pearson, on the other hand, in his book "The Grammar of Knowledge," suggested it was unwise to set limits to knowledge, and asked with Galileo, "Who is willing to set limits to the human intellect?" Pearson stated that notions and axioms go through a process of natural selection; those that best symbolize and describe sense-data will in time become established, whereas the others will fail to survive.

Darwin appears to have proved that Nature herself uses the Baconian method of empirical experiment in both the plant and animal worlds. In fact, if that were consistently true, there would be no room left for teleology.

The phrase "the survival of the fittest" was coined by Herbert Spencer to express Darwin's term "natural selection."

191

The fittest, of course, is that which best adapts to the existing environment, and thus may be either a higher or lower type, an evolution if the former and a devolution if the latter. Lord Balfour pointed out that on the basis of a thorough-going selectivist philosophy the only proof of fitness is survival. Hence, it appears to beg the question. If it should be maintained that man is higher than his ape ancestors, a consistent selectivist would have to say that even our judgment in that respect is itself formed from natural selection. Thus, there appears to be no way out of the dilemma.

As suggested by some, the order in which we place creation is a matter of racial religion. For instance, the Oriental Buddhist considers existence an evil, and consciousness an even greater evil. This idea, we recall, influenced Schopenhauer. Thus, according to the Oriental Buddhist, progressive regression to inorganic matter would be the ultimate good.

Natural selection was never considered by Darwin as completely explaining the evolutionary process. Natural selection, after all, only cuts off the useless and does not create the variations themselves. And mutations are not necessarily improvements but more often not. The problem of life itself, and its ever-increasing pressure, still remain unsolved. Darwin's theory of evolution revealed an underlying unity in the entire organic creation, from the one-celled animals to man. However, it is only one aspect of the problem of existence. The method of science is indispensable to analysis, but the problem of synthesis eventually falls on philosophy.

XVIII.

TWENTIETH CENTURY SCIENCE

Biology—Embryology

Twentieth century mathematics and physics broke away from the Newtonian picture of the Universe, and caused a profound change in philosophic thought. Biology of the twentieth century, however, is still following the general lines established in the prior century. Darwin's theory of natural selection had almost become a scientific creed and resulted in the temporary discontinuance of studies of inheritance. The attention of laboratory workers in biology was now occupied in studying embryology as a result of von Baer's hypothesis that the progressive development of the embryo reveals the history of the species.

The exceptions, however, were de Vries and William Bateson (1861-1926). De Vries continued his experiments on variation, while Bateson questioned the logic of the evidence for von Baer's contention, and advocated a return to Darwin's original methods of research.

There were two difficulties to be overcome in explaining evolution: first, the difficulty of rationalizing the origination of species based on small or initial variations; and secondly, the difficulty of overcoming the swamping effect of inter-crossing. Both deVries and Bateson had learned from their own experiments that large discontinuous mutations occur, a phenomena which plant and animal breeders had already observed.

Genetics, Resulting from Rediscovery of Mendel's Research

The previously overlooked experimental work on garden peas of Gregor J. Mendel, an Augustinian Monk, was rediscovered by deVries and others in 1900. Mendel, it was learned, had questioned natural selection as an adequate explanation of variation; he, therefore, proceeded to experiment on garden peas in the monastery garden.

This rediscovery of Mendel's published results initiated the study of heredity as an exact experimental science. Mendel really introduced what may be termed as an atomic or quantum conception in biology, that heredity is determined by certain indivisible units which carry certain transmissible characters. These observed characters were found to occur in pairs, one dominant, such as tallness in peas, and the other recessive, such as dwarfness. Either the true dwarfs or the true talls, if self-fertilized, bred true in type. When crossed with each other, however, all outwardly resembled in the first generation the tall parent as tallness, as we mentioned, is a dominant character. However, when the tall hybrids are self-fertilized, one-quarter of them are dwarfs and three-quarters are tall. The one-quarter that are dwarfs breed true to type as their pair of genes are recessive. The three-quarters that appear tall breed one-third true tall plants, while the remaining two-thirds repeat in the next generation the same products as the first hybrids mentioned.

It was found that biological qualities follow the same mathematical laws as in physics, the law of probability. However, certain characters were found to be sex-linked.

Sir Roland Biffen applied his knowledge of genetics in producing a new species of wheat which was immune from rust, possessing high cropping power and certain baking qualities.

After the discovery of Mendel's laws of inheritance, investigation of the cell nucleus revealed the presence of a definite number of thread-like bodies. As these invisible bodies became visible on staining with certain dyes, they were given the name chromosomes. These bodies proved to be the chemical bearers of the genetic characters. The phenomena of inheritance was explained by observing the chromosomal divisions taking place within the nucleus of the germ cell at the time of fertilization.

T. H. Morgan and his co-workers in New York in 1910 worked out more fully the relations between chromosomes and so-called genes, using the fruit fly Drosophila as the experimental animal. Biologists have determined that there are four chromosomes in the germ-cells of the fruit fly (drosophila melanogaster) and that there are twenty-three in the germ-cells and forty-six in the body cells of man.

Karl Pearson and his co-workers in London have made a study of the application of statistical laws to work on heredity. The normal curve of error is usually observed in a study of large numbers. DeVries, in his work on the evening primrose, called attention to certain dangers in the use of statistics. He found it impossible to tell from the statistical data on all seeds how many varieties were involved. He plotted separately on a graph what he considered as three varieties. On the horizontal axis he plotted the length of the fruit and on the vertical axis the number of individuals. Of the three varieties, his "A" and "C" varieties were found to have a characteristic mean size of fruit and their curves closely resembled the normal "bell-shaped" curve. However, the "B" variety showed indications of being divided into at least two separate groups. If all varieties had been grouped as one at the beginning, the normal curve would have resulted.

Pearson determined that if the average height of the men of a race be 5 foot eight inches, the sons of men six foot tall would produce sons on the average five foot ten inches; in other words, two inches taller than the average. Such a correlation is expressed in statistical terms as one half, or 0.5; perfect correlation would be 1.0 and no correlation would be zero.

At one time there arose considerable controversy between the Mendelians and the Biometricians who used these statistical methods. For a complete study of heredity, however, it was concluded both systems are advantageous.

As paleontological evidence has accumulated, the evolutionary theory as a general description of the life process, has become more firmly established. For instance it has been found that there were gymnosperms but no angiosperms (higher plants with protected seeds) in carboniferous times.

Some biologists today still believe that natural selection, given enough time, is adequate to explain evolution. Others see in Mendelian mutations the explanation of the appearance of new species. However a third group of biologists, among them some of the leaders of modern thought, are not satisfied that the true explanation of the origin of species has yet been found. In fact, Bateson stated in 1922, "In the dim outline evolution is evident enough. From the facts it is a conclusion which inevitably follows. But that particular and essential bit of the theory of evolution which is concerned with the origin and nature of species remains utterly mysterious." As Dampier-Whetham brings out, neither Darwinian variation nor Mendelian mutation as used in experiments, seems to reach those basic differences which systematists still recognize as distinct species.

F. O. Bower has assembled evidence that in ferns especially, long continued environmental differences may produce heritable characters. This would support the theory of Lamarck. Yet, the possibility of inheriting environmental influences (acquired characters) in plants has been explained by the fact that the segregation of germ and body cells do not occur at such an early stage as in that of animals.

Another difficulty is that variations appear to depend on elements being lost rather than gained, a regressive process. Such has been Bateson's observation in the case of his genetic experiments with the fruit fly. Bateson states in part, "Our doubts are not as to the reality or truth of evolution, but as to the origin of species, a technical, almost domestic, problem."

The fossils collected by paleontologists appear to indicate evolution along definitely directed lines. The fact of a progressive appearance of species in a time sequence is not in question. Varieties within species have been explained by natural selection and mutations. But the explanation of the appearance of new species in the first place is still an unanswered question.

Effects on Society of the Studies of Heredity

Something will now be mentioned about the results of the studies of heredity as effecting society as such.

Nettleship made studies on deficiencies such as color blindness and congenital cataract, and found them to follow Mendelian laws in their descent. The almost exact equality in the number of male and female babies born suggests that this too is a heritable character. It has been determined that if all female germ cells carry the female gene and half the male cells carry maleness and half femaleness, it would produce an approximate equality between male and female babies. Genetic experiments on man, of course, run into obstructions as they do not produce as fast or reach maturity as quickly as fruit flies or white mice. However, enough observations have been made on man to show that Mendelian laws also apply to him. The importance which Galton assigned to the effects of heredity in man have been substantiated by such researchers as Hurst, Nettleship and others; as well as by the mathematical work of Karl Pearson and his colleagues. They have determined that whereas environment and education may help the individual in fuller expression of the inherited characters, they cannot create or modify these characters. As education and experience cannot be inherited, able men are born, and are not the product of environment.

A race is not benefitted unless the fittest, that is the more intelligent, have the greatest number of children. Studies of population show that the more intelligent have a progressively decreasing birth rate, while the opposite is true of the less intelligent, especially so among the feebleminded. The so-called more intelligent have been found to either maintain an unaltered population or even show a small progressive increase. It has been determined that an average of about four children to each fertile marriage is needed to maintain an unaltered population.

The Mental Deficiency Act in England has cut down the prolific number of feeble-minded children in that country. But, there is always an uneasy feeling among the average middle class as regards this method of control, fearing that eventually such a Deficiency Act would progressively be applied nearer to them. Yet certain smug individuals would suggest that such fears may be more imaginary than real as someone has to be around to perform the so-called menial tasks.

The tragedy of the acts of such superior "wild-men" as Hitler becomes apparent when one considers how he deliberately arranged to place before the firing squad the men of superior ability in conquered nations, and ironically, but for emotional reasons, within his own nation.

Bateson called attention to the fact that the progress of civilization has resulted solely from the work of exceptional men; the rest he maintained merely copy and labor. However, we should not under-rate the importance of the contributions of those who copy and labor. After all, history records the necessity for all, including the self-classified superior group, to move away from the accumulating stench piles to build another city because of the non-existence of sanitation men. True, they sometimes would return to rebuild after the sands of the desert storms had buried the former stench heaps.

It has been said that the hope for future civilization lies in the sense of responsibility of the better stocks in the race. Possibly the more practical way of expressing it would be that the future of civilization rests upon the sense of the sociological responsibility of all classes of mankind, with emphasis on the word "responsibility."

Physiology—Vitamins, Glandular Secretions and the Nervous System

Rise of Biochemistry

The marked feature of twentieth century physiology was the application of the methods of physics and chemistry to its problems. Physiology has now been divided into biophysics and biochemistry, as the problems of analysis necessitated that trend.

As protoplasm, which constitutes the contents of a living cell, consists of colloids and the nucleus, the physics and chemistry of colloids now became important in physiological research. The distinction between crystalloids and colloids was observed by Graham in 1850. Colloid particles were observed to be large as compared to crystalloids. It was also recognized that a crystalloid solution, like sugar, formed a homogeneous liquid. The solution of a colloid, however, proved to be a two-phase system, with a definite surface of separation, enough to show so-called surface tension.

In 1908 Perrin proved that the so-called Brownian movement was caused by the bombardment of neighboring molecules. The invention of the "ultra-microscope" by Siedentopf and Zsigmondy in 1903 enabled the investigation of the smaller colloid particles.

The theory of colloids was advanced by a study of their electrical qualities. In this connection Sir W. B. Hardy observed that as the surrounding liquid changed slowly from being faintly acid to faintly alkaline, the charge of certain colloids was reversed. At the so-called "iso-electric" point where the charge was neutralized, the colloid was precipitated from its solution.

Hence, the electric charge proved to be important in a

colloid solution. In 1882 Schultze noticed that the coagulation power of a solution depended on the valency of the ions of the salt. In 1895 Linder and Picton found the average coagulative powers of uni-valent, di-valent and tri-valent ions to be proportional to 1:35:1023. Hardy in 1900 found that the active ion was the one of opposite sign to that on the colloid particles. Dampier-Whetham in 1899, by the application of the theory of probability, and using the method of the chemical valency of the ions, determined the proportion to be 1:32:1024, to compare with the observed values of Linder and Picton of 1:35:1023.

The properties of colloids, especially the electrical, are of interest to the biologist inasmuch as the structure of protoplasm is made up of colloids. Faraday had observed that the precipitating effect of "salt" on colloidal gold could, by adding a trace of "jelly," be stopped. Mines (1912) and other physiologists have made a study of such protective colloids.

The electrical conductivity of water, if purified by repeated distillation, drops toward a limit equivalent to a concentration of hydrogen ($H+$) and hydroxyl ($OH-$) ions of about 10^{-7} gram-molecules per litre. This so-called hydrogen-ion concentration (Ph) of pure water is expressed in negative logarithmic terms, 10^{-7} or a Ph of 7. As water is acidified, the concentration rises. Thus the Ph has become a measure of the acidity of a medium, not only in general physical chemistry, but also in physiology and in the science of soils. Lime treatment of soils is determined by the Ph, as is also the normal acidity of the blood as against that which is incompatible to life.

Haldane and Priestley (1905) demonstrated that the nervous centers of the lungs are sensitive to small increases of carbon dioxide in the blood, and instantly institute increased breathing to counteract it. In other words, the body is equipped with automatic controls to maintain the required chemical equilibrium. Natural selection, with mutations, even with great time periods, has really taken on quite a task in explaining the existence of these marvelous automatic mechanisms.

Vitamins

The experiments of Sir Frederick G. Hopkins in 1912, brought out that a diet sufficient to supply energy requirements of the body may not contain certain substances to maintain growth. After feeding chemically pure food to rats he noticed that they failed to grow until small amounts of fresh milk were added to the diet. A subsequent study by him of these so-called "accessory food factors," later called vitamins, revealed the nature of their respective effects. He discovered vitamin A and D are found chiefly in animal fats. Vitamin A is a protection against infection and from a form of eye-disease. Vitamin D is required for the proper calcification of bones in growing animals. Vitamin B, taken from the outer layers of certain grains, in yeast, etc., will prevent the nervous disease of beri-beri. Vitamin C, present in fresh vegetables and in certain fruits, was found to prevent scurvy. A fifth vitamin was found which is connected with the maintenance of fertility.

Glandular Secretions

The glands, which are organs of internal secretion in the body, have been found to be of great importance in the control of proper chemical equilibrium within the body. Their function long remained a mystery. However, in 1902 Bayliss and Starling discovered that secretion from the pancreas is produced by a chemical substance formed by the action of acid on the intestine and carried to the pancreas by the blood. This substance, called secretin, is formed during digestion when acid contents of the stomach enter the intestine and require the action of pancreatic juice.

The discovery of secretin led to finding of other similar secretions also carried by the blood stream. Hardy called these secretions "hormones," a term which was later adopted by Bayliss and Starling, and has become a term in current use.

Banting and Best in 1922 discovered a hormone named insulin, which serves as an alleviation to human diabetes. These researchers injected dogs from which the pancreas had been removed, with an extract from the pancreas of sheep; and they thereupon observed a reduction in the abnormally high concentration of sugar in the blood of the experimental animals. The pancreas was thus proved to serve a double function, of secreting insulin into the blood stream, and of supplying pancreatic juice through a duct into the intestine.

Malfunctioning of the thyroid gland in the young not only slows down growth but causes a variety of idiocy called cretinism. In the adult, malfunctioning of this gland causes a state called myxiedema. The condition can be corrected by treating

200

with thyroid extract. On the other hand excess activity of the thyroid gland causes exophthalmic goitre.

Kendall in 1919 succeeded in isolating thyroxin, the active factor of the thyroid gland, and Hannington in 1926 was successful in synthesizing it in the laboratory, and learned that it contained a large amount of iodine.

The parathyroid glands have been found to control the amount of calcium within the body. Malfunctioning of these glands have currently been determined as one of the causes of kidney stones.

Steinach in 1910 initiated experiments on the effects of the removal of the sexual glands of frogs. He found that if castrated frogs were injected with the substance taken from the testes of other frogs, the former qualities returned in the castrated frogs.

The secretions of the small pituitary gland have been found to effect growth; excess secretion produces gigantism, and a deficiency causes dwarfism.

The adrenals near the kidneys secrete adrenalin into the blood stream in times of fright, and stimulate the so-called splanchnic nerves. Injection of adrenalin will produce physical symptoms which accompany the emotion of fear.

Some scientists have recently suggested that the difference between races can be partly accounted for by the differences of glandular secretions, thus suggesting an influence on organic evolution.

Nervous System

The study of the nervous system is considered one of the most important branches of physiology. Sponges, very primitive animals, have been found to possess contractile tissues but no nerves as such. Jellyfish possess receptors or sense organs which are connected with the muscles by a nerve-network. However, in the earth worm a centralized nervous system appears. Sensory neurones are connected with the motor neurones either directly or through so-called "association neurones." The nervous system of the higher animals gains in complexity to that of man, where the most intricate system is centralized in the brain.

Sir Charles Sherrington from 1906 on made a careful study of the nature of nerve tissue. He observed that while the neurones were in physiological continuity with one another, they possess properties indicating an absence of protoplasmic continuity. Sherrington calls the sense of sight and hearing, "distance receptors" and the brain is developed in connection with them. The cerebrum, especially the cortex, was found by Sherrington to be the seat of the mental functions. In 1870 Fritsch and Hitzig first investigated the effects of electrical stimuli on the brain. Sherrington, Horsley, Graham Brown, Burnett and Head were some of the later physiologists to continue the work of Fritsch and Hitzig.

It was discovered that the so-called small brain, the cerebellum, was concerned with the sense of balance, posture and movement. It reacts to stimuli from the muscles of the body and from the semi-circular canals of the ear.

Gaskell (1886-1889) and Langley (1891-   ) first investigated the involuntary nervous system. They observed that it is essentially an outflow from the cerebro-spinal system, although it possesses a certain degree of independent action.

Psychology

Pavlov (1910) experimented with dogs, producing the so-called conditioned reflex. Pavlov was able to condition a flow of saliva in a dog by simply ringing a bell prior to bringing the meat in sight of the dog. This method does not involve the intervening consciousness, and the idea was immediately seized by psychologists, resulting in the behavioristic school.

Weber in the nineteenth century initiated the methods of experiment in psychology. Thereafter it was felt that the field of psychology could be classed among the natural sciences. During the twentieth century mechanical devices were used in the study of sight, taste, smell and feeling. Memory, attention, association, learning, and the like, were studied by more complex tests. In these investigations so-called objective and analytic methods were used.

While physiologists studied the physics and chemistry of the central nervous system, the psychologists studied the mental aspect of these same physical manifestations.

During the First World War (1914-1918), neurologists had an opportunity to observe the mental effects of localized injuries to the brain.

The basic ideas of the associationist school and the conditioned reflex school (leading to J. B. Watson's Behaviorism in 1914) were outlined by Lloyd Morgan. It was Morgan who founded the American school of animal psychology. It involved the interpretation of behavior based on observation without involving consciousness. First psychology lost its soul and now its consciousness, as was suggested by some psychologists. But yet it took consciousness to observe and interpret the results. What it actually did accomplish was to provide a method whereby more than one consciousness could make concomitant observations.

The behaviorists run into the same difficulty as the mechanistic philosophers who underrate the contributions of the mind and thought. According to Watson, thought is a secondary product gained through the habit of language, as a skill at tennis is acquired by muscular activity. The so-called circular-reflex theory used by the behaviorists in explaining how a bird builds its nest is a most fascinating one, though placing somewhat of a strain on one's credulity. The stimulus-response psychology of Robert S. Woodworth then provides a broader viewpoint from which to rationalize behavior without the contortions required in behaviorism; yet Woodworth's psychology also remains amenable to the scientific approach.

Industrial psychology is a specialized application of psychological principles to industrial problems. It is used in employee selection, as well as studying such factors as bodily and mental fatigue as affecting production, and the like.

Psychology in education is another application of the science. Tests of mental alertness, emotional stability, personality traits and tests for the determination of vocational interests have been devised.

The field of abnormal psychology is, of course, the most intriguing field in psychology, at least to many students of the science. Such contributors to this field as Charcot of France, Freud (with his emphasis on the sex instinct), Adler (with his emphasis on the self-preservative instinct), Jung (with his depth psychology of archetypes) and others, have done much to throw light on so-called abnormal behavior of mankind. Ironically no adequate study of the normal has ever been made. William McDougall and Morton Prince made most significant contributions to the organization of the personality which threw considerable light on so-called normal behavior as well as on the abnormal.

Psychical research is another field in which there is active research currently going on. The studies in extra-sensory perception by Dr. H. B. Rhine of Duke University have opened a promising new field of psychological research. At first this aspect of psychological investigation was gingerly by-passed as off-limits to so-called true scientists, but now the evidence is gradually reaching the point where these phenomena are given scientific recognition.

The complexity of the phenomena of physiology and psychology on one side and the apparent difficulty of natural selection to explain evolution on the other, led to a division in opinion following the year 1900. Experimental physiologists and psychologists, working on the assumption that the laws of mechanics, physics and chemistry are applicable to living organisms, have continually enlarged the field where mechanisms appeared to explain vital phenomena. Yet, some biologists, aware of the ignorance over wide areas of knowledge or impressed with the apparent purposefulness of living organisms, concluded that the facts can only be explained by regarding living organisms as organic entities or wholes. Wolfgang Köhler in his Gestalt Psychology reflects this awareness in the psychological field.

Problem of Organization in Living Organisms

Uexküll (1922) called attention to the fact that living organisms are units in time as well as in space. J. S. Haldane (1913) stressed the tendency of animals to maintain constancy amid external and internal changes. Driesch considered that early embryonic development can only be explained by a non-material guiding force.

E. Rignano, a philosopher, insisted that the essence of living matter is teleological, a striving for a goal. He cited the fact that living substance selects from a mixture of chemical substances those which will maintain itself, which selection would indicate a purposive aspect.

Needham, on the other hand, emphasized the need of the mechanistic view to supply hypotheses for use in experimental research, and that the teleological view must remain outside of science. Lawrence Henderson, in turn calls attention to the fact that the environment as such bears the mark of teleology and thus merges organic teleology in universal teleology. As certain thinkers have brought out, the mechanists have assumed since Descartes onwards that physical science has revealed reality. However, it has been found on further inspection to be simply another abstraction. Thus, we have the periodic oscilla-

204

tions of emphasis as between mechanists and vitalists. When science by analysis makes certain promising discoveries, the mechanists hold sway. However, during a lull in discoveries and the synthetic whole still remains a mystery, the vitalists take over with their speculations. While the field of physics formerly was the chief support of mechanists, now with analysis in that field going beyond the powers of visibility, their problems have necessitated a retreat from the field of visual observation to that of logical construction and mathematics. The principle of indeterminacy created by wave mechanics raises a question concerning the scientific argument for philosophic determinism.

Physical Anthropology

Now some attention will be given to the field of physical anthropology. Paleontological discoveries led to the conclusion that apes and men were probably differentiated as early as the middle of the miocene period, about fifteen million years ago. Bones of the so-called Neanderthal man were discovered in 1856 in the valley bearing that name. The Neanderthal man is reconstructed by anthropologists as an individual with a flattened head and prominent eyebrow ridges, and they conclude he represents a species preceding and more brutal than that of homo sapiens. Sir Arthur Keith has acknowledged the mistake of early evolutionists in assuming a straight line of human descent leading back to a general fossil ancestor common to both hominoids and anthropoids. However, it is now generally agreed that the line is zigzag, and that the Neanderthal man is no direct ancestor of homo sapiens—in other words, the Neanderthal man was an offshoot from the main trunk.

The bones of the tall, long-skulled Cro-Magnon race were discovered in Europe subsequent to the Neanderthal man, and the anthropologists classed the Cro-Magnon man as a true variety of homo sapiens. Their flint implements were of a much better type and their paintings on the walls of caves reveal considerable artistic ability.

Ratzel (1886), Schmidt (1910) and Graebner (1911), all representing a German school, traced the origin of similar artistic cultures to intermingling of peoples. The English and French had previously considered that similar civilizations could arise independently from races in different parts of the world.

A point of view similar to that of this German school was arrived at independently by an anthropologist named W. H. R. Rivers, in his study of relationships of language and social organization in the Pacific islands. This view was further supported by Elliott Smith in his research work on embalming. The widespread practice of erecting monoliths and other stone structures, oriented to the Sun or stars, also points to a common origin of civilization.

Social Anthropology

Social anthropology in the twentieth century took off in different directions, for instance: the study of the psychology of primitive peoples; the study of Greek religion; and the extensive collection of world-wide data by J. G. Frazer, published in "The Golden Bough," which has become a classic in its field.

Frazer brings out that Greek and Roman society was built on the principle of the subordination of the individual to society, of the citizen to the state. The welfare of the state was considered the supreme aim of conduct, even above that of the safety of the individual. The religions of the Middle East (Zoroastrianism, Judaism, Christianity, and Islam), however, were concerned primarily with the welfare of the individual. They considered the communion of the soul with God and its eternal salvation as the only things worth living for. The importance of the status of the individual soul, therefore, made the objects of material prosperity and even the existence of the state appear insignificant in comparison. Frazer goes on to maintain that the Middle East religions halted the march of civilization until Roman law, Aristotelian philosophy, ancient literature and art were again revived at the close of the Middle Ages. He stated that it "marked the return of Europe to native ideals of life and conduct, to saner, manlier view of the world." Of course, Frazer's conceptions have since been both concurred with and disputed, both rationally and emotionally.

Physical Science—Discovery of Radio-active Phenomena

For a short period it appeared as if physical science had arrived at a stage where all that was left was to determine the physical constants with more accuracy. This opinion, however, was upset when Professor Wilhelm K. Röntgen of Munich

(1845-1923) accidentally discovered X-rays in 1895. He observed that photographic plates, although protected from light, became fogged up and thus spoiled when placed near vacuum glass tubes or bulbs through which electric discharges were passing. Apparently rays of some nature emitted by the discharge tubes passed through the covering of the photographic plates. He further noticed that a screen covered with a phosphorescent substance lighted up near such a tube. The fact that the rays registered an effect roughly proportional to the thickness and density of the absorbent led to its application to surgery.

After the discovery of X-rays had been announced, J. J. Thomson and others discovered that when the rays passed through a gas, the gas became a conductor of electricity. Rutherford observed that in a conducting gas the current up to a certain point was proportional to the applied electromotive force; thereafter the current increased more slowly up to a saturation point.

The discovery of X-rays also led to research in radio-activity. Henri Becquerel in 1896 and 1897 discovered that uranium and its compounds emit rays which affect a photographic plate through black paper or any substance opaque to light. This led to the discovery of ultra-atomic particles much lighter than the atoms of any chemical element. Hittorf (1869) and Goldstein (1876) discovered certain rays which Goldstein gave the name cathode rays. In 1890 Schuster measured the ratio of the charge to the mass of these so-called cathode ray particles. Hertz in 1892 observed that cathode rays would pass through thin gold leaf or aluminum. These discoveries were followed by Perrin's discovery in 1895 that the rays gave a negative electric charge to an insulated conductor. In 1897 the work of several physicists solved the problem of their nature, and determined the velocity as about one-tenth that of light, and the ratio of the charge (e) to the mass (m) of the particles as 2000 to 4000 times as great as the value for the hydrogen atom in liquid electrolytes.

J. J. Thomson observed that in a high vacua these rays could be deflected by either an electric or a magnetic field. This would suggest that these rays possess their own magnetic field. C. T. R. Wilson in 1897 showed that ions, like particles of dust, act as cloud nuclei for the condensation of water droplets in moist air. Thomson in 1898 and in 1899, using the method of the Wilson cloud chamber, measured the charge on the ions produced in gases by X-rays. Soon thereafter, Townsend measured the rate of diffusion of ions through gases and calculated the charge from the result. In 1899 Thomson completed the proof by measuring the "e" by the cloud method, and the e/m by magnetic deflection for the same particles. The value attained in all the measurements agreed very closely with the charge on a univalent liquid ion. In view of these results it became certain that it is not the electric charge which is greater than the charge of the liquid ion but that the mass is smaller. Millikan in 1919 by improved methods determined that the corpuscle or electron is one 1830th part of that of the hydrogen atom. At last the problem originally raised by the Greeks of whether different kinds of matter have a common basis was solved. Thomson at the time put his views in these words: "I regard the atom as containing a large number of smaller bodies which I will call corpuscles; these corpuscles are equal to each other; the mass of a corpuscle is the mass of the negative ion in a gas at low pressure. . . . On this view, electrification essentially involves the splitting up of the atom, a part of the mass of the atom getting free and becoming detached from the original atom."

Light, according to Maxwell's theory, was a system of electromagnetic waves emitted by vibrating electric systems. Just preceding Thomson's discovery, an electrical theory of matter was in process of being formulated by Lorentz. Lorentz reasoned that if light spectra or waves appear to be characteristic of elements and not their compounds, the vibrator must be atoms or part of atoms. Hence, the light spectra should be affected by a magnetic field. Zeeman in 1896 realized this expectation and observed a broadening of the lines in the sodium spectrum when the source of light was placed in the magnetic field of a strong electro-magnet.

Johnstone Stoney had previously named the vibrating electric particles "electrons," a name which Lorentz adopted. The measure of the Zeeman effect showed that they were identical with Thomson's corpuscles. Larmor suggested that the electrons must possess, because of their electric energy, an inertia which is equivalent to mass. Thus, Thomson explained electricity in terms of matter, while Lorentz expressed matter in terms of electricity.

It was later learned that electrons could be obtained in other ways, such as from substances at high temperatures and from metals under ultra-violet light. Since then the heat effect has become of practical importance in the development of wireless means of communication.

Whereas cathode rays were found to proceed from the negative electrode (or cathode), the corresponding positive rays from the anode were discovered by Goldstein in 1886. The positive rays were found to consist of positive particles which possess masses comparable to ordinary atoms. The magnetic deflection was observed to be inversely proportional to the velocity of the particles, while the electric deflection to the square of the velocity. Thomson gave the name "electric atomic weight" to the ratio of m/e for any element to its value for the hydrogen atom.

Thomson, in examining the element neon (atomic weight 20.2) observed two lines, indicating respectively weights of 20 and 22. This discovery suggested that neon might consist of a mixture of the same element but of different atomic weights. This condition Soddy later named "isotope," a condition which was later explained by certain radioactive phenomena. F. W. Aston continued Thomson's experiments in this field, and discovered that the phenomena appearing in neon were also noted in other elements. Aston's observations also supported Prout's hypothesis that the successive increments in atomic weights are all multiples of that of hydrogen.

It was observed that uranium rays, like X-rays, produced electric conductivity in air and other gases. In 1900 M. and Mme. Curie discovered that pitchblende and several other minerals containing uranium, were more radio-active than uranium itself. In the chemical analysis of pitchblende, they found salts of three very active elements; these they named radium (the most active), polonium and actinium.

In 1899, Sir Ernest Rutherford, then in Canada, discovered that the radiation from uranium consists of two parts, the first named alpha rays, and the second, beta rays. At a later date gamma rays were detected. The alpha rays produced the most noticeable electric effect, and were later found to consist of helium and to possess a velocity of about one-tenth the speed of light. The beta rays were found to be negative electrons, with velocities varying from 60 to 95 per cent of the velocity of light. While the beta rays can be deflected by magnetic or electric forces, and the alpha rays to a much less extent, gamma rays register no effect to these forces. The gamma rays, like Xrays, consist of waves of the same nature as light, though of much shorter wave-lengths. These were measured by C. D. Ellis and Fräulein Meitner.

Sir William Crookes in 1900 observed that if uranium were precipitated from solution by ammonium carbonate, and the precipitate were dissolved in an excess of reagent, a small quantity of insoluble residue remained. Crookes named this residue uranium-X, which was found to be exceedingly active when examined photographically. The re-dissolved uranium, however, was observed to be photographically inert. Becquerel, however, observed that when these substances were put aside for about a year, the formerly active residue had lost its activity, and that the inactive uranium had regained its radiating quality. Rutherford and Soddy subsequently discovered a corresponding effect in thorium.

M. and Mme. Curie in 1899 observed that a rod would acquire radio-active properties if exposed to the emanation of radium, and the rod was noticed to ionize gas in a testing cylinder.

In 1902 Rutherford and Soddy investigated the rate of activity of decay of thorium-X and discovered that the rate during each short period of time is proportional to the amount of activity at the beginning of that interval. It showed the same law as does the decrease in the amount of a chemical compound dissociating molecule by molecule into simpler products.

Curie and Laborde in 1903 remarked about the fact that compounds of radium constantly emit heat. It was found that one gramme of radium in equilibrium with its products gives off 135 calories per hour, the rate being unchanged by either exposing to high or low temperatures. Rutherford subsequently correlated this heat with the radio-activity. He determined that of the total of 135 calories, 5 calories are caused by the beta rays, 6 calories by the gamma rays, and the remainder by the alpha rays. The heat effects of the alpha and beta rays were ascribed to the kinetic energy of the projected particles.

The phenomena of the continual development of heat by compounds of radium led to many attempts to explain the source of this apparently continual energy supply. In 1903 Rutherford and Soddy explained this phenomena by the theory that radio-activity is caused by an explosive disintegration of the atoms themselves. Whenever one atom out of many millions explodes, an alpha particle, or a beta particle and a gamma ray are ejected, resulting in a different atom left behind. If an alpha particle has been thrown out, this new element will be less in atomic weight by the four units of a helium atom.

The end products of the distintegration of uranium are three isotopes of lead; these appear to be the only isotopes found in nature in isolated condition. Crookes was the first one to observe with a magnifying lens scintillations of alpha particles on a fluorescent screen of zinc sulphide exposed to a speck of radium bromide.

By a method developed by Rutherford, the life of radium was calculated. It was determined that a mass of radium would diminish by one-half in approximately 1600 years. C. T. R. Wilson used his cloud-chamber method for this same purpose.

Rutherford's work on radio-activity finally revealed the possibility of the transmutation of matter. However, it has been found easier to destroy than to build up atoms, and it appeared unlikely that man would ever be able to reverse the cosmic process of breaking up of complex atoms into simpler atoms and radiant energy. However this is now possible.

Röntgen found that Xrays are not refracted like ordinary light waves, nor are they deflected by magnetic or electric forces. Laue in 1912 suggested that if Xrays were ethereal waves of very short wavelength, the regular arrangement of atoms in a crystal might be found to diffract them. After Laue worked out a complex mathematical theory, Friedrich and Kipling successfully tested the theory experimentally. As a result, Xrays were shown to be electromagnetic waves, shorter than those of light. Later research into the structure of crystals was carried on by Sir William Bragg and others. As an outcome of this research, radiation is now known from the long waves in use by radio, to the short waves of Xrays and gamma rays, a frequency range of approximately 60 octaves. Visible light, incidentally, consists of only about one octave. Apparently, much is going on in nature without our seeing it. Suspicion as concerns natural phenomena may prove a productive trait.

With the use of the crystal method, H. G. J. Moseley, a promising young English physicist killed in the First World War, discovered that the frequency of vibration of the characteristic lines in the Xray spectrum undergoes a simple change when the target bombarded by cathode rays was changed from one metal to another. By this method he was able to get a series of atomic numbers ranging regularly for all solid elements examined from aluminium 13 to gold 79. This method revealed that there are only two or three places left for undiscovered elements.

Quantum Theory—Planck's Energy Constant

As mathematical investigation indicates that oscillators of high frequency should radiate more energy than the oscillators of low frequency, one would conclude that visible light would give off more heat than the invisible infra-red rays, and the ultra-violet rays more than light. However, this is contrary to well-known fact. This problem served as Planck's motivation in 1901 to conceive the so-called "quantum theory." According to this theory, radiation is not continuous but must be considered like matter, as individual units of atoms. The sizes of these units of energy radiated would be proportional to the frequency of the oscillation. As the high-frequency oscillations of ultra-violet would require more energy in order to radiate, the chance of many units being available and radiated would be very small. In the case of the low-frequency oscillations, the probability is great that many units will be available and radiated. However, since each unit is very small, the total energy is also small. The intermediate frequency, however, with a unit of medium size, the number radiated would be fairly large, and hence a maximum of total energy. This theory would explain the apparent inconsistency in the amount of heat given off by light and ultra-violet rays versus infra-red rays. To do so, Planck's quantum of energy must be supposed to be proportional to the frequency, i.e., inversely proportional to the period of vibration. Hence, he derived the formula

$$e = hv = \frac{h}{T}$$

e being Planck's quantum of energy, v being the frequency, T the time period, and h a constant.

Planck's Constant Supported by New Conception of the Phenomena of Heat and Light

Planck's theory was received at first with scepticism until Einstein, Nernst, Lindemann and Debye used it successfully in explaining the phenomena of specific heat. Einstein successfully explained the phenomena of specific heat by pointing out that if energy could only be absorbed in definite units or quanta, the rate of absorption would depend on the size of the unit, and hence on the frequency of vibration, and thus on the temperature. Light, according to this theory appears to consist of a stream of minute gushes of energy, or atoms of light somewhat similar to Newton's corpuscles.

More recently deBroglie has framed a theory of light in which the properties of waves and particles are combined mathematically in a new form of wave-mechanics. The term facetiously used for this conception is "wavicle," that is, a moving particle behaving as a group of waves.

Gradual Development of the Modern Conception of the Atom

The modern conception of the atom began at the close of the nineteenth century with the discovery of the negatively charged corpuscle which was named an electron. Electrical properties of atoms were to be explained in terms of an excess or deficiency in the normal number of electrons, and their optical properties in terms of electronic vibrations.

Physicists soon became aware of the great empty space within a so-called "hard" atom. As the mass of an electron was found to be so small compared with that of an atom, it was concluded that nearly all the mass must be in the nucleus of the atom.

The nucleus of the hydrogen atom was determined by J. J. Thomson to be the positive unit (proton) to correspond with the negative unit (electron). The mass of the proton was found to be 1837 times the mass of the electron. It was conceived that the electron of the hydrogen atom moves around its proton nucleus at great speed, in other words, a miniature solar system. This ascribed similarity, however, later proved to be hasty.

In 1913 Niels Bohr of Copenhagan first applied Planck's quantum theory to the problem of atomic structure. He based his research on the theory of planetary electrons. Bohr supposed in the case of the hydrogen atom that the electron had four possible so-called stable orbits. An electron, according to Bohr's idea, can only move in one of a few paths. When it goes from one path or orbit to another, the jump is instantaneous. As an electron falls in from an outer to an inner orbit, it loses energy of position and gains energy of motion. In jumping from one orbit to the next, the electron absorbs or radiates energy $h\nu$, where h is Planck's unit of action and v the frequency of vibration.

It has been found that radio-activity is caused by an explosive disruption of the nucleus; Xrays, on the other hand, proceed from the inner layers of the electrons outside the nucleus; and light comes from the outermost electrons. These electrons are detached more easily and are involved in the phenomena of cohesion and chemical action.

Statistical models of atoms were constructed by Kossel, Lewis, Langmuir and others. These models served to explain valency and other chemical properties. However, physicists at that time preferred Bohr's more dynamic conception of the atom.

The phenomena of temperature and pressure effect on spectra were investigated by such physicists as Saha, H. N. Russell, R. H. Fowler and E. A. Milne. They applied the new theories by means of thermo-dynamic methods. Their findings have resulted in renewed activity among astro-physicists in the measurement of stellar temperatures.

Bohr's theory of the atom proved successful in accounting for the line spectrum of hydrogen and of ionized helium. It failed, however, with the heavier atoms, and by 1925 his theory was replaced by other explanations. Heisenberg in 1925 framed another theory of quantum mechanics based on the frequencies and amplitudes of radiation absorbed and given out by the atom, phenomena which can be observed. The mathematical formulation of the theory was based upon these observations. The theory has been developed by Dirac, and shown to lead to the formula or "ladder" by J. J. Balmer, a Swiss mathematician. In 1885 this mathematician, in his attempt to arrive at a formula to account for the various frequencies of emission of an atom of hydrogen, calculated that a number 3,287,870 divided by 1^2, 2^2, 3^2, 4^2, 5^2, 6^2 produced the distances between the frequencies. Forty years thereafter Niels Bohr proved out the formula as the relative distances between the various shells within the atom.

In following up the work of deBroglie on phase-waves and light quanta, Schrödinger in 1926 came up with a theory mathematically equivalent to the Heisenberg theory from the view that material points are nothing but so-called "wave systems." The medium carrying the waves is considered dispersive, as transparent matter is to light. It becomes possible for waves of two frequencies to be present together. It can be compared to a group of waves in a storm; the velocity of a group of waves is not the velocity of an individual wave in the group. The group waves thus manifest themselves to us as particles. The frequencies of the waves manifest themselves as energies. This leads to the constant relation between frequency and energy as in Planck's constant h. Schrödinger in more complex atoms succeeds in getting the right number of frequencies to explain the phenomena of spectra; it was here where Bohr's theory failed.

As the wave group expands, there is a certain indeterminacy of position of the electron. It appeared that the more accurate the position was attempted, the less accurate the momentum, and vice versa. This condition is now generally known as the principle of uncertainty.

This new quantum mechanics produced another revolution in physical science. Both Heisenberg's and Schrödinger's mathematical formulations are equivalent to each other, although they are mathematical equations only.

Experiments on electrons during the 1920's by such physicists as Davisson, Kunsman, Germer, and G. P. Thompson have supported Schrödinger's theory that a moving electron is accompanied by a series of waves, comparable to those of Xrays, the wave-length being only about a millionth part of the wavelength of visible light. If the electron is accompanied by a train of waves, the assumption is that it must be vibrating in unison with the waves. Hence it appears that the electron is no longer the ultimate unit of matter or of electricity. Mathematical investigation reveals that the energy of the electron is proportional to the frequency of the waves. It also shows that the product of its momentum and the wave-length is constant. However, discontinuity is still indicated, and thus we are back to the quantum theory.

G. P. Thomson's experiments lead to the interpretation that an electron possesses both the nature of an electric charge and a train of waves. Schrödinger goes further and states it is a wave system. Thus it appears at present as if matter has been analyzed to the point of becoming a set of mathematical symbols.

Development of the Theory of Relativity

In 1676 Olaus Römer, a Danish astronomer, observed that the intervals between successive eclipses of one of Jupiter's satellites were longer when the Earth was receding from Jupiter and shorter when approaching. Thus he concluded light required time for its passage through space. He estimated that light travels at 192,000 miles per second.

In the nineteenth century Fizeau and L. Foucault separately determined the velocity of light over short distances on the Earth. The most modern result for the speed of light gives a value of 186,384 miles per second, so Römer's original determination of 192,000 miles per second was comparatively close to that determined by modern techniques.

The determination whether the so-called luminiferous ether has any effect on the velocity of light was ascertained in 1887 by Michelson and Morley. They set up an apparatus consisting of a system of mirrors which enabled the experimenters simultaneously to observe light reflected by the mirrors that could be adjusted in relation to different angles of the movement of the Earth. They arrived at the conclusion that there is no appreciable relative motion of the Earth and the ether. If there is an ether, the Earth appears to drag ether with it.

G. F. Fitzgerald made a useful suggestion which was developed by Larmor and Lorentz. The suggestion was that if matter be electrical in essence or bound together by electric forces, it may contract as it moves through an electromagnetic ether in the direction of motion. Hence Michelson's and Morley's apparatus might change in dimensions as it rotated and thus compensate for the displacement produced by the Earth's movement through the ether.

Einstein in 1905 pointed out that the ideas of absolute space and time were only metaphysical concepts not derived directly from the observations and experiments of physics. The only space we can experience is that measured between the scratches on a bar, and the only time, that measured by a clock set by astronomical events. Thus, time and space are merely relative to the observer. This led to the first discovered law of the new physics of relativity, namely, that time and space are shown to be such that light always travels with the same measured velocity relative to any observer. Therefore, from this viewpoint no explanation is needed of the fact that the velocity of light, in any circumstances, is always the same. The apparatus of Michelson and Morley, tested by our constant standard of the speed of light, shows no change in linear dimensions as it rotates because the experimenters are moving with it.

According to Einstein's principle of relativity, mass and

energy are equivalent to one another, a mass (m), when expressed as energy being mc², when c is the velocity of light, or the equation $E=mc^2$. This also conforms with Maxwell's theory of electromagnetic waves.

These principles lead to fantastic conclusions; for instance, a metal rod on an ether plane would, to an outside observer, become shorter and shorter as its acceleration approached the speed of light, in fact the rod would disappear at the speed of light. A clock, on the other hand, would go slower and slower as it approached the speed of light. That is the way it would appear to an observer on the Earth. On the other hand, the observer on the ether plane would see things as perfectly normal on his plane, but the appearance of a like set-up on the Earth would seem identically abnormal as the rod on the ether plane appears to the observer on the earth. (Of course, it should be kept in mind that these conclusions are drawn from idealized experiments consistent with the mathematical equations, for at such speeds no actual experiments could be conducted. Because of the nature of Einstein's research, idealized experiments were his only technique.)

Both of these observers are right according to the theory, for length, mass and time are not absolute quantities. The so-called measurements are true only relative to one specified observer within his own co-ordinate system.

Minkowski in 1908 pointed out that the changes in space and time compensate each other, that is, a combination of the two produces the same result for all observers. Minkowski maintained that, in addition to length, breadth and thickness, we must look on time as a fourth dimension in this combination of space and time, one second being equivalent to the 186,324 miles which light travels in that time.

The term "interval" comes up in the relativity theories. Bertrand Russell in his book "ABC of Relativity" speaks of the interval (space-time relationship) between two events as "a physical fact about them, not dependent upon the particular circumstances of the observer." He goes on to cite three possible cases:

(1) The interval may be zero, as when an observer is present at both events, as when lightning strikes.

For so-called "space-like" and "time-like" intervals he very considerately supplied the following construction:

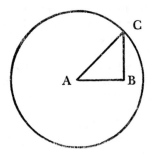

Figure 1

(2) "Space-like" intervals are those in which the space is greater than the distance light would have travelled in the time. In that case, line AB in the foregoing construction would be drawn as long as the distance light would travel in the time. The distance in space, represented by line AC, would be the distance between the two events. Then the line BC drawn perpendicular to AB to meet C at the circumference of the circle would represent the "interval," which would be the same for all observers.

(3) If it is physically possible for a body to be present at both events, then the interval is said to be "time-like." AC would then represent the distance light would travel in the time, while AB would be the distance in space between the two events. The perpendicular drawn from AB to the circumference of the circle to meet C would represent the "time-like" interval between the two events, and would be the same for all observers.

In determining the so-called "Fitzgerald contraction," AC would represent the distance light would travel in a second, and AB the distance the object, moving relatively to ourselves, on which we wish to measure lengths would have travelled in a second. Then the ratio between AC and AB would be the ratio in which apparent lengths are changed by the motion.

It should be emphasized that the foregoing construction is only significant in the case of objects traveling at a speed approaching that of light, i.e., 186,324 miles per second.

In the realm of relativity, number, thermodynamic entropy, and action (product of energy and time which gives us the quantum) still remain as so-called absolute quantities.

When it was determined that light had a speed, the absolute "now" of former ideas became a merely relative "seen-now."

The equations of ordinary dynamical systems are reversible and can be read either way whether terrestrial or astronomic. However, the rise of the entropy of an isolated system towards a maximum is a physical process which can only proceed in one direction and corresponds with the passage of time in the human mind.

The phenomena of the planets circling around the sun, together with the tendency of a projectile to fall to the earth, leads to the conclusion that near matter there is something analogous to a curvature of space-time. Any matter entering this region has a tendency to move towards or around the matter in a fixed path.

In a so-called "idealized" experiment (a technique used by Dr. Einstein along with his mathematical method), a person in a free-falling elevator would not be conscious of motion and could drop an apple and still have it remain near his hand. Thinking about this so-called "principle of equivalence" turned Einstein's thinking from relativity to that of gravitation. The thought occurred to him that the movement of a body towards the Earth or in an orbit, may simply be the following of the natural path in a curved region of space-time. This conception, if true, would make Newton's hypothesis of a gravitational attraction unnecessary.

A so-called crucial experiment was devised to determine whether Newton's or Einstein's conception was true. Calculations showed that the deflection of a ray of light by the Sun under Einstein's principle would be twice that which Newton's theory would indicate. The opportunity for the crucial experiment came during the eclipse on May 29, 1919. Eddington at the Gulf of Guinea and Crommelin in Brazil determined that the image of the nearer star was displaced to the amount required by Einstein's calculation.

Another way in which Einstein's calculations were determined to be more accurate than those of Newton was to correct the discrepancy of 42 sec. of arc per century in Mercury's orbit around the sun. Also under Einstein's relativity theory, an atom should vibrate more slowly in a gravitational field. This appears to have been confirmed by experimental evidence which showed that the lines in the Sun's spectrum were displaced toward the red in comparison with corresponding spectra on the earth. Thus, Einstein's new conception of the universe has produced a change in the direction of physics, in the quantum theory and the relativity theory. Matter as something extended in space and time is now conceived of as a system of waves in space-time according to Louis de Broglie and others.

Hilbert in 1915 proved that the minimum principle, previously espoused by a number of scientists during and prior to Newton, also applied under the relativity theory. He found that gravitation acts so as to make the total curvature of space-time a minimum. Whittaker in his book "Space & Spirit" expresses it in these words: "gravitation simply represents a continual effort of the universe to straighten itself out."

In 1929 Einstein indicated that he had discovered the solution to the problem of unifying gravitational forces with the forces of electro-magnetism. In his new Unified Field Theory, in which he considered space to be something between that of Euclid and that of Riemann, he makes electromagnetism a metric property of space-time the same as gravitation.

Development of Theories in Astro-physics

In the field of astro-physics, scientists with the use of mathematics and observations have determined that the distance between the earth and the sun is 92,800,000 miles. The diameter of the sun has been determined as 865,000 miles, its mass as 332,000 times the mass of the earth, and its average density as 1.4 grams per cubic centimeter as compared with that of the earth of 5.5.

The diameter of the solar system is approximately 5600 million miles, determined by the orbit of the planet Neptune. It takes Neptune 165 years to move around the sun, as against that of the earth of only one year.

The nearest star has been determined by the parallax method to be Proxima Centauri, about 24,000,000 million million (4.1 light years) miles from us. Thus, the intervening space between us and the first star is vast indeed. Yet, our solar system is only a very small part of the lens-like Milky-way, our particular galaxy; our sun is 60,000 light years from the center of our galaxy. It has been estimated that the Milky-way is at least 300,000 light years wide at its maximum diameter; in other words, it takes light, traveling at 186,324 miles per second, 300,-

000 years to travel across it. And there are untold galaxies of stars in the universe.

Stars were classified by Hipparchus in the second century B.C. according to six so-called "magnitudes" (degree of apparent brightness). This scale has now been continued to the faint stars beyond the twentieth magnitude, about a millionth part of the first magnitude stars.

Hartzsprung and H. N. Russell have independently determined that there are more stars in the higher and lower absolute magnitudes than in the intervening. The stars of the high absolute magnitudes are known as "giant" stars; those in the lower, as "dwarf" stars. The dwarf stars are of great density, however, and because of this they generate immense heat in their interiors, and hence are potentially explosive. Stars are now considered as thermo-nuclear furnaces, especially so the dwarf stars.

Many stars which appear to be single stars have been found on closer inspection to be a group of two or more stars. For instance, the so-called pole-star or North Star, used by mariners in determining their location, has been found spectroscopically to be made up of four stars, two stars of which revolving around one another in four days, a third star with an orbit period of twelve years, and a fourth star with an orbit period of some 20,000 years.

Dr. Hubble of the Mount Wilson Observatory in California has estimated that about two million suns are visible in the 100-inch telescope at the Observatory. On a clear night the naked eye can detect only a few thousand such suns. The more recent 200-inch telescope now at Mt. Palomar has increased the distance seen two times, that is, from 500,000,000 light years to 1,000,000,000 light years.

It has been found that the difference in mass between different stars is not great. On the other hand, the differences in density and size are very great.

The classification of stars according to their spectra was initiated by Father Secchi in Rome about 1867. This system of classification was considerably improved and extended at the Harvard Observatory in the United States. The visual color of stars has been found to differ, and at Harvard these differences were distinguished by the letters O, B, A, F, G, K, M, N, R, the bluer stars coming first and ending with the red. Our sun is classed under type G. The spectra also reveals the types of elements predominating. The spectra were also observed to estimate the temperatures of the various types of stars.

From the agreement of various methods of estimating stellar temperatures, it has been found that stars just visible have a temperature of about 1650°C. For the hottest stars known, the temperature reaches 23,000°C. These temperatures naturally apply only to the outer radiating layer. The interior of stars is estimated to be much hotter, with temperatures estimated to rise to many million degrees centigrade, this extreme temperature being the result of gravitational pressure. Work in the field of stellar temperatures was performed by such men as Saha, R. H. Fowler, E. A. Milne, and others.

The division of stars into so-called "giants" and "dwarfs" appears more marked in those stars falling into the cooler group from type K classification on. In the hotter group, for instance in type B, the divisions have practically disappeared, and are all "giant" stars. This observation has led some authorities to conclude that all stars go through a roughly identical evolutionary course. Each star is considered to begin as relatively cool, gradually rising in temperature to a maximum, and then receding down the temperature scale until it again becomes relatively cool. As it reaches its maximum, it emits a large amount of light and is classed as a "giant" star. As it cools, its luminosity becomes less and less until it becomes a so-called "dwarf" star. Russell traced out this process of stellar evolution and determined that it was in accordance with the dynamics of a mass of gravitating gas, as worked out by Lane and Ritter.

This process cannot explain all the heat evolved by our sun, and it is now thought that atomic disintegration may explain the additional heat evolved. Hence, new knowledge of atomic structure has led to a modification of the process by Eddington and others. Stars are now considered thermo-nuclear furnaces, building up elements.

McLennan, Kolhörster, Millikan and others have detected extremely penetrating rays of minute quantity coming from space and continually passing through our atmosphere. Jeans, in his Eos or The Wider Aspects of Cosmogony, has this to say of these rays: "In a sense this radiation is the most fundamental physical phenomenon of the whole universe, most regions of space containing more of it than of visible light or heat. Our bodies are traversed by it night and day . . . it breaks up several million atoms in each of our bodies every second. It may be essential to life or it may be killing us."

Eddington in 1924 computed that the greater the mass of a star the more it should radiate. His calculated theoretical relation checked with the facts. It appears now that the sun, as well as the other stars, are in effect gaseous, even though denser than water. This condition is possible as it appears that most of the elements of the sun are minus their electrons and hence take up less space. However, there is sufficient space between the nuclei of the atoms to consider them in a gaseous state. It is assumed now that the atoms in the depths of the stars must be heavier than those on the earth.

By various methods, astro-physicists have come up with an estimate of from five to ten billion years as the probable age of the stars in our galaxy. For lives of such length, enormous supplies of radiant energy are required. In this connection Einstein's theory suggested the possibility that the source of this energy might be the product of the mutual annihilation of positive protons and negative electrons. It has been estimated that the sun radiates fifty horsepower from each square inch of surface, meaning that the sun as a whole is losing mass at the rate of 360,000 million tons a day.

Now that the age of the stars has been estimated, the next natural question is how they came into existence. The existence of nebulae, areas of luminosity, have been known for a long time, as the one in the constellation Andromeda was observed by the naked eye prior to the invention of the telescope. Huygens discovered another in 1656 in the constellation Orion, which is an irregular-shaped nebulae.

In addition to irregular-shaped nebulae, there are smaller bodies of regular shape called planetary nebulae. The most fascinating, however, are like great whirlpools of light known as spiral nebulae. Our own Milky-Way is such a nebulae.

The Milky-Way, the so-called "island-universe," is one of some one hundred million galaxies. It is our home in space, our solar system being 35,000 light years from the center of a spiral of 2,000,000,000 stars, about 100,000 to 200,000 light years in diameter and 10,000 to 20,000 light-years thick at the center of its lens-like shape. Our earth is an average of 93,000,000 miles from the sun.

Now that we have placed our earth in a relative position within the Milky-Way, our "island home," let us proceed to the nearest sister to our Milky-Way, namely, the Andromeda nebulae or galaxy.

The Andromeda galaxy is very similar to that of the Milky-Way, in size, mass and structure. It gives astronomers an opportunity to study a galaxy from the outside. Rotating around its center are its spiral arms. The spectra and the distribution of its stars appear also to be the same as the stars in the Milky-Way. It also has the two Magellanic clouds and the flock of so-called globular clusters. The so-called Magellanic clouds are made up of stars extraordinarily hot and bright. Most of the recognizable stars in the Magellanic clouds are "blue supergiants." They are considered young as they are connected with the "cloudy" material believed to be the building material of stars.

A great number of globes of extremely hot stars, known as globular clusters, flies through space with our Milky-Way. They have been likened to "squadrons of airplanes escorting a ship," and make a most impressive sight according to astronomers.

Harlow Shapley has made a concentrated study of these globular clusters. They appear to be dispersed over a space twice as large as the galaxy. Most of the clusters, however, appear to be near to the center of our galaxy. Shapley reports that the distribution of the stars within a cluster appears to be arranged in accordance with the pattern of an ideal crystal structure. In other words, it is a celestial crystal comparable to an atomic crystal. The explanation of why these so-called stellar crystals are found around galaxies everywhere is a mystery awaiting explanation.

There are some three hypotheses expounded for explaining the formation of the stellar universe, i.e., the hypothesis of the exploding universe (the so-called "big-bang" theory), the hypothesis of the pulsating universe (the breathing universe), and the hypothesis of the continuous creation of the "balanced universe," (the so-called "steady-state" theory).

First, we shall briefly review the so-called "big-bang" theory. Edwin Powell Hubble of California observed that 80 per cent of the spectra of the extragalactic nebulae revealed a displacement of their spectral lines toward red. This would indicate that the islands of the universe are moving away, the farther away the galaxy, the faster it is receding into space.

Belgian astronomer, Abbé Georges Lemaitre, was the first astronomer to interpret the apparent whirling away of the galaxies from a common center as an exploding mass, each fragment a galaxy. The creation of the universe, in other words, was a primordial explosion of a highly compressed and overheated cloud mass which contained all the matter in the universe today; it was, in fact, a super-galaxy. It is estimated that this original explosion took place from five billion to eight billion years ago.

Naturally the next question is, where did the original primordial mass come from? In this connection Gamow has speculated that inasmuch as matter can be transformed into radiation and radiation into matter, the primordial cloud was a cloud of photons. Paul Adrien Dirac, a Scottish physicist, has determined that the temperature of the cosmic cloud was one trillion degrees at the zero hour of the hypothetical explosion. As the explosion of an atom bomb creates in a split second by fusion and fission radioactive isotopes before non-existent, just so the primordial cloud of photons created by chain reactions in minutes the elements of our universe. Dirac has calculated that at the end of ten seconds our universe had the size of the sun, with the mass of our moon. The physicists themselves could but wonder how the universe could come into existence by the explosion of a cosmic atom bomb, but that is the conclusion toward which their equations point. Arthur Eddington, a leading English astrophysicist, now deceased, admitted in these words—"The theory of the expanding universe is in some respects so preposterous that we naturally hesitate to commit ourselves to it. It contains elements apparently so incredible that I feel almost an indignation that anyone should believe it—except myself."

The hypothesis of the *pulsating universe* will next be reviewed. Upon the formation of mass, the gravitational field extends outward at the speed of light. The gravitational field may be identified with "space." Space is considered curved. If a positive curve, it would make a full circle and return to form a ring. A negative curve is likened to a hairpin with the spreading ends. The space of the solar system forms a positive curve; the type of curve of the universe is still undetermined. Universal space is subdivided into innumerable curved fields. In a positively curved space, stars would move closer the farther they are from the eyes of the observer. This phenomena may be noted in looking upward at a large dome containing equally spaced electric lights. As to a negatively curved space, Gamow has pointed out the reverse of this phenomena is observed in looking up from a valley and noting the greater spread between trees as our gaze moves up the side of the mountain. Hence, based on this observation, the curve of cosmic space appears to be negative, as the space between the island universes appear to become greater the farther away they are from the supposed center of the galactic universe.

Under the pulsating theory, the various stars will extend their gravitational fields while they are expanded and in a hot condition, and draw in their gravitational field as they cool off. The diminishing of the stars will increase their density, in turn producing heat and pressure causing them again to expand. Thus the universe pulsates like the heart in pumping blood to and from the tissues of the body. It has been estimated that one pulsation takes billions of years, and that at present the universe is inhaling.

The third hypothesis is the so-called *"steady-state" theory.* This theory was first expounded by Hermann Bondi and Thomas Gold, both young English cosmogonists. They now have supporters to their theory. The theory was formulated as the result of their endeavor to solve the problem of the receding galaxies. They accepted the premise of Lemaitre that the red shift of the spectral lines was caused by an actual recession of the galaxies. They also took into consideration Einstein's theory that no body can reach the speed of light as the mass at that speed reaches the value of infinity. Hence, they considered that the galaxies as they approach that speed disappear. New matter is progressively created to make up for the galaxies disappearing over the "brim," like a continually overflowing fountain of water. In this connection it is comforting to learn that the present estimated speed of our Milky-Way in space is not faster than several hundred miles per second. As the speed increases and approaches the speed of light, or 186,000 miles per second, we may expect to become magnetic waves at the edge of the universe, and thus form new matter.

Dr. Fred Hoyle, a Cambridge astronomer and a former strong supporter of the "steady-state" theory, has recently retreated from his position in view of recent astronomical evidence which appears to favor the "big-bang" theory.

Quite recently (1964) astronomers have reported an exciting discovery (by means of a combination of optical and radio astronomy) of a series of so-called "lighthouses" at the distant edges of the universe. They shine with an incredible light of one-billion sun-powers. They are not stars or galaxies but new wonders of the heavens. So far they have located about twenty-five of them, and have christened them "quassars," a contraction of quasi-stellar. Of course, this discovery has greatly excited the astronomers and astrophysicists.

As has occurred so many times before in all fields of research, it will no doubt develop that the final theory accepted will incorporate the views of all three theories.

XIX.

TWENTIETH CENTURY PHILOSOPHY

Introduction

Philosophy in the twentieth century is represented by a rather motley group. There is the predominantly American school, Pragmatism, represented by such men as Peirce, James and Dewey. There is the French Existentialist school led by Sartre. Sartre was influenced by Kierkegaard, a Danish clergyman of the nineteenth century and the original founder of the school. Sartre was also influenced by such men as Nietzsche, Jaspers, and Heidegger. Then there is the school which first called themselves Logical Positivists, originally made up of former physicists of the so-called Vienna Circle. They subsequently changed the name to Logical Analysts, then Logical Empiricists and finally Scientific Empiricists. They included such men as G. E. Moore, Bertrand Russell, Rudolph Carnap, and Ludwig Wittgenstein. Finally there were the so-called "whole" philosophies. In this group we have such representatives as Jacques Maritain, Marx and Engels, Santayana, Croce, Bergson, Husserl, and Whitehead.

We shall briefly consider the various philosophies sponsored by the foregoing group, beginning with Pragmatism.

Pragmatism

Although Charles Sanders Peirce (1830-1914) put forth the original basis for pragmatism, it was William James (1842-1910) who generally made it known by his application of the concept in support of religion, and in the establishment of a practical meaning for truth.

Charles Peirce never published a book on philosophy during his lifetime. He was born in Cambridge, Mass. His father was a distinguished mathematician, and his son Charles also became a mathematician at his father's encouragement.

Briefly the main concept he espoused was a theory of scientific meaning. He suggested that all ordinary categorical singular statements should be restated in an "if-then" form, such as: "If operation O were performed on this, then E would be experienced." To illustrate, let us take the statement: "This is hard." According to Peirce's suggestion, the statement should be restated in an "if-then" form, such as: "If one were to try to scratch this, one would not succeed."

In short, there are three main aspects in his doctrine: (1) restatement of the original singular statement in hypothetical form; (2) his insistence that the "if" clause specify something for the experimenter to do; and (3) his insistence that the "then" clause should indicate what the experimenter should experience or observe provided test conditions are followed.

In his essay "How to Make our Ideas Clear" Peirce states his conception of truth and reality as follows: "The opinion which is fated to be ultimately agreed to by all who investigate, is what we mean by the truth, and the object represented in this opinion is the real. That is the way I would explain reality."

Peirce objected strenuously to the use of his method by James in his theory of truth, and thereafter Peirce insisted his method should be called "pragmaticism" rather than "pragmatism."

William James, the pragmatic philosopher of religion, started out as a physician, and then turned to psychology. In 1890 he wrote his famous work "Principles of Psychology." He finally completed his career as a philosopher, espousing Pragmatism applied particularly to religion. He reacted against being "fenced in" by the dogmatists of the nineteenth century science, that anything outside of the particular fields of science is of no importance or of no significant meaning. He used the method of Peirce to support his ideas. James was an admirer of Bergson; it is easy to recognize the similarity of thinking in James' psychological "stream of consciousness" and Bergson's main concepts of intuition and duration.

229

James published in 1907 his Pragmatism. In this treatise he divided philosophers into two general classes:

The Tender-Minded	*The Tough-Minded*
Rationalistic	Empiricist
(going by "principles")	(going by "facts")
Intellectualistic	Sensationalistic
Idealistic	Materialistic
Optimistic	Pessimistic
Religious	Irreligious
Free-Willist	Fatalistic
Monistic	Pluralistic
Dogmatical	Sceptical

James states: "The pragmatic method is primarily a method of settling metaphysical disputes that otherwise might be interminable"—"to try to interpret each notion by tracing its respective consequences." He suggested that perhaps all scientific laws are only approximations, and their principal use is to summarize old facts for convenience in leading to new facts. He maintained that Pragmatism is "uncomfortable away from facts." His application of the pragmatic method to religion is revealed by his following statement: "If theological ideas prove to have a value for concrete life, they will be true, for pragmatism, in the sense of being good for so much. For how much more they are true, will depend entirely on their relations to the other truths that also have to be acknowledged. . . ." James' treatise on "Varieties of Religious Experience" and his essay "The Will to Believe" are two of his well-known works on religion. He later stated that his essay "The Will to Believe" should have been entitled "The Right to Believe."

James was a brilliant and original thinker, as well as a witty and charming personality. Even though Russell opposed his Pragmatism, he had a high regard for James as an individual; he considered him a "natural aristocrat."

John Dewey (1859-1952) applied the pragmatic method in ethics, education and politics. He chose to call his branch of Pragmatism, Instrumentalism or Experimentalism. It is unique to find three so-different contemporary personalities as Peirce, James and Dewey all espousing the same school of philosophy.

John Dewey was born in Burlington, Vermont. After receiving his PhD from Johns Hopkins in 1884, he became a professor of philosophy successively at the Universities of Minnesota, Michigan, Chicago and finally in 1904 at Columbia University. He was associated with Columbia at the time of his death in 1952.

He was a moral philosopher, educator and political thinker. As a philosopher he started out by making a serious study of Hegel. According to Dewey, Hegel left an enduring influence on him by emphasizing the historical, cultural, and social context of all human thought and activity.

His original field in philosophy was ethics. He then turned to logic, applying to that field the same methods he had worked out in the study of morality. New meanings are given to all categories by the new uses to which they are used in dealing with new problems. "If we put ourselves in the attitude of a scientific inquirer in asking what is the meaning of truth per se, there spring up before us those ideas which are actively employed in the mastery of new fields, in the organization of new materials. This is the essential difference between truth and dogma, between living and the dead and decaying. Above all it is in the region of moral truth that this perception stands out. Truth means the effective capacity of the idea 'to make good.'"

In education he formulated the tenets and guided so-called progressive education. In politics he was an ardent supporter of American democracy as against communism.

Existentialism

Jean-Paul Sartre was born 1905. He, along with certain other fellow Parisians, adopted for their particular philosophy the name Existentialism.

First let us review some of the early influences leading up to Existentialism. This philosophy had its roots in the writings of *Sören Kierkegaard* (1813-1855), a Danish religious thinker. Kierkegaard was brought up in a conservative Christian environment; he was a sensitive, frustrated personality. He reacted against the orthodox clericalism of Christianity as he also did against Hegelianism. He maintained, among other things, that God is beyond man and reason, that Christianity stands opposed to this world, and that Christian ethics is attainable only in eternity. Man, he asserts, is an egotist and hence must experience feelings such as boredom, anxiety and dread. Kierkegaard's existents appear to be "God-is," and persons or personalities. He seems to ignore physical objects as existents. Kierkegaard's

231

interest was in the development of the individual as a concrete human personality, through the successive stages of esthetics, the moral, and the religious. It will be recalled that Comte's three stages of development were the religious, the metaphysical, and the scientific stage. Thus for Kierkegaard the highest stage was the religious, while for Comte it was the scientific stage, a stage which Kierkegaard ignored.

Friedrich Nietzsche (1844-1900), another frustrated thinker, is credited with the discovery and description of "resentment," along with the concept of the "superman," which was to stamp him as an outstanding philosophical psychologist. His superman philosophy appeared to be a dominant and positive reaction to an intense feeling of frustration and inner emotional turmoil. His writings undoubtedly influenced the existentialist movement.

Karl Jaspers (1883-), a German thinker, conceded the influence of both Kierkegaard's and Nietzsche's philosophical psychology on his thinking. Following a scientific method, he analyzed the possible attitudes of man toward the world around him, the decisions with which he is faced as regards the problems of change, struggle, guilt and death, and the different manners in which man meets these problems. Jaspers objects to being labeled an existentialist. As he as a Catholic believes in the existence of God, he is naturally sympathetic toward Kierkegaard's existent "God-is."

Martin Heidegger (1889-) is another German philosopher who espouses existentialism and like Jaspers objects to being labeled an existentialist. As an atheist, he of course cannot accept Kierkegaard's existent "God-is." He received his basic philosophical training under the influence of Husserl's school of phenomenology, involving the structural analysis of so-called pure consciousness. He directed his attention to the methodical analysis and description of the conceptual meanings of single phenomena, devoting his efforts to analyzing human existence from the viewpoint of its historical and temporal aspects.

Jean-Paul Sartre was of course influenced by the writings of the foregoing thinkers. He was trained as an academic philosopher, and taught until 1942. He resigned to devote his time to writing, not only in philosophy but also as a novelist and playwright. He was active with the French underground resistance movement during World War II.

His basic contention is that each individual makes his own

personality by his choices, for which choices he and no one else is responsible. For this reason man carries the burden of the effects of these choices not only as concerns himself, but for the rest of humanity as well. As Sartre does not attempt to explain human existence on anything more fundamental, some existentialists speak of human existence as an "absurdity." This, of course, would not apply to Kierkegaard's true followers, who assert "God-is." Sartre asserts that the belief which all existentialists have in common is that existence comes before essence, that we must begin with the subjective. He attempts to explain the meaning of this by citing as an example the procedure in the manufacture of a paper-knife. The artisan must first have a conception of it and its purpose, and the pre-existent method of producing it. Hence, thinking, a subjective process, precedes the existence of the paper-knife. Production, in other words, preceded its existence. He goes on to say that man possesses first a "human nature," which is a universal conception of man. This conception of man precedes the man or personality of man as essence, which comes into being by man's own choices and actions. "Man is nothing else but that which he makes of himself. This is the first principle of existentialism." ". . . And, when we say that man is responsible for himself, we do not mean that he is responsible only for his individuality, but that he is responsible for all men." Sartre explains this assertion by stating that man is not only free as an individual subject, but that he cannot pass beyond this human subjectivity. Hence, when he chooses for himself, he chooses for all men. For instance when a man chooses between this or that he is really affirming the value of that which is chosen, something that is good or better for him. As man chooses always the better, nothing can be better for us unless it is better for everyone. As we fashion ourselves according to our own image, the image is really valid for all.

Sartre explains such existentialist terms as anguish, abandonment, and despair. Anguish is the feeling man experiences when he commits himself to anything, fully realizing that he is not only choosing what he will be but at the same time decides for all mankind. In other words, he cannot escape from a sense of profound responsibility. Sartre goes on to amplify this by stating that some would insist that man is only deciding for himself alone. The existentialist would ask, "What would happen if every one did so?" They would answer, "Everyone does not do so." To this Sartre goes on to state: "But in truth one ought always to ask oneself what would happen if everyone did as one is doing; nor can one escape from that disturbing thought except by a kind of self-deception. The man who lies in self-excuse by saying 'Everyone will not do it,' must be ill at ease in his conscience, for the act of lying implies the universal value which it denies."

The term "abandonment," a word often used by Heidegger, means only that it is necessary to assume the consequences of the belief to the very end that God does not exist. Sartre calls attention to Dostoevski's statement "If God did not exist, everything would be permitted." Sartre agrees that everything is permitted, and that this very fact makes man forlorn as he discovers that he is without an excuse. Sartre asserts that man is even responsible for his own passion. He also maintains that the Kantian ethic of never regarding another as a means but always as an end, is a difficult one to follow in practice.

Sartre states that "abandonment" results in "anguish." "Despair" is defined by him as an expression meaning "that we limit ourselves to a reliance upon that which is within our wills, or within the sum of the probabilities which render our action feasible."

Sartre, in short, maintains that man exists only in so far as he realizes himself. He is nothing other than the sum of his actions, for which he is fully responsible. "In life, a man commits himself, draws his own portrait and there is nothing but that portrait."

Scientific Empiricism

The so-called school of philosophical analysts, an analytic movement which generally characterizes current philosophy, has among its sponsors G. E. Moore, Bertrand Russell, Rudolph Carnap, and Ludwig Wittgenstein. It is the unity of science movement, and originated with the so-called Vienna Circle founded by *M. Schlick* (1882-1936). R. Carnap was a member of this original circle. At first they called themselves logical positivists, but now they seem to prefer the name logical empiricists, or scientific empiricists. They appear to have been influenced by: the ideas of the older empiricism and positivism espoused by such thinkers as Hume, Mill and Mach; the methodology of science as developed by scientists since the middle of the 19th century, such as Helmholtz, Einstein and others; and the symbolic logic and logical analysis of language as developed by such thinkers as Boole, Frege, Whitehead and Russell, and Wittgenstein. Russell was the first one of the group to combine these various aspects.

George Edward Moore (1873-) and Bertrand Russell (1872-) started out at the turn of the century as neo-realists, both being anti-Hegelianists. Russell speaks of two distinct elements in 20th century realism; the first, which involves the common-sense belief that physical objects such as the sun and its planets exist independently of the mind; and the second, by its highly uncommonsensical belief that such things as platonic ideas or universals also independently exist. Moore maintained that some idealists believed that trains had wheels only at stations. Under the second element would come the conception of "wheelhood." Russell, especially, argued for this particular element on the basis of the principle of "Occam's Razor," which stated that entities are not to be multiplied beyond necessity.

Both Moore and Russell later turned their attention toward philosophical analysis, Moore in the direction of analysis of language, and Russell in the realm of mathematical logic. Moore's formative training was mainly linguistic and classical, while Russell's background was principally mathematical. Moore's influence has been principally academic, as professor of philosophy at Cambridge, and also as editor for many years of one of the leading philosophical journals, Mind. Moore is considered a philosopher's philosopher.

Moore states in his treatise "Some Main Problems of Philosophy" that the first and most important problem of philosophy is: "To give a general description of the whole Universe. Many philosophers (though by no means all) have, I think, certainly tried to give such a description: and the very different descriptions which different philosophers have given are, I think, among the most important differences between them. And the problem is, it seems to me, plainly one which is peculiar to philosophy. There is no other science which tries to say: Such and such kinds of things are the only kinds of things that there are in the Universe, or which we know to be in it." Apparently when he wrote this he was occupied more with so-called whole philosophies and prior to his concentration on the problem of philosophical analysis. But then too, one must have something on which to apply the analytical method.

Bertrand Russell (1872-) is generally rated as one of the most brilliant thinkers of the present period. He is a mathematical logician, philosopher, and journalist. He was a utilitarian before the age of eighteen after reading the works of John Stuart Mill, but after going to Cambridge in 1890 and coming under the influence of Bradley of Oxford and McTaggert of Cambridge, he became an Hegelian. He and his friend, G. E. Moore, of course, later became anti-Hegelians. It may be assumed that Hegelianism served as good background material for their later analytic work.

Russell is a lover of liberty, and as an extra-curricular activity he delights in making iconoclastic statements. He, like other analysts, is hostile to speculative and obscurely written metaphysics. He avoids advancing a moral philosophy as such, or a so-called "rounded philosophy." For this reason he rejects the pragmatism of James and Dewey, and no doubt the later philosophy of his close friend Whitehead. He, like the other analysts, believes the proper activity of a philosopher is to analyze and clarify the meanings of such terms as right, wrong, evil and good. Russell, however, is blunt in expressing his opinions on moral questions, although he generally makes it clear at such times that he is not speaking as a philosopher.

Among the published works of his early days are the "The Principles of Mathematics" (1903), which was followed by "Principia Mathematica" (1910-13), a three-volume work produced in collaboration with A. N. Whitehead. "Our Knowledge of the External World" is another significant treatise, published originally in 1914 and revised in 1928.

His major contributions to philosophy are his discovery of the world of logic and his efforts to identify the methods of philosophy with those of the sciences. He also ingeniously solved the puzzle in Meinong's famous "golden mountain argument." He pointed out that the puzzle was created in the first place because of the poor syntax in the sentence "The golden mountain does not exist." He also solved the antinomies of Kant involving infinities and continuities, as well as the point-instant problem.

Lord Russell is an agnostic and a pacifist; and during World

War I he was imprisoned for his pacifism. His time during that period was well used, however, as it was devoted to study and writing. More recently he has engaged in demonstrations against the atomic bomb. As a layman and not as a philosopher he has stated—"I say that what the world needs is Christian love or compassion." Also, "If you wish to be happy yourself you must resign yourself to seeing others also happy."

There are very few philosophers, if any, whose style is so clear and understandable as Lord Russell's; it must be a reflection of his orderly thinking. Of course, when his emotional nature becomes involved, his opinions are as skewed as that of any other individual. At such times, however, he will generally make the statement that he is not speaking as a philosopher.

Rudolph Carnap (1891-) was born in Germany, and went to the University of Vienna in 1927. He became an active participant in the discussions of the Vienna Circle. At that time, as heretofore mentioned, the group called themselves logical positivists, but because the word positivism suggested Comte's school which they considered narrow, the name was later changed to logical empiricism. When Hitler came into power, his philosophical prejudices forced the school to move out of Central Europe. Carnap came to the United States in 1936 as professor at the University of Chicago.

Because such thinkers in America as Peirce, James and Dewey had previously created a favorable influence for science and logic, the logical empiricists were treated quite civilly in the United States. It should be recalled that the original group of logical positivists were formerly scientists who became philosophers; and naturally the old line metaphysical school of philosophers somewhat resented the instrusion of these former scientists. Carnap, himself, had a prior background in physics, and also was an accomplished logician.

To avoid the waste of time in disputing over meaningless questions among philosophers, Carnap as a logical empiricist espoused the empirical criterion of meaning. It disallowed as nonsense any scientific or philosophic statement which could not possibly be affirmed. This sounds like good pragmatism but Carnap would not concede that influence, as he argued against Dewey's ideas on ethics.

Carnap also insists on the recognition of a basic distinction

237

between empirical truths based on experience arrived at inductively, and the truths of mathematics which are a priori, true independent of experience.

He considers that much of metaphysics is cogitatively meaningless, such as Heidegger's "The nothing naughts," and certain so-called moral laws. He concedes, however, they may have an "emotive" meaning. In view of this situation, Carnap concludes that philosophy is neither more nor less than the logical analysis or syntax of science.

Ludwig Wittgenstein (1889-1951) devoted his philosophical efforts in the analysis of language, but ironically he is acknowledged generally as one of the most difficult philosophers to understand. Wittgenstein left Europe to go to Cambridge as lecturer in philosophy in 1929, becoming head of the department in 1939.

Moore had a high regard for Wittgenstein, who succeeded him in 1939 as department head. Moore attended his lectures, and while he considered Wittgenstein a most profound thinker, yet he had this to say about him: "He has made me think that what is required for the solution of philosophical problems which baffle me, is a method quite different from any which I have ever used, a method which he himself uses quite successfully, but which I have never been able to understand clearly enough to use it myself." Russell also knew Wittgenstein well in his early logical period and regarded him a genius. However, Russell lost touch with him after 1919, as he appeared to develop a sort of mystical tendency.

Wittgenstein's first treatise "Tractatus" (1921) used the logical symbolism revealing Russell's influence. In his second and final work "Philosophical Investigations" (1945) he more or less departed from logical symbolism and used the more common language of Moore.

He avoided too close ties with the Vienna Circle and preferred to be uncommitted to any school. However, the Vienna Circle was influenced by his "Tractatus." His main contribution to present-day philosophy has been his demonstration of the importance of a study of language and syntax. Philosophical language, he maintained, should mirror a one-one correspondence with the "world." He pointed out that much philosophy endeavors to say what can only be shown. His later work, which was out of sympathy with logical positivism, embodied a more relativistic approach to language, and his efforts were directed more to the inculcation of a therapeutic method, more or less of a pragmatic approach, toward the elimination of senseless philosophical questions. "Whereof one cannot speak, thereof one must be silent," is one of his dictums, as also his often stated slogan, "The meaning is the use." His analysis of the word "game," appearing in his "Philosophical Investigations," reveals his later philosophical tendencies. He likened this analysis leading to a "family" class, to spinning a thread; one fibre does not follow through the entire length, yet the intertwining of the various fibres results in the completed thread.

Sponsors of "Whole Philosophies"

Dialectical Materialism

Karl Marx and Friedrich Engels, while really philosophers of the 19th century, their philosophy (known as dialectical materialism), did not become popularized until Lenin froze and wove it into the structure of communism during the first part of the twentieth century. It was a political philosophy built around a theory of economics.

Karl Marx (1818-1883) received his education at the Universities of Berlin and Bonn. The genius of Marx, according to Lenin, "came as a direct and immediate continuation of the teaching of the greatest representatives of philosophy, political economy, and socialism." From Hegel's philosophy he received his dialectics, although in an inverted form; from Feuerbach he received his materialism. His contacts in Paris with French socialists influenced his social philosophy, and his sojourn in London, absorbing the political economic theories of Adam Smith and David Ricardo, gave him his background in political economy.

Marx emphasized in his economics the relation between classes of men, whereas the classical economists emphasized the relation of commodities. Marx has no parallel among the philosophers as to the impact of his philosophy on subsequent political and social structure. His social theory was mainly formulated around economic determinism and the class character of society. Because he dwelt on the abuses in the capitalistic society of the time, he naturally had a large following among the working class. This condition, coupled with his atheism, led to Marxism becoming almost a religion, or rather in fact a negative religion, and ironically this negative religion became even more emotional than any positive religion, hate being its basic emotion.

Marx maintained a strong belief in the dynamics of economic change setting the course of history, and for that reason he became increasingly reluctant to define his concepts. It seems reasonable therefore to conclude that if Marx were alive today, his philosophy and social theories would have been considerably modified. As he died before the Russian revolution, Lenin could "freeze" Marx's philosophy at the time of his death and use it for his (Lenin's) own practical political purposes in the organization of the Russian revolution.

The economic system which Marx first espoused he called Communism, which he later changed to Scientific Socialism. His principal work is "Das Kapital."

Friedrich Engels (1820-1895) came from a long line of German industrialists who were political conservatives and of religious orthodoxy. He had originally planned to become a poet but a period of service in the Prussian Army and his subsequent contacts with Marx in London led him to espousing the views of his new friend and devoting his life to the realization of Marx's plans for the working class. He became both the financial supporter and collaborator of Marx; and after the death of Marx edited the second and third volumes of "Das Kapital" of Karl Marx.

Engels' significant contribution was his theory of class morality. From his "Morality is Class Morality" we quote the following excerpts—"But when we see that the three classes of modern society, the feudal aristocracy, the bourgeoisie and the proletariat, each have their special morality, we can only draw the one conclusion, that men consciously or unconsciously, derive their moral ideas in the last resort from the practical relations on which they carry on production and exchange."
. . . "From the moment when private property in movable objects developed, in all societies in which this private property existed there must be this moral law in common: Thou shalt not steal. Does this law thereby become an eternal law? By no means. In a society in which the motive for stealing has been done away with, in which therefore at the very most only lunatics would even steal, how the teacher of morals would be laughed at who tried solemnly to proclaim the eternal truth: Thou shalt not steal!"

240

The present-day communist regimes would like Engels' prediction to be true among individuals within their own borders, but alas not. Likewise those nations bordering upon a communistic nation possessing large undeveloped land masses, would hope that they would be relatively free of aggressive activity by it, direct or via infiltration, but alas they too are sadly disappointed.

The economic system created by Marx and Engels seems to reflect a gap in their espousers' educational background, especially in the basic principles of dynamic psychology. To advocate a system whereby a nation of men surrenders its freedom to a bureaucracy of men in the naive belief that all their former problems stemmed from the evils of a particular economic class indeed appears to reflect such lack of knowledge. The basic cause of evil, as dynamic psychology reveals, lies in the individual self-centeredness of men as presently constituted, and when a bureaucracy of such men are given dictatorial powers and placed over a nation, woe unto its citizens. Moreover, man requires a certain amount of freedom for his choices to keep alive his incentive for progressive effort. (Mankind's creator allowed for man's freedom of choice and the wide world in which to exercise it. It would appear therefore that if man does not value it enough to fight for it, he deserves to lose that freedom.)

True it may be charged that selfish bureaucracies exist in other systems as well, but at least the long-suffering citizenry can periodically "kick the scoundrels out" without the need of a bloody revolution.

Engels labored under the false notion that in a communistic society stealing would occur only among "lunatics." He apparently was not aware of the existence of men, who incidentally are not considered lunatics, of whom it may be said "insist on crawling under the tent even though they hold a free ticket to the circus in their back-pocket."

Vladimir I. Ulianov (Lenin) (1870-1924) was the leader of the Bolshevik party in 1917 when it seized political power in Russia, thereby beginning a new chapter in history both as affecting Russia and the world at large. Lenin was a great natural revolutionary, and devoted approximately twenty years in the process of organizing the Russian revolution.

Lenin made an intensive study of the strategy of civil war, especially the tactics of sabotage, of the weak points in the arguments of opposing groups, and of the psychology of the

Russian people. He apparently capitalized upon, but kept secret, his acquired knowledge of the Russian people, for there is no indication that he subsequently established a chair of Dynamic Psychology in a Russian university. He rather seized upon and encouraged experiments with animals involving the conditioned-reflex approach of Pavlov.

Lenin early realized that he must have a philosophical base, a need which was especially urgent for he was an avowed atheist and hence had only a negative religious base. Therefore Lenin quickly seized upon the philosophy of Marx and Engels as a base consistent for his purposes. Because Marx was dead he was able to establish Marxian socialism as a rigid system and the ruling dogma in Russia. He stated that Marx sufficiently explained the world and it was up to him (Lenin) to change it.

He forthwith built himself up as a mythical infallible personality for he realized that the continuance of his leadership depended on his skill in cowing critics and ability to maintain discipline. The dogmatism of a positive religion cannot "hold a candle" to the dogmatism of Leninism. While Lenin himself made practical temporary deviations to attain his ultimate ends, yet any deviations from his rigid system set up on Marxian socialism by anyone else were considered by him as heretical, resulting in the elimination of the heretic.

Lenin both attacked and placed on the "index" the writings of such men as Richard Avenarius (1843-1896), whose philosophy incidentally placed emphasis on the significance of man as an individual. Ernst Mach (1838-1916) was given a like treatment for like reasons. Under Leninism the individual becomes subordinate to the State, and the State is a self-perpetuated hierarchy—not unlike the so-called feudal aristocracy mentioned by Engels. Khrushchev, who in his later life traveled extensively, gradually became aware of the weaknesses of the system created by Lenin and endeavored to institute reforms giving the individual Russian citizen more incentive, which meant more freedom. The hierarchy became uneasy and soon ousted Khrushchev.

The weaknesses of atheistic communism are that it freezes an ideology around a state hierarchy, takes away the motivating forces of the individual, and leaves him frustrated, stranded and alone in a deterministic universe.

If Marx and Engels were alive today and were shown the Berlin Wall, they would stare incredulously, especially upon learning that it was hastily erected to prevent the proletariat of their "dream society" from escaping to the "evil society" of capitalism.

But it is over-reaction which brings the pendulum back the sooner to sanity, so let us withhold judgment, for evil at times serves some ultimate good purpose.

Jacques Maritain (1882-   ) was born in Paris and studied at the Sorbonne with H. Bergson. He was converted to Catholicism in 1906. He subsequently studied biology with H. Driesch for two years, and Thomistic philosophy with Father Clérissac. Thereafter he became an ardent follower of the philosophy of St. Thomas, stressing its adaptations to modern problems. Yet Maritain does not maintain that the Christian Middle Ages should be considered as a necessary model of human civilization. He does maintain, however, that the value of the human person is founded upon an order created by God and which strives for God. He considered the Church as the refuge of sinners and not the home of the elect.

Maritain's view of the Creator's purpose is reflected by his following words: "The divine plan is not a scenario prepared in advance in which free subjects would play parts and act as performers . . . On the contrary, everything is improvised, under the eternal and immutable direction of the almighty Stage Manager."

Benedetto Croce (1866-1952), another philosopher of the twentieth century belonging to this group, spent his early child-hood in Naples. He was left an orphan following the death of his parents in an earthquake in 1883. His parents were wealthy landowners, leaving their son relatively free of financial worries. He was brought up by his grandfather, whose taste in philosophy influenced his grandson to make that field his career. Croce, however, found time also to engage in political activity, serving in the Italian senate and holding several cabinet posts. Being unsympathetic to fascism, he went into retirement when fascism came into power in Italy.

Although Croce criticized Hegel's philosophy, as also Kant's, he more than any other 20th century philosopher remained closer to Hegelianism. Croce was an idealist, and hence reacted strongly against empiricism and positivism. Douglas Ainslee, in his introduction to Croce's "Aesthetic," states: "The philosopher feels that he has a great mission which is nothing less than the leading back of thought to belief in the spirit, deserted by so many for crude empiricism and positivism. His view of philosophy is that it sums up all the higher activities, including religion, and that in proper hands it is able to solve any problem. But there is no finality about problems, the solution of one leads to the posing of another, and so on. Man is the maker of life, and his spirit ever proceeds from a lower to a higher perfection."

Croce considers all human experience an historical experience, and hence philosophy and history are identical. His "Aesthetic" defines art as an expression of sentiment, as a language. He regards all history as contemporaneous. His elaboration of pure concepts entirely appropriate to historical experience is unequaled in philosophy.

Croce also identifies the subject-matter of philosophy as a spiritual activity, which he divides into intellectual activity and practical activity. He sub-divides intellectual activity into two forms, intuition and abstraction. Practical activity is sub-divided into economic and ethical activity. Intuition produces the discipline aesthetics, which studies the concept of beauty. Out of abstraction came the discipline of logic, which analyzes the concept of truth. Economic activity produces the discipline economics, with its concept of utility. And finally ethical activity, which attends to the study of the concept of goodness.

George Santayana (1863-1952) was an American philosopher and poet. He was born of Spanish parents in Madrid, Spain. After being graduated in 1886 at Harvard, he became an instructor and later served as a professor of philosophy at that university from 1907 to 1912. Thereafter, he lived in Paris. The "Life of Reason" was his principal philosophical work. He called himself an atheist and yet a Catholic. While he rejoiced in the poetry and the ritual of its religious ceremony, yet he rejected its theology, a position somewhat similar to that of Whitehead.

While he did not agree with Croce that history was the essence of philosophy, he did believe that a philosopher might use the works of historians to suit his particular preference. He gave moral philosophy a central position between Moore's tendency toward analysis and Croce's identification of philosophy with history.

His general thesis is that consciousness reveals reality rather than distorts it. Reality so revealed is an infinity of essences (Platonic ideas), subsisting by themselves; some of which are entertained by minds, and some enacted in a non-mental substratum or matter, giving them concrete existence. Whereas this substratum cannot be rationally proved, it is assumed in action by so-called animal faith. Matter is external to and independent of consciousness; it is extended and is capable of becoming conscious. It is actuated by efficient causation and predetermined by prior situations.

Matter may become conscious in organic bodies. Mind, while being unsubstantial, is an activity of the body and is not causally effective, but entertains and contemplates essences both existing and non-existing.

His work "The Life of Reason" is in five volumes and covers the subjects of commonsense, society, religion, art and science. It is a critical survey of the transformation of man's natural impulses into high ideals.

As to religion he considers it an allegorical and metaphorical rendering of moral truth. In his third volume of this work, there appears the following excerpts revealing his views on this subject: "Experience has repeatedly confirmed that well-known maxim of Bacon's that a 'little philosophy inclineth man's mind to atheism, but depth in philosophy bringeth men's minds about to religion.' ". . . "Even the heretics and atheists, if they have had profundity, turn out after a while to be forerunners of some new orthodoxy. What they rebel against is a religion alien to their nature; they are atheists only by accident, and relatively to a convention which inwardly offends them, but they yearn mightily in their own souls after the religious acceptance of a world interpreted in their own fashion." . . . "The Life of Reason is the seat of all ultimate values. Now the history of mankind will show us that whenever spirits at once lofty and intense have seemed to attain the highest joys, they have envisaged and attained them in religion. Religion would therefore seem to be a vehicle or a factor in rational life, since the ends of rational life are attained by it." . . . "Religions are many, reason one. Religion consists of conscious ideas, hopes, enthusiasms, and objects of worship; it operates by grace and flourishes by prayer. Reason, on the other hand, is a mere principle or potential order, on which, indeed, we may come to reflect, but which exists in us ideally only, without variation or stress of any kind." . . . "And yet this struggling and changing force of religion seems to direct man toward something eternal."

Edward Husserl (1859-1938) and *Alexius Meinong* were

pupils of Franz Brentano (1838-1917). He stimulated his pupils to initiate new philosophies devoted to studying objects of reference or so-called "intensional objects." Meinong called his particular contribution in that direction "The Theory of Objects," while Husserl called his "Transcendental Phenomenology." If Wittgenstein were to have broken up the varieties of phenomenology, he would have found as many kinds as he found in the "game" family.

Husserl's philosophy took hold better than that of his colleague Meinong who, incidentally, is famed for his "golden mountain" argument which Russell analyzed. Husserl's philosophy greatly influenced both Heidegger and Sartre. He reserved for philosophy, as against that of the sciences, that function of seeing the structure of things by intuition. Phenomenology is defined as the descriptive analysis of subjective processes. Psychology and phenomenology differ in that psychology sets up causal laws to explain what phenomenology merely describes. Phenomenology is said to be pure insofar as the phenomenologist distinguishes the subjective from the objective and does not investigate either the genesis of subjective phenomena or their connection with somatic and environmental circumstances.

Husserl has this to say with regard to the so-called world of "natural standpoint." "Our first outlook upon life is that of natural human beings, imaging, judging, feeling, willing, 'from the natural standpoint.'"

As to the cogito, he has this to say: "In the natural urge of life I live continually in this fundamental form of all 'wakeful' living, whether in addition I do or do not assert the cogito, and whether I am or am not reflectively concerned with the Ego and the cogitare." . . . "Perhaps I am busied with pure numbers and the laws they symbolize: nothing of this sort is present in the world about me, this world of 'real fact.'" . . . "The arithmetical world is there for me only when and so long as I occupy the arithmetical standpoint." . . . "The two worlds (natural and arithmetical) are present together but disconnected, apart, that is, from their relation to the Ego, in virtue of which I can freely direct my glance or my acts to the one or to the other."

As to the "other" ego-subject he has this to say: "Whatever holds good for me personally, also holds good, as I know, for all other men whom I find present in my world-about-me." . . . "But this in such wise that I apprehend the world-about-them as

246

the world-about-me objectively as one and the same world which differs in each case only through affecting consciousness differently."

It is quite obvious that Husserl never passed through an Hegelian stage as most English philosophers did during this period. He began as a realist and anti-idealist from Brentano's influence; then he became a so-called transcendental idealist, and finally a great influence on the existentialists.

Henri Bergson (1859-1941) was a French philosopher of Jewish descent, born in Paris the same year as both Dewey and Husserl were born.

Bergson's philosophy was a reaction against the crude and dogmatic naturalism, the static and mechanistic materialism which reached its height during the second half of the nineteenth century.

So-called "real time" to Bergson is not time as conceived by science, but duration. "Pure duration is nothing but a succession of qualitative changes which melt into and penetrate one another, without precise outlines, without any tendency to externalize themselves in relation to one another, without any affiliation to number." For practical purposes, science and common sense externalize this time and separate it into discrete moments in a line. Real time or duration is experienced only when we withdraw ourselves from our practical interests. Then "we no longer measure duration, but we feel it." Duration rather than intuition is the main doctrine of his philosophy, the very "substance" of philosophic tradition.

Bergson was the first philosopher to try to give the term "intuition" a scientific basis. His conception of that term represents a fusion of scientific objectivity and artistic directness.

Intellect, he states, is unable to do justice to the nature of life and of spirit, inasmuch as the intellect is a function of life developed to deal with what is spatial alone. Instinct would enable us to understand life except that instinct does not aim at understanding but is directed towards a particular concrete object. Intuition, however, is what is needed, as it is an "instinct which has become disinterested, self-conscious, capable of reflecting on its object and of enlarging it indefinitely." Bergson believes that all previous philosophies have been constructed by intellect alone.

Some of the characteristic phrases, other than that of dura-

247

tion, appearing in his philosophy are "vital impetus," or "elan vital," and "creative evolution." Bergson considers that life is an unceasing, continuous, undivided process, a sort of cosmic movement of which we are expressions, the motivator being this so-called "elan vital."

One of the chief contributions of Bergson's philosophy was his defense of freedom. He offered the theory of creative evolution as the only alternative to mechanism, that we can characterize and explain evolution by reference to purely physical and chemical transformations, and also to teleology, in short, the view that everything proceeds by prearranged plan.

One can appreciate from the foregoing the reason Bertrand Russell has difficulty in appreciating Bergson's philosophy, for how can one analyze life in motion? The point-instant is essential for analysis of nature, as in mathematics.

Alfred N. Whitehead (1861-1947) was an English mathematician and philosopher. He was a Fellow of Trinity College, Cambridge, from 1911 to 1914, and Professor of Applied Mathematics at the Imperial College of Science and Technology at London to 1924. From 1924 until his retirement in 1938 he served as Professor of Philosophy at Harvard University. He wrote certain treatises on mathematics prior to collaborating with Russell in their classic joint work on the derivation of mathematics from logic, published in three volumes as Principia Mathematica (1910-1913).

Whitehead is the only outstanding philosopher of the twentieth century to pass from the field of logical analysis to a so-called "whole philosophy." His logical and mathematical phase was during his stay at Cambridge and London, while his metaphysical phase occurred during the period beginning at sixty-three years of age and while connected with Harvard at Cambridge, Mass. It was at Cambridge, Mass., that he produced his "Science and the Modern World" (1925), "Process and Reality" (1929), and his "Adventures of Ideas" (1933).

All of these works at Harvard were devoted to his exposition of his so-called philosophy of organism. One cannot but suspect that the influence of Harvard, and of American life in general, had something to do with his shift from a philosophy of analysis to a philosophy of synthesis. It must also be conceded, however, that the conclusions of the physicists in their analysis of the atom raised questions in his mind as to the adequacy of the old conceptions. His mind apparently was much younger than his years to change over from a universal algebra to a universal biology, as he did in his philosophy of organism. Modern physics has replaced the conception of empty space to the idea of a field of force and incessant activity. As Whitehead put it, "Matter has been identified with energy, and energy is sheer activity." The modern physicists' picture of the universe of "bare activity" leaves the philosopher the task of answering the larger questions: "Activity for what, producing what? Activity involving what?"

In his "Modes of Thought" (1938) Whitehead states, "The status of life in nature . . . is the modern problem of philosophy and of science." "The very meaning of life is in doubt. When we understand it, we shall also understand its status in the world. But its essence and its status are alike baffling."

Here are some of his further thoughts in his own words: "The first step in the argument must be to form some concept of what life can mean. Also we require that the deficiencies in our concept of physical nature should be supplied by its fusion with life. And we require that, on the other hand, the notion of life should involve the notion of physical nature. Now as a first approximation the notion of life implies a certain absoluteness of self-enjoyment."

He goes on to say: "The process of self-creation is the transformation of the potential into the actual, and the fact of such transformation includes the immediacy of self-enjoyment."

Whitehead states that it is nonsense to conceive of nature as a static fact. Another character required in a description of life according to Whitehead is "aim."

"All philosophy," he says, "is an endeavor to obtain a self-consistent understanding of things observed." It must possess a coherent self-consistency as well as elucidate the things observed.

Whereas sense-perceptions are without doubt the most prominent in our conscious experience, yet "it is very superficial in its disclosure of the universe." He goes on to say that science conceived as relying on only sense-perception is bankrupt.

He maintains that we are directly conscious of our purposes as directive of our actions; otherwise no doctrine could in any sense be acted upon.

Whitehead makes a rough division of six types of so-called occurrences in nature: (1) human existence, body and mind; (2)

249

all sorts of animal life other than human; (3) all vegetable life; (4) single living cells; (5) all large-scale inorganic aggregates; and (6) all happenings on an infinitesimal scale disclosed by modern physical analysis.

As regards all the foregoing six types, all function within nature, all influence each other, and lead on to each other.

As to his thoughts on the body-mind relation, he claims a unity, namely, that the human individual is one fact, body and mind. He also maintains that the functioning of our body has a wider influence than just the producer of sense-experience. The emotional state, he goes on to explain, arises just because the heart, lungs, bowels, kidneys, and the like, are operating without our being directly conscious of their operation.

The notion of the soul is vaguer than the definition of our body with its continual exchange of molecules with its environment. The soul "has to leap gaps in time. We sleep or we are stunned. And yet it is the same person who recovers consciousness."

He states that "the weakness of the epistemology of the eighteenth and nineteenth centuries was that it based itself purely upon a narrow formulation of sense-perception," and thus excluded the really fundamental factors of our experience.

In the words of Niels Bohr, "we are both the actors and spectators in the great drama of existence." Whitehead as his conception of existence has this to say: "Existence is activity ever merging into the future. The aim of philosophic understanding is the aim at piercing the blindness of activity in respect to its transcendent functions." He went on to say: "Philosophy begins in wonder. And, at the end, when philosophic thought has done its best, the wonder remains." His reaction in this respect would seem to be somewhat similar to that of Dr. Einstein who is quoted as having said: "The most beautiful and most profound emotion we can experience is the sensation of the mystical. It is the sower of all true science. He to whom this emotion is a stranger, who can no longer wonder and stand rapt in awe, is as good as dead. To know that what is impenetrable to us really exists, manifesting itself as the highest wisdom and the most radiant beauty which our dull faculties can comprehend only in their most primitive forms—this knowledge, this feeling is at the center of true religiousness."

XX.

INTERMEDIATE GENERAL REMARKS UNDER PART TWO

So far in Part II of this treatise we have reviewed man's progressive creation of his so-called intellectual culture. At this point it should again be re-emphasized that the same identical human organism as pictured in Part I hereof functioned at the very dawn of both philosophy and science as at the present time. The only advantage which a later generation had over a prior one was the knowledge of the scientific discoveries and philosophical advances which had taken place between the two time periods; the tool for analyzing and correlating was identical.

It would appear that the advances in science have been discrete or discontinuous according to its periodic discoveries; in other words, the quantum theory appears to have been applicable. The advances in philosophy, whereas they too may appear discrete, yet they would seem to have been initially the product more to intuitional activity—a certain feeling and intuitional reaching for the truth, prior to the subsequent reasoning process of putting these resultant intuitions into a logical and coherent whole. Much as some will dispute the statement, philosophy and science make an essential team in solving the mysteries of existence. The speculative philosopher ventures out where a scientist has hit a so-called blind alley. The scientist at such times appears to want to say: "Mr. Philosopher, you 'stick your neck out' and suggest a possible new tangent, as I do not want to endanger my professional scientific standing." Periodically, of course, the speculative philosopher must readjust and modify his philosophy to the subsequent verified facts of the scientist.

Conservative philosophers, of course, will not venture a philosophy except one based on so-called scientific facts or hypotheses. However, such philosophical conservatives are sometimes left stranded in the next generation because of the discovery of new so-called facts. However, the methods used by the scientists with their hypotheses suggested by verified facts, and the methods of speculative philosophers acting as both generalizers and pioneering scouts into the unknown vastnesses, are quite comparable to that of the one-celled animals with their trial and error activity of alternate extension-advancement, or extension-withdrawal of their pseudopodia, according as the medium is alkaline or acid—agreeable or disagreeable.

As the present logical positivists or empiricists were formerly scientists (mathematicians or physicists), their philosophies are "withdrawal" philosophies rather than "trail blazers." Bergson's "elan vital" and "duration" school, as well as the pragmatic and existentialist schools, are reactions against this "withdrawal" type of philosophy, as they are again "extending the pseudopodia" of knowledge into new fields, even under the sharp criticism of the logical positivists. Yet both types are essential, as the observation of the Amoeba Proteus has taught us.

one another. The proton is known as the nucleus of the atom. The electron, of negligible mass, is pictured circling the proton of the hydrogen atom at great speed and at a relatively great distance from its nucleus, thereby creating the atom's form, unit volume, or occupied space if you like. If we picture the nucleus of the hydrogen atom as a cherry, its electron, like a mosquito, would be a half-mile away flying at great speed around it. The atom comes into being by the marriage, we might say, of the proton and the electron.

As we go up the atomic scale, the number of protons increases within the nucleus, with a corresponding increase in the number of circling electrons within fixed orbits around the nucleus. This progressive increase in the number of protons and electrons within the atom results in atoms of differing characteristics. Various theories have been expounded to explain why an atom nucleus does not explode if it is true that protons, or positive charges, repel one another. One novel theory is the so-called "tennis ball" theory. This theory postulates the analogy of a tennis game going on inside the nucleus: mesons, being the tennis balls, are volleyed back and forth millions of times per second between the players—protons and neutrons (a combination of both protons and electrons). In that manner the balance is maintained between the protons within the nucleus. Truly we must agree with the statement of the Greek philosopher to the effect that nature is a study of more and more about less and less. The microcosm and its analysis would seem to be infinite, limited only by man's analytic tools.

But be that as it may, we find that the electrons progressively arrange themselves in regular orbits around the nucleus as the number of protons increases. The number of electrons in the outer orbit of each atom determines its reaction to other atoms of a differing number of outer orbit electrons. The resulting reaction of mutual attraction, neutrality or repulsion of atoms is known as a chemical reaction. If such atoms attract one another, we have the next higher form of inorganic organization of matter, the molecule, which is the product of the marriage of positively and negatively charged atoms. There was and is no way of predicting the product of such combinations. For instance, knowledge of the nature of both the hydrogen and the oxygen atoms would be of no use in predicting that two hydrogen and one oxygen atom would produce water. Such knowledge is gradually accumulated by trial and error. For that reason the science of chemistry owes much to the labor of the early alchemists who tried diligently to convert cheaper metals into gold.

Carbon, the so-called sociable atom, with its four negative charges, appears to be the core of most molecules; hence the first matricidal society. Oxygen, with its two negative charges, also serves as a molecular core.

The foregoing molecular phenomena occur in the world of chemistry.

The Organic or Biological Stage

From the world of chemistry we enter the next higher stage of nature study, namely that of botany and zoology. We find in so-called living matter, that is, self-producing organisms, practically all molecular forms, which in turn contain nearly all known atoms. Three-fourths of the atoms in living matter consist of oxygen atoms, approximately ten percent of hydrogen, another ten of carbon, with nitrogen a little over two percent, and the many remaining elements making up the balance.

Biologists have speculated on the inception of life to have occurred some 2,000 million years ago, in the warm shallow primeval seas swarming with carbon chains. In this warm "soup," nucleic acid and protein molecules united to form the larger molecules called nucleo-proteins. These nucleoproteins were pretty much naked genes destined to form the nucleus of the first living cells, the protista, which are unitary cells which gradually developed into the cell made up of the nucleus, the centrosome, cytoplasm and cell membrane. The protista, through some unexplainable process, first branched off to develop chlorophyll, found only in plant cells. It was only after this branch was established that the animal branch appeared on the scene, as it is dependent on the plant branch for its carbohydrates.

Some biologists will classify living organisms into the following four groups:

1—Plants, which are synthesizers of carbohydrates from carbon dioxide and water, using the radiation of the sun to supply the necessary energy for the so-called photosynthetic process;

2—Nitrogen-fixing Bacteria, who extract nitrogen from

255

the air and bring it into the soil for the sustenance
of plants;

3—Fungi, whose function it is to break down dead plant
and animal organisms again to useful rebuilding
forms;

4—Animals, who rely on the foregoing organisms for
their sustenance.

Other biologists will classify the foregoing four groups into
only two divisions, placing group one, two and three under
Division 1—Plants, with Division 2 comprised of Animals. For
purposes of brevity, we shall follow the two-division classification, and shall proceed first with the plant division.

Plants or Metaphyta—The plant, with its miracle ingredient
chlorophyll, along with light energy from the sun, sets free
hydrogen (the simplest of the elements) from water, H_2O. However, hydrogen is at the same time the most potent of the elements, in fact the building blocks for all material creation. It
does not take hydrogen long to tie up with carbon dioxide to
give us carbohydrates, the source of energy for animal life. All
of this was made possible because of the mutual attraction of
opposites, first by the marriage of the proton and the electron
to give us the atom, followed by the marriage of atoms of
positive and negative valences to give us molecules.

The protista progressively developed into the various algae,
and multicellular fungi; liverworts and true mosses; ferns, club
mosses, and horsetails; and finally pine and fir trees known
technically as gymnospermae; and flowering plants which include nut trees, vegetables and cereals, all known technically
as angiospermae.

Animals—With carbohydrates made available by plants for
animals, there progressively developed the following groups of
animal life, requiring an estimated period of approximately two
billion years. They have been classified in ten different phyla, as
follows:

Protozoa—Single-celled animals;

Sponges—Clusters of cells, with harder skeletons; Mostly
marine life;

Polyps and Medusae—Many celled, with bag-like shape.
Mostly marine life;

256

Flatworms—Ribbon-like bodies;

Roundworms—Cylindrical bodies without segments;

Segmented Worms—More or less cylindrical bodies, segmented and with unjointed legs;

Echinoderms—Body usually with five divisions; spiny shells,—all marine life;

Arthropoda—With bodies segmented, legs jointed; considerable chitin in skin; includes crustacea, horseshoe crabs, arachnids, millipeds, centipedes, and insects;

Molluscs—Includes snails, clams, slugs, octopuses—generally with external shells;

Vertebrates—Bony skeleton; includes fish, amphibia, reptiles, birds, and mammals.

Comparative Behavior of Certain Animals as to Reflexes, Instincts and Intelligence

Plants have been excluded in comparative behavior as active movements are hardly necessary in organisms which secure their nutrition by photosynthesis or as parasites and saprophytes. Our attention shall thus be devoted to some of the species of organisms who actively must seek their existence in their environment.

In this connection it is well first to clearly define our basic terms, as follows:

A *reflex* may be defined as "an immediate, unlearned response to a specific stimulus."—Harriman;

An *instinct* is "often defined as a complex pattern of unconditioned reflexes or as an unlearned inner drive to biologically purposeful action."—Harriman;

Woodworth differentiates a reflex from an instinct as follows: "Typically, a reflex is a prompt reaction. It occurs at once, on the occurrence of the stimulus, and is done with. What is characteristic of the instinct, on the contrary, is the persisting 'tendency,' set up by a given stimulus and directed toward a result which cannot be instantly accomplished."

Intelligence may be considered as "a common capacity (or group of capacities) underlying, in greater or lesser amounts, specific activities" (Spearman), involving "the ability to maintain a direction, adaptability, and auto-criticism." (Binet).

Animals of different species have correspondingly different

instincts. The reason ascribed by authorities for this is that they are differently equipped with sense organs, motor organs, nerves and nerve centers.

Protozoa

In tracing the primitive beginnings of the reflexes and instincts, which are the roots of man's personality, we find among the one-celled animals, the aquatic organism protozoa, a predominance of reflex action, a complete reflexive response to any stimulus from its environment.

In satisfying its primary need of food, the most important response mechanisms of these one-celled animals are its means of locomotion, such as cilia or pseudopodia. When a potential food particle is contacted, digestive enzymes are secreted. The food is treated and absorbed into its body through its cell wall, a semi-permeable membrane.

As to self-protective reactions, the principal one is the avoiding reaction to a harmful chemical or temperature medium. Active fighting is probably rare as their principal enemies appear to be in the inorganic world. Colonizing or forming of aggregates seems to be a form of protective behavior against an unfavorable environment. Encystment (crawling into one's shell) also is generally regarded as another form of native response of these one-celled animals to unfavorable conditions.

As to reproductive behavior, the primitive mating response, conjugation, has been observed occasionally to take place between two protozoa, during which an interchange of nuclear material takes place. However, this act is not directly associated with fission, which is a splitting of the nucleus and cytoplasm, with the end result of two similar organisms in place of one. This phenomenon occurs with great frequency and seems to be determined by the growth stage of the organism.

As to group behavior, the tendency to colonize may be considered as a general behavior pattern of these one-celled animals. The persistent tendency of the protozoa appears to be to maintain itself in as favorable an environment as possible for its immediate bodily needs and for its self-perpetuation. It has been observed that protozoa will modify its initial reactions in an otherwise unfavorable environment when forced to do so.

Fish

The next aquatic animal which we shall consider is the fish. It should be kept in mind, however, that considerable time has elapsed between the one-celled intracellular organized protozoa and the appearance of the many-celled and comparatively complex intercellular organized fish. The fish appeared on the scene approximately five hundred million years ago.

The behavior of fish is largely a matter of instinctive mechanisms. These animals are well equipped with reflex mechanisms, but lack a highly developed brain. There is some modifiability of behavior. For instance a pike, separated by a sheet of glass from minnows, will dart at the minnows only to run its nose into the glass. Eventually, however, it will discontinue this activity, even to the extent of leaving the minnows unmolested when the glass is removed.

The hunger drive appears to be by far the strongest motivating factor in the behavior of fish. This drive appears to account for the gregarious tendencies of schooling, as fish will school at the best eating grounds. However, when the spawning season comes, generally once a year, some fish will stop eating entirely until the eggs are laid by the female and fertilized by the male. During the spawning season certain species, such as the salmon, are oriented to swim against the current to shallow water to lay its eggs. Eels, on the other hand, will swim from shallow water to lay its eggs in the ocean depths.

Mating occurs with certain species of fish. A male stickleback will build a rather neat and durable nest and conduct the female there to lay its eggs. After the eggs are fertilized the male will guard the nest until the eggs hatch. After hatching, no maternal or paternal interest appears to be taken by the parents toward the offspring.

Certain play activity has been observed with some fish. And, when two males are placed together, especially during the spawning season, active fighting will take place between them.

Amphibians

The amphibians, who appeared approximately 400,000,000 years ago, are the first animals to accomplish the transition from water to land vertebrates within their life cycle. In their larval stage, as the tadpole, they are fishlike and breathe through gill slits. As they reach the adult stage, they lose their fishlike tail and become land animals, using lungs for breathing, as the frog. They then hop about on land feeding on insects, worms, and such like.

Another order among the amphibians embraces the salamanders and newts; they do not lose their tail in the adult stage. They get about by running rather than hopping as do the toads and frogs, as their front and hind legs are practically the same length. Another interesting fact about salamanders is their regenerative capacity. If they lose a tail or a leg, another one grows in its place within a short time—a truly remarkable phenomena, in fact a phenomena which must give the materialistic determinist cause for convenient blindness.

The frogs and toads are largely herbivorous in their fishlike stage, but become carnivorous in their land stage. They have a tongue fastened in the forepart of the mouth with a sticky substance at the end of it. This is quite effective in catching insects and other food as the animal lies in wait.

Amphibians take in more water through the skin than by drinking. Many amphibians can take in large amounts of food, which enables them to survive months of starvation. The amphibians' principal means of defense is concealment by blending of their skin color with the background of their natural habitat. Some frogs, too, are adept at death-feinting as a defense mechanism.

Most amphibians lay their eggs in water. Frog-mating takes place during the migrating season, apparently determined by internal glandular changes and change of temperature. The male will pursue and mount the female, occasionally however making the mistake of mounting a male. The forelegs of frogs are adapted to the clasping reaction.

Many amphibians hibernate during the winter season, either by burrowing under water or on land. The amphibians are the first of the vertebrates to possess vocal cords that produce sound when breathed upon. The croaking of frogs during the mating season is a common sound in the countryside. This croaking follows a rather fixed daily rhythm.

It seems that only during the mating season the amphibians show any particular social tendency. Feeding and breeding appear to be the main factors to bring amphibians together. (The same might be equally stated of homo sapiens, although in addition he has the factors of sporting events, religious activities, and the like.) Lack of the parental instinct among amphibians is, of course, unfavorable to development of social life.

Like most other animals, the hunger drive seems to be the chief motivating factor in their behavior, except during the mating period, when the sex drive takes precedence and dominates behavior.

Surprisingly, evidence so far does not appear to rate amphibians over fish in learning ability, although the frog and the toad have a better developed forebrain. As between the toad and the frog, the toad appears to rate higher in learning ability. For instance if a glass obstacle is placed in front of the food, the toad will hop around the obstacle even though it may lose sight of the food during the interim. The frog, on the other hand, must have the food constantly in view or it will seem to forget what it started hopping after.

The amphibians, who effect the transition from water to land habitat within their life cycle, should be sentimental favorites of the members of homo sapiens, for reasons which will become apparent later in our study.

Mammals

The mammals are the highest class among the vertebrates, and appeared about 200,000,000 years ago when the dinosaurs existed. They are distinguished from among the other vertebrates by nourishing their young with milk. They are warm-blooded, air-breathing animals, most of them four-footed. True mammals nourish their young in the uterus until they are old enough to be cared for by their parents.

The sense of taste and smell are well developed for food seeking and it is generally agreed that all mammals possess a sense of hearing. The eye of the sub-primate mammals is generally the same as that of man.

The grazing mammals are almost entirely herbivorous and their most common form of protection is running away from enemies. The carnivores, however, are able to attack their enemies by their claws and teeth.

In some species the rutting period is seasonal, and sexual activity in both male and female is limited accordingly. In others, rutting in the female is cyclic throughout the year, with that of the male being continuously active.

The maternal instinct is strong among mammals, at least until the young are able to shift for themselves. So far as is known, sleep is common to all mammals. Most mammals lie down during sleep, although the horse often remains standing, while the opossum hangs from a limb.

Characteristic noises, the beginnings of vocalization, are associated with certain forms of behavior as mating, feeding, fighting, fleeing, playing, and nesting.

Group behavior of most sub-primates is fairly simple and centers around the reproductive functions. Among grazing mammals the young often come together and form bands or herds after leaving the parents. This herding tendency may be determined in part by social motives, although the presence of a common feeding ground is undoubtedly an important factor.

Hunger and food searching is a powerful motivating factor in mammalian behavior, but during the mating season the sex drive takes precedence.

From test results it seems reasonable to conclude that the mammal ranks higher than the other vertebrate groups so far as modifiability of behavior to environment is concerned.

The *apes*, of course, come under the sub-class of true mammals, the order Primates, sub-order Anthropoides, and Family Simiidae. Incidentally, Man, the classifier, has classified himself in the highest group of all, family Hominidae (primitive and modern man).

The Simiidae Family are man's nearest phylogenetic relatives, our poor relatives shall we say to ease the shock. As in man, their olfactory membranes are restricted to the upper portion of the nostril and they do not have a wet nose or snout as most other mammals, except if allergic. They are warm-blooded and will shiver in cold weather. The palms of the forefoot are especially sensitive and are used in manipulating objects. In this connection it should be mentioned that it has been experimentally determined that a chimpanzee in a form matching test can select from a bag of objects of various patterns the proper object by contact cues only.

While a chimpanzee apparently possesses an ear like man, he failed in tests to train him to associate the word "banana" to the fruit. A dog, in fact, rates higher in associating words with objects.

Monkeys, apes and man are the only mammals having color vision. The eye of a chimpanzee is comparable to that of man.

Incidentally, one experimenter was led to believe he had trained a chimpanzee to solve simple mathematical problems, such as selecting cards bearing the proper numeral from a long rack placed between him and the trainer. It was discovered, however, that the chimpanzee used visual cues in choice of response, carefully watching the head of the trainer as it oriented from one card to another.

It has been determined that great apes are little disturbed by fairly strong electric shocks. Monkeys, on the other hand, are quite sensitive. It is, of course, not surprising that monkeys and apes are much superior to man as regards the sense of balance, especially in motion, the factor of alcohol excluded.

It is generally agreed that the upright bodily posture in the great apes resulted from ages of brachiation. The gorilla, because of his weight, spends much of his time on the ground, and makes very little use of his front limbs in walking while on the ground. He often sleeps on the ground as he appears to fear no other animal.

While monkeys and apes are omnivorous, they seem to prefer dairy products, fruits, and grains.

A chimpanzee and gorilla both prefer flight to fight, but fight they will if they are challenged, at which time they acquit themselves well. It has been determined with a dynamometer that only one out of one hundred college students can with both hands reach the 500-pound mark, yet a chimpanzee, weighing only 135 pounds, made a record of 847 pounds with only one hand.

The sounds made by the apes can be classed as emotional cries, which appear to have social meaning. Strangely, apes make no attempt to imitate man's vocal sounds while in captivity. They make a better showing with gestures than with voice.

Food is the great motivator in behavior study of animals, especially with monkeys. A monkey has been observed to work for a half-hour on a puzzle device to secure a raisin as prize. It has also been observed that the sex drive in male monkeys is especially stimulated by novelty.

It is recorded that a gorilla under three years of age was kept in a home in London for two years. He proved to be friendly and clean, and learned to use the lavatory facilities after six weeks training. His table manners, too, were good. But he could not be taught to say the most simple words.

The Human Organism—The Psycho-Social Stage

Classification and Evolution

Man, that remarkable organic entity who has the capability of both observing himself as well as the rest of nature, has classified himself biologically in the following impressive manner:

Kingdom:	Animalia
Phylum:	Chordata
Class:	Mammalia
Order:	Primates
Family:	Hominidae
Genus:	Homo
Species:	Sapiens

Biologists maintain that man is the product of two billion years of biological evolution. Pasteur's experiments having eliminated the belief in spontaneous generation, and based on the assumption that all forms of life came from prior life, any plant or animal can also claim an ancestry going back two billion years. Man's ancestry, however, had the very good fortune of having evolved from the periodic lead branches of the biological tree. All other forms of life were deployments from the main trunk, which eventually led to blind alleys, with further evolution coming to a stop.

Three stages of evolution of man from the lead branch have been distinguished. First, the deployment of so-called pre-men which began about ten million years ago. The original pre-men were pre-human apes which differentiated into numerous species, all possessing trends toward the acquisition of more human characteristics. The so-called Australopithecine ape, the remains of which have recently been discovered in South Africa, is cited as one of the later branches of this deployment.

The second stage in the evolution of man involves the so-called proto-men who were possessed of larger brains. They are credited with having discovered fire, and the art of making certain crude tools and clothing. They also undoubtedly had developed some form of true speech and social customs. They are said to have flourished about 1,200,000 years ago. This group includes the so-called Peking man, and the Java ape man, Pithecanthropus. Types such as the Heidelberg and Neanderthal man, which are only different species, all were biologically discontinuous. In other words, they were offshoots from the main trunk and became extinct. However, there are some biologists who feel that possibly the Neanderthal man could have exchanged genes with homo-sapiens if they were not an extinct species.

The third stage is homo-sapiens which appeared about 25,000 years ago. This group of individuals were the direct forebears of present humanity, with its differing races and civilizations. The only way in which they differed from man today is apparently in knowledge. This group did not make any significant numerical progress until toward the end of the last ice age, or about six thousand years ago. The group then quickly increased in number and diverged out in all directions. It evolved adaptations to adjust to differing climatic conditions, which adaptations according to some authorities resulted in the different races of man, generally classified as white, yellow and black. Divergence at present has apparently run its course, and there is at present a tendency toward convergence, or intercrossing. In other words, the tendency toward discontinuity has reversed itself, and according to some authorities further biological evolution has come to a stop. Hence, mankind, at present at least, constitutes the lead branch of the evolutionary tree.

In passing it is interesting to note how certain persistent conceptions of beauty will tend to favor the perpetuation of certain physical types. For instance, the Mayan civilization had a preference for such physical facial characteristics as big noses, retreating foreheads, weak chins and cross eyes, the very opposite of the present American preferences. It was at first thought that the profiles on Mayan monuments were caricatures, but now it is known that they represented the Mayan conception of classic beauty.

The Law of Biogenesis

It is appropriate at this point to mention a strange phenomena observed in the development of every biological organism. This phenomena has been incorporated under the Law of Biogenesis, which law has been formulated as follows:

265

Every organism in its individual development repeats the life history of the race to which it belongs.

This phenomenal recapitulation on the part of an organism of its prior biological background will appear during the progressive development of its egg or embryo. With some animals a part of this biological phase will take place outside of the initial egg or embryo, as in the case of a frog who comes out of its egg as a fish (tadpole), and subsequently loses its gills, tail and fins, and develops lungs and legs to become an adult frog. Likewise, a moth will go through the worm stage as an apparently true worm outside its egg, which worm subsequently spins a cocoon around itself in the fall of the year. The following spring the heat from the sun will cause the cocoon to break open and release the adult moth.

In this connection it is interesting to observe that a flounder, a so-called flatfish, with its two eyes and its fins on one side of the body in its adult stage, was hatched out as a normal fish, which gradually changed to a flatfish to adapt itself to so-called bottom-feeding.

The embryo of man during its progressive development within the womb of the female is no exception to the Law of Biogenesis. His embryo has been observed to pass through roughly the various stages of his particular biological history. The embryo starts out as an egg (one-celled protozoa), then develops into a ball of cells (the blastula stage), which in turn changes to a double-walled cup (the gastrula stage) corresponding to the adult stage of sponges and coelenterates. It then goes through the worm stage with its primitive digestive organ, and the fish stage with a series of bones through which a nerve-cord passes, the primitive nervous system. The fish stage is especially prominent in the vertebrate including man, for babies have been known to be born with open gill-slits in the neck. Babies also are known to become especially hairy prior to birth. At birth the grasping reflex muscles are stronger relatively than at any later time in its adult life. This does not mean that man was once a monkey, but rather a form of so-called man-ape now extinct.

All organs of the body develop progressively within the embryo with that of the race. For instance during the development of the embryo the heart will go through the two-cham-

266

bered heart of fishes, the three-chambered heart of frogs, and finally the four-chambered heart of a mammal.

The physical brain also develops from the primitive form, from the small double ganglion of gray matter of the worm to the five basic parts found in all organisms from fish up to and including man, namely, the olfactory lobes (for smell), cerebral lobes (for thought), optic lobe (for sight), cerebellum (for equilibrium), and the medulla.

These foregoing observations should not be interpreted as indicating that man has been through the prior history of all animals, including the arthropods, all mammalia, and even the monkey and baboon. Rather man came up the trunk (anagenic branch) of the so-called evolutionary tree and his direct forebear have long since become extinct, only the so-called lead branch being currently active.

Julian Huxley's Conclusions as to Man's Responsibility for Future Evolution

Julian Huxley has stated that man has not improved biologically since homo-sapiens was evolved about 25,000 years ago; in fact he feels that man's genetic structure has degenerated because of present tendencies to shield the individual from the action of natural selection. This has resulted in the perpetuation of unfavorable mutant genes. He advocates that man should be guided by the advice of geneticists, although he concedes that man at present is not receptive to such advice. He maintains, however, that "once the fact is grasped that we men are the agents of further evolution, and that there can be no action higher or more noble than raising the inherent possibilities of life, ways and means will somehow be found for overcoming any resistances that stand in the way of that realization."

Huxley cites both the present population explosion and the potential explosion of atomic bombs as the greatest obstacles to the future progressive evolution of mankind. (It appears that it is a case of overreaction in both directions, an irony of fate.) He has suggested that man submit to the guidance of geneticists to overcome the first obstacle, population explosion, and a form of religion, preferably what he calls evolutionary humanism, as the solution of the potential explosion of atomic bombs. Although he does not dogmatically exclude the contributions of any religion involving the belief in a god, he appears definitely allergic to anything involving the word "supernatural."

Julian Huxley's perspective is vastly greater than the average scientist or philosopher. He sees life as progressive and never regressive, and he pictures man as the responsible bearer of the torch toward the future formal progress of life. He speaks of man as requiring not only the three-dimensional map of the bees but also the fourth dimension of time to properly chart his position and the direction of his future course. He cites human history and human destiny as parts of a larger evolutionary process. "Only by getting some over-all view of reality, in its dual aspect of self-transforming pattern and continuing process, can man hope to get a clearer view of his place—his unique place—in the process, and steer a better course into the future."

We are indeed greatly indebted to Julian Huxley for his sincere and effective efforts to make man conscious of his responsibilities as an individual in contributing toward the shaping of the future course of the evolutionary process.

Cultural Creations of the Human Organism

Man's primary claim of superiority over the rest of animal creation is the fact that only he possesses a genuine culture. A culture, incidentally, involves such diversified traits as associated with tools and gadgets, technical skills, customs, beliefs, and social institutions (in fact everything we have so far reviewed). Man alone domesticated himself and created a culture which is evolving along many different lines. It should not be overlooked that this culture, in turn, is reacting not only on mankind in a general sense, but that each specific culture is reacting on each individual who through fate was born therein. Also, biological and cultural forces are at present interpenetrated to the point that it is difficult, if not impossible, to separate the two.

Warden has stated that "the primary purpose of the cultural regime is to create a human being out of the growing animal." In other words, childhood is a period of cultural habituation.

Whereas cultural traits are the traits of a civilization, personality traits are the traits of an individual human being. The individual is not a total slave of the culture in which he is born. On the other hand, the culture of a civilization is the ever-modified product of the contributions of each individual, living or having lived, within that civilization. In other words, it is definitely the joint creation of man, the individual, and mankind as a whole.

There is a tendency among anthropologists to emphasize the conception that the essence of culture is habit, that as the noted anthropologist Malinowski maintains, "each generation of human beings is a laboratory in which reflexes, impulses, and emotions are formed during the period of development." While to a large extent this is true, yet this emphasis should not lead one to overlook the fact that the ideological contributions of one or two individuals can entirely change the course of a culture, as in the case of Buddha, Confucius, Jesus, Muhammad, and more recently with a political emphasis, Marx and Lenin.

What are the specific capabilities of man that enable him, alone among all natural biological entities, to create a culture? Warden has brought out three specific unique capabilities of man to explain the phenomena. First, he can invent; second, he can communicate by means of the spoken and written word; and third, he can pass on his knowledge to future generations, in short, social habituation. Some will properly ask, what about the bees? In answer to that question Warden brings out that bees are entirely guided by instinct; in fact, slaves to instinct which cannot be modified and such modification passed on to future generations of bees. Incidentally those authorities who assert that man is nothing more than the product of his culture is really asserting that he is a slave to his culture, just as the bees are slaves to their instinct. It is both significant and stimulating therefore, that as outstanding an evolutionary biologist as Julian Huxley has come to the conclusion that the choices of man as an individual are all important and significant in the further evolution of life itself.

Of the general cultural traits found in primitive as well as in modern cultures, the majority are oriented around food-gathering and food-preparation, to meet the physical needs of the body. Such traits would include fire-making, cooking, knife, spear, basketry, pottery, hunting, fishing, gaming nets, bow and arrow, and the domesticated dog. Artifacts such as basketry and pottery also became a medium for artistic expression, an outlet for the appreciation of the beautiful.

The institution of marriage undoubtedly had an instinctive

motivation, as the higher mammals have a tendency to pick permanent partners. This tendency was no doubt motivated by the needs of the young who required a longer time period to reach maturity and independence. Then, too, man would pick his love objects, in the more general sense, for a more or less permanent period. In fact, his love objects were woven into his personality as sentiments, which pretty largely determines his sense of values.

The practice of magic is especially prevalent in a primitive society. This practice is possibly motivated by a desire to break away from the frustrations of living and to rationalize the mystery of natural phenomena. Eventually magic bifurcated, one aspect evolved into science in its primitive stage, and the other evolved into certain forms of religion.

Man, the individual, apparently possesses an innate creative urge, the expression of which is most satisfying to him. The female of the species would seem to derive her primary satisfaction in the creative endeavor of producing children and their subsequent education, the man assuming the impregnation function. The male of the species, on the other hand, appears to express his creative urge mainly on a mental plane, some of which are materialized as artifacts, with the female often being the motivator for such activity.

There is one artifact found generally in present cultures which serves as an ideal illustration of man's creative effort, and that is, the automobile. In fact, we shall briefly retrace the progressive developmental stages of this modern useful and important artifact.

It started with the wheel, an invention of the early Sumerian civilization. Even the wheel came into being as a gradual process; in fact, it is difficult to say which came first, the wheel or the axle. The need was a means of moving or transporting objects. Man originally started out by carrying objects on his back. He later transferred his load to the backs of animals, making them so-called "beasts of burden." Man eventually discovered that an animal could carry more if the load was placed between two poles and drawn by the animal. He later conceived the sledge. But one day a man stepped on a log and it rolled out from under him. While sitting on the ground where he had sprawled, he made the enlightening discovery that a log rolled when a weight was placed unevenly upon it. This discovery was the first step in the evolution (or was it creation) of an automobile. Primitive man subsequently rolled heavy stones on a group of logs, moved progressively in front of the stones. After centuries of trial and error he chopped a wide notch between the two edges of the log to keep the load from sliding off the ends. Now he had the beginning of the wheel and the axle, although they were still of one piece. Later he reinforced the wheel section by cross-pieces to keep the wheel from splitting; eventually the axle became a separate unit.

Wheeled chariots are mentioned in the Bible. The Sumerians used them in warfare. The Egyptians used them around 1500 B.C. to pursue the Israelites. It has been suggested that in the soft muck of the Sea of Reeds the chariots bogged down as the wheels did not revolve evenly; disaster to the army resulted.

Eventually the wheel was made of iron with spokes. Later in place of two-wheeled vehicles, four-wheeled carriages were conceived by the Romans between 300 and 500 B.C.

Late in the nineteenth century compression-type wheels, where the weight was borne by the lower spokes between the axle and ground, were replaced by the suspension-type wheel, where the weight on it hung on tightened spokes from the rim above. These wheels appeared first on the bicycle.

Eventually, after the covered wagons served their useful purpose during the pioneering days in America, the automobile appeared, not however, until appropriate motive power was invented. Each year new inventions and features are incorporated in automobiles, stimulated largely by the competition between the various automobile manufacturers. Automobiles now are not solely used as burden carriers for man, but as a pleasure medium as well. They have largely become the core of a nation's economy, almost a sub-culture you might say, as some people practically worship their automobile—a modern form of idolatry.

Was the automobile evolved by chance factors alone, or did men's minds contribute something to the process? One of the leading manufacturers of automobiles in the United States once stated that the reason he loved the automobile industry was the opportunity it afforded him to express his creative urge.

Whereas we have heretofore noted that the early expressions of cultural traits were oriented around food—its gathering and preparation, the later cultural traits appear to be largely influ-

271

enced by the type of religion. In fact, many times a particular religion will even determine what kind of food is permitted among its adherents and what food is taboo.

Cultural traits are seldom pure units or elements, but rather trait complexes. Generally speaking, the two principal cultures today are the oriental and the occidental. Here we observe the influence of religious conceptions. For instance, the Muhammadan (occidental) culture in Pakistan clashes with the predominant Hindu (oriental) culture of India. For example, the Hindus consider cows sacred because of their belief in the transmigration of souls. Hence, the Hindus are vegetarians, and thus cows will block the streets of an Indian village unmolested while there are starving people milling around them. The Pakistanians, on the other hand, do not face this problem as they entertain no compunction because of their religion to killing and eating their cows.

There are also obstacles to cultural integration within a general branch. For instance, in the occidental branch, the Islamic culture of the Algerians created clashes with the Christian culture of the French. These clashes resulted eventually in the French withdrawing from Algeria.

In Part III, which now follows, we shall review some of the present outstanding religions as basic determinants, not only of value but in the larger sense, of the cultural direction of the present evolutionary trends.

PART THREE

WHITHER

XXII.

RELIGION

Introduction

In a general sense we have up to this point applied mathematical formula to physical phenomena. Now we must consider the factor of direction, to establish an overall vector so to speak. In a larger sense, life is not a system of two way equations, but more a system of vectors.

The individual's choice of love objects, as suggested in Part I of our discourse, would appear largely to determine the nature and direction of his activity. For example, love of parents will lead a child to respect their moral teaching. Particular incidents of failure to live up to that teaching will result in twinges of conscience, for conscience would appear to have its birth in love and not in fear. No conscience exists in a personality who possesses no loves but that of love of self; yet he is not free of fear. Love of self exclusively produces the so-called psychopathic personality, a most dangerous individual from the standpoint of society.

Love of one's wife and children is a projection of one's self-love to that of the welfare of the family, and in most cases is extended to that of relatives, or most of them.

One's love of country, commonly known as patriotism, is a further extension of one's self-love. A nation depends upon its patriotic citizens in times when it is threatened. But as Nurse Cavell stated on the evening of her death: "Patriotism is not enough" as an integrating love for all mankind.

Love of God, however, represents the highest, most encompassing form of love a man can possess, but a love many shy away from expressing, as it appears to involve a covenant, a covenant involving the love of fellow-man and the love of truth. ("Al, you are too honest." "What do you want me to be, 50% honest with you?" "No! No!")

The nature of our loves determines our motivations and sense of values; and these in turn determine the direction of our activity. A man's works are overt expressions of his loves, for "by their works ye shall know them."

In a larger sense a society and its culture is a composite expression of the loves, with their values, of the individuals making up that society. The same principle applies to each civilization.

It appears logical, then, that the more encompassing love would be the very core of a civilization's culture. That core of love appears to be found in religion.

In his book "Man: His First Million Years," Ashley Montagu states that: "Culture represents man's response to his basic needs. Culture is man's way of making himself comfortable in the world." As all civilizations have a religion, we may reasonably conclude that it is a response to a universal need of man.

Certain Definitions of Religion

It is appropriate, at this point, to seek a definition of religion. Charles Francis Potter, in his book "The Great Religious Leaders," defines religion in these words:

"Religion is the endeavor of divided and incomplete human personality to attain unity and completion, usually but not necessarily by seeking the help of an ideally complete divine person or persons. . . . Religions are systems of belief and practice which arise among the disciples of some man who has attained a satisfying measure of success in his endeavors to unify and complete his personality."

In other words religion is the rationalization of the felt needs of the personality to attain a relative degree of peace of mind, the lack of which he is vaguely aware of.

Four other definitions of religion will be cited:
(1) that of Tomasso Campanella, an Italian philosopher of the seventeenth century—

"Religion is a universal phenomenon and has its source
in the dependence of all things on the absolute Being."

(2) that of Bertrand Russell—

"I regard religion as a disease born of fear and a source
of untold misery to the human race."

(3) that according to Vladimir Ulanov (Lenin) religion is an
opiate for the people; and

(4) that of Alfred N. Whitehead:
"Religion is the vision of something which stands beyond,
behind, and within, the passing flux of immediate things;
something which is real, and yet waiting to be realized;
something which is a remote possibility, and yet the
greatest of present facts; something that gives meaning to
all that passes, and yet eludes apprehension; something
whose possession is the final good, and yet is beyond all
reach; something which is the ultimate ideal, and the
hopeless quest."

Of course, in primitive times, as at present in the case of
the growing child, the ever recurring question "Why?" was
raised. Why does the sun rise in the morning and set at night?
Why the lightning and thunder? Why am I?, and the like. Some
imaginative individual would explain that the sun-spirit takes
a ride each day on his Wheel of Fire to look over the world,
and if the people of the world did not pray and praise him
daily, he might stop taking his daily rides and leave the world
in darkness. The sun-spirit led to the moon-spirit, and so on.
Soon families would claim a particular spirit in nature as its
own and call upon it when in danger or desire revenge on a
neighbor. The spirits became innumerable and man lived in
a state of continual fear of unfriendly spirits. This plurality of
individual spirits or gods eventually led to a spirit or god for
the tribe, and finally to one God.

Ye shall know a civilization by its culture, and the culture
in turn is largely the product of its particular form of religion,
founded or modified by an individual leader.

In the words of Julian Huxley: "Only man has a sense of
the sacred, to use Professor Otto's phrase, and only man organizes religions around that sense." Religion may be the product

of fear motivated by necessity, or motivated by love. The first source of motivation produces opportunism with no stability; the second produces steadfastness and stability. They may be compared respectively to the electromagnet and the permanent magnet.

With this introduction, let us now briefly review the principal religions at present in existence.

XXIII.

CURRENT EASTERN RELIGIONS

Hinduism

Hinduism is the oldest of the living religions. It is prehistoric, and it is unique in that it has no original individual founder, although many modifiers.

The greatest number of the adherents of this religion live in India, as it is the national religion of that country. There are, of course, also followers in Siam, Ceylon, South Africa, and Bali. They number a little over 300,000,000. The differences between their numerous sects are great; yet they all have in common the belief in Reincarnation and the Nirvana. These beliefs appear to be made possible by their belief that man is both a body and a soul, the soul only surviving death and hence being the most important part of man. The soul passes from one body to another until it attains a state of Nirvana. Yet strangely they will define soul as knowledge.

Early Hinduism took the form of worshipping spirits, trees, rivers and other nature objects. This form of worship is still in evidence in the hill-country of India.

Hinduism is the only religion with a caste system, starting out with four castes, namely, the priestly caste, the nobility including the warriors, the administrative group including merchants and land-owners, and the largest group made up of the people who perform the common tasks of a society. There are also the so-called "untouchables" or "out-castes," now abolished by law, mainly through the influence of Gandhi. When an "out-caste" desired to purchase something in a store, he had to stand outside and shout his desires to the storekeeper within. The out-caste then placed the money in payment at a prescribed place and backed away while the storekeeper placed the item of purchase at the prescribed place and picked up the payment therefor. (Was this the source of the reference to money as "filthy lucre?") Be that as it may, the money was invariably retrieved. The out-caste thereupon returned and picked up his purchase.

The number of sub-castes now number some 19,000. The members of the different castes are segregated as to social contacts, marriage, temple attendance, and the like. A member of one caste cannot change his caste status during his life-time. The change may only occur via the process of reincarnation, during another life cycle of the soul, dependent on his behavior and performance of duty in his present life cycle.

Brahma, or World Soul, the central thought of Hinduism, is also called Trimurti, the Three-in-One God, because he personifies Brahma, the Creator, Vishnu, the Preserver, and Shiva, the Destroyer. The Hindus believe the Brahma created the first man, called Manu, and the first woman known as Shatarupa; they were the original parents of all mankind. Even though they came from the same parentage, mankind was from the beginning segregated into the four castes previously mentioned. To the question raised by some people in the lower castes that if a man born in a low caste can never enjoy the advantages of the higher castes, what is the advantage of being good—to this the Brahmin priests replied that if they are good in this life, they will be rewarded in their next reincarnation by being re-born in a higher caste. Reincarnation, incidentally, consists in the belief that people's souls enter again into another body after they die, life-cycle after life-cycle until they are in a sufficiently purified state to enter Nirvana, a state in which the individual soul completely loses its identity in Brahma, the World-Soul. All souls are considered a part of Brahma. The priests further explained that the Law of Life provides that good should be rewarded with good (be re-born in a higher caste), while evil with evil (be re-born in a lower caste and with less advantages). This law is known as Karma or the Law of the Deed.

Hinduism appears to have been able to absorb or tolerate any other religion but Muhammadanism. The principal reason therefor being the fact that the Muhammadans have no com-

280

punctions about eating meat whereas the Hinduists are strict vegetarians.

Reformers of Hinduism

Hinduism has been reformed from time to time from within. The first significant reformer was Siddhartha Gautama, The Buddha (563-483 B.C.). The form of Hinduism founded by him is known as Buddhism, and because of the great number of its adherents, it will be treated separately hereafter.

Nataputta Vardhamana, called Mahavira, is another reformer of Hinduism during the sixth century, whose established religion is known as Jainism. This religion, too, will be treated separately hereafter.

About 500 years ago, Kabir of Benares, an adopted son of Muhammadan parents, reformed Hinduism, the form of his reformation reflecting the influence on him of the thoughts contained in the poetry of the Poet Ramanand. Kabir was receptive to Ramanand's teaching that there is only One God (apparently the influence of Muhammadanism), that Truth is one of Man's greatest friends, and that the way to Nirvana is living a simple life. He himself worked as a weaver. He also expressed his objections to the Caste-system of India and to the worship of idols. His followers called themselves Kabir Panthis, meaning followers of the Kabir Path.

Another reformer of Hinduism was Nanak, born of noble Hindu parents thirty years after the birth of Kabir. Nanak was later known as Guru Nanak, and became the founder of a religion later to be known as *Sikhism*. He early showed his dislike for work, and enjoyed spending his time reading the poetry of Ramanand and Kabir. The teachings of these two poets were apparently adopted by Nanak, the only difference being that he advocated eating meat, provided the animal was slaughtered by one blow of the sword. He also taught that people must have a leader, a Guru, to facilitate serving the One God. Consequently, he became Guru Nanak.

The opposition of the leaders of the other religions to the missionary work of a later guru, namely, Guru Arjan, angered that leader to the point where he established an army and spread his religion with the sword, following the method previously used by the Muhammadans when they originally forced their religion on the Indians.

281

At Amritsar, their Holy City, they constructed a beautiful temple known as the Golden Temple of the Pool of Immortality. The adherents of Sikhism number about 3,000,000, and are distinguished from other Hindus by their long hair in which is inserted a wooden comb, their white drawers, and an iron bracelet. They carry a short dagger when on the street.

Another more recent reformer of Hinduism, Dayananda, was born about a hundred years ago. His father was of a very high Hindu caste. He was taught by the best Hindu teachers, studying religion and languages. While attending The Fast of Shivarati with his father, he observed a mouse at the top of the idol Shiva crunching rice which the worshippers had brought to their god. He quickly asked his father, "But if Shiva is a god, can't he even drive a mouse away?" "Ask no questions," his father retorted: "an unbeliever asks questions." Dayananda apparently was dissatisfied with this answer, for he thereupon told his father that he would stop worshipping idols, and went home to bed.

Dayananda began a search for a more satisfactory religion, and finally came upon the teachings of Rammohun Roy. This teacher, who incidentally was born the same year as Dayananda, had likewise become dissatisfied with some of the teachings of Brahmanism (Hinduism) and had made an intensive search for a more satisfying religion. He was well prepared for such a search as he had studied Arabic, Persian, Sanskrit and Hebrew. He carefully read the Bible, the sacred scriptures of the Christian missionaries. In that book he discovered some teachings which he desired to incorporate into the teachings of Brahmanism. The sect he established was known as *Brahma Samaj*.

The experience of Rammohun Roy led Dayananda thereupon to make an independent study of the Bible of the Christians. He became convinced that he should cease believing in many gods but to believe in only One God. He also became convinced that if a man repents the evil which he has done, God forgives him. Among his other conclusions was that man is not born into any caste but that some people were born more intelligent than others. However, his belief in Reincarnation and Nirvana remained unchanged. In 1875 he organized his adherents into the new sect of Hinduism known as *Arya Samaj*.

Shinto is another prehistoric religion, and like Hinduism has no known founder. It was at one time the state religion of Japan. After World War II it ceased to be the state religion and is now on a competitive basis with Buddhism, Confucianism, and Christianity.

The word Shinto is a derivation of the Chinese word "Shen" meaning good spirits, and the word "Tao" meaning The Way. Hence, the word Shinto (Shen-Tao) means The Way of the Good Spirits. The Japanese later named their religion Kamino-Michi.

It is a form of nature-worship; in other words, animistic polytheism. Its early form involved phallic worship. There are thousands of shrines in Japan honoring their various nature gods, the Sun Goddess, Amsterasu, being the center of Shinto worship. Hence, the appearance of the red sun on the Japanese flag.

All the gods are descendants of Izanagi, the Sky Father, and Izanami, the Earth Mother, the original divine pair. They gave birth to three noble children, the Sun Goddess and her two brothers, the Moon-God and The Storm-God. The Sun goddess, Amsterasu, sent her grandson to be the original ruler of the islands of Japan; this was the source of the belief in emperor worship. However, the Emperor of Japan after World War II renounced his divinity. Yet the belief continues with the majority of the common folk, who continue worshipping the various gods. The more thoughtful Japanese, however, will speak of the divine manifested in nature rather than of the various specific gods.

During the early period of Shintoism, it was believed that at one time there was a bridge between Heaven and the Japanese Islands; that it was possible to visit it; and that the beauty of Japan came originally from Heaven. This bridge broke down and was never again repaired. They also believed in an underworld; that they could visit it through an entrance; but it was not as pleasant a place in which to live as on the earth. An earthquake, however, permanently closed the only entrance to this underworld.

As a result of their nature worship, the Japanese sees and considers himself as a part of nature, a feeling which is not equally true of the average European or American.

Love of the beauty of nature is reflected in the interior

decorations of the Japanese homes, one of the national characteristics generally noted by a visitor to the islands of Japan. This is one of the influences of their nature worship. Like China, Japan appears to be able to entertain all religions. Shinto, however, still remains their original basic religion.

Omi Okura well expresses the spirit of Shintoism in the words: "The ways of shining Heaven are far; turn thee! Ah! turn to things yet near; turn to thy earthly home, O friend! And try to do thy duty here."

The sacred books of Shintoism are Kojiki (Records of the Ancients), Nihongi (Chronicles of Japan), and also a later work Yengis-hiki (Hymns and Prayers).

Religions Founded around The Sixth Century B.C.

Introduction

With the exception of the prehistoric religions, such as Hinduism and Shintoism, along with the principal historic religions of Judaism, Muhammadanism, and Christianity, it is a rather unique and interesting coincidence that Buddhism, Jainism, Taoism, Confucianism, and Zoroastrianism were all founded by historical religious leaders during the sixth century B.C. Something of the character of the founders, with a brief outline of the nature of the religions they founded, will next be considered, beginning with Buddhism.

Buddhism

The founder of Buddhism was Siddhartha Gautama (563-483 B.C.), called The Buddha. His father was King Suddhodhana Gautama of the Sakyas, a clan of Hindus living about 2500 years ago on the plains of the Ganges at the foot of the Himalayas. King Suddhodhana long wanted a son, and when he finally got his wish, he naturally spared no wealth and efforts to give that son all the advantages of a prince. He was sent to the best teachers for his education.

When his son finally put on the Sacred Thread at twelve years of age and took the Vow of Allegiance to remain true to his parents' religion Hinduism, he was considered a so-called Twice-Born Hindu. This vow he later broke as his views on religion changed. Some consider he reformed Hinduism; others that he founded a new religion known as Buddhism.

It was the father's main desire that his son should become the ruler of his kingdom after his death, and all his son's training was directed in that direction. He arranged for his son's marriage, which proved a happy union.

His father unwisely tried to keep his son from witnessing any of the suffering which existed among the common people of his kingdom. However, he did not succeed in this effort for eventually the son on one of his expeditions on horseback with his servant Channah, saw a man writhing on the ground in pain. Surprised and shocked, he asked his servant Channah what was wrong with the man. He was told he was ill and that illness was the way of life; all people became ill. This knowledge caused sadness in the unsophisticated prince. This sadness and concern were later aggravated by the sight of an old trembling bent-over man walking with canes. This condition Channah informed him was the way of old age. As a climax he happened to witness a funeral procession, with the widow and her son following it and weeping bitterly. As an explanation of this scene Channah informed him that this was the way of every man, as death comes to all whether king or pauper.

Following these sights he brooded over the facts of sickness, old age, and death. Something must be wrong, he thought, and determined to find out the cause. This led him eventually to leave, secretly in the middle of the night, his wife and newly-born son in his palace. He left them in order to seek an answer to what was wrong. He became a monk, for he had at one time observed the serenity of expression on a monk's face.

He went from place to place asking teachers and holy men for the causes of sickness, old age, and death. He even resorted to fasting as a means to find the answer. However, he gave up this method as he soon found out that fasting did not improve his reasoning power. Finally, after sitting in deep contemplation under a wild fig tree, the answer suddenly flashed into his mind, and he exclaimed that he finally found the Key to Wisdom and the First Law of Life. "From Good must come Good, and from Evil must come Evil." This was one of the Brahministic teachings, the Law of the Deed. He immediately returned to five monk friends whom he left after giving up fasting, and after he explained to them his enlightenment they became his first disciples. His next thought was to go back and tell King Bimbisara of the Mogadah Kingdom whom he had previously promised to inform as soon as he discovered the answer to the riddle of life. (This compulsion to keep a promise was an indication of a good trait of character in Siddhartha Gautama.) This king, incidentally, also became a convert.

Buddha thereupon began training other monks to go out individually in all directions to spread his doctrine, which briefly was as follows:

He reasoned that if from Good must come Good, and from Evil must come Evil, then prayers and sacrifices were foolish. Thereupon, he declared that the Vedas, a collection of the holy books of Hinduism, was not sacred. He also declared himself against the caste system, as all people fell into two classes, either good or bad, according to their own individual choice and deeds. He conceded, however, that some were born more intelligent than others.

He further stated he did not believe Brahma created anything, reasoning that the world is going to exist forever and that it will never come to an end, and that anything that has no end also has no beginning.

He counseled his disciples to keep away from two extremes, one a life of selfish and ignoble pleasure and the other a life of self-torture, as these two extremes did not lead to a Good Life. He, on the other hand, advocated the so-called Eight-fold Path—Right Belief, Right Resolve, Right Occupation, Right Speech, Right Effort, Right Contemplation, Right Concentration, and Right Behavior. Right Behavior involved the Five Commandments of Uprightness: Do not kill; Do not steal; Do not lie; Do not commit adultery; and Do not become intoxicated at any time.

Continual questions were raised by his disciples as to how to explain suffering which was not apparently accountable to bad behavior of the individuals experiencing the suffering. This more or less forced Buddha to bring in the belief in Transmigration of souls and Nirvana, beliefs espoused by Hinduism.

Buddha taught that the cause of unhappiness was desire. Hence, to the extent that a person kept his desires to a minimum, the happier he would be. Total elimination of desires resulted in a state of Nirvana.

He also taught that "hatred does not cease by hatred at any time; hatred ceases by love."

286

He found to his own satisfaction an answer to the problem of unhappiness, which is one form of suffering. However, the problem of sickness and death he apparently left unsolved. A weeping mother, it is related, approached him stating that her only son had died and wanted to know if there was any way to bring her son back to life again. He is said to have replied that if she would bring him some mustard seed from a house in which neither parent, child, relative, nor servant had ever died, he would bring her child back to life again. She came back to report that all people had told her that the living are few but that the dead are many.

Buddha died at 80 years of age, his death reportedly being caused by overeating on fresh pork. His sermons were included in the Tripitaka (The Three Baskets of Wisdom), which was divided into sermons, rules of the priesthood, and the Buddhist doctrine in detail.

After Buddha's death, his followers eventually divided into two main branches of Buddhism, *Hinayana Buddhism,* the so-called Path of Self-Reliance, the conservative branch, and *Mahayana Buddhism,* the Path of Mutual Aid, the reformed branch.

The Hinayana Buddhists follow strictly the original teachings of their teacher. They are mainly all monks and have no priesthood. The adherents of this branch are found mainly in Thailand, Burma, and Ceylon. The Buddhists are practically non-existent in India, possibly because they are not vegetarians. The adherents of the Hinayana branch believe that each individual is responsible for his own salvation, a person's past, present and future being a personal responsibility. Because of the relatively smaller number of adherents to this branch, it is known as the Small Vehicle or Raft.

The reformed branch, Mahayana Buddhism, has departed considerably from the teachings of Buddha, and have formed many sects. The majority of the adherents of this branch are found in Tibet, China, Korea, and Japan. The scriptures of Buddhism were greatly changed to meet the needs of the common people. Certain authorities state that the Buddhist priests in the Mahayana branch incorporated some of the teachings of Christianity into Buddhism to prevent the missionaries of that religion from converting their followers. Then, too, for practical reasons all followers of Buddhism could not become monks in order to seek their own salvation, so it was maintained that there is not just one Buddha but many. These various Buddhas, because of their way of life, built up what might be termed a reserve of good deeds from which the common people could draw by prayer and sacrifices at the innumerable Buddhist temples built in China, Mongolia, Korea and Japan. At these various temples were idols of the various Buddhas, which idols were objects of worship.

Although Buddha told his disciples at his bedside when dying that he would remain with them after his death by way of his various teachings, stories after his death stated Buddha actually had about 530 lives, 42 times as a god, 85 times as a prince, 22 times as a learned man, 2 times as a thief, once each as a slave and a gambler, and numerous times as a lion, a deer, a horse, a bull, a snake, and a frog. However, in all these lives he was always wise. (The subsequent followers of a religious leader invariably distort and modify his original teachings.)

One of the sects of Buddhism given considerable publicity today are the so-called *Zen Buddhists* of Japan. Its philosophers maintain that all ideas and religious practices are only so-called pointers, and that its followers should give attention to what they point to rather than devote their time with the pointers themselves. They emphasize meditation and intuition as methods of learning rather than obtaining it from books. (One can understand why certain students are interested in this religion.) Further, they advocate that truth should be sought in individual experience and not by thinking about it or trying to derive it from the experience of others. They even teach that a person who says the word "Buddha" should wash out his mouth.

The number of adherents to the various branches of Buddhism today is difficult to determine as many of them are also Confucians and Taoists. However, the estimates vary widely from 150,000,000 to 500,000,000.

Jainism

Jainism is another religion founded in India in the sixth century B.C. Its founder is Nataputta Vardhamana (599-427 B.C.). He was called Mahavira, meaning The Great Hero, after he managed as a boy to subdue a stampeding bull-elephant and bring him back to the royal stables.

His life ran so parallel to that of the life of Buddha that at one time it was thought that he was the same individual. Prince Mahavira was the second son of King Sreyama of the Kingdom of Mogadah. His parents were very religious and when Mahavira was twenty-eight years old, the parents died, having starved themselves to death in order to attain a Holy Death. Mahavira subsequently became a wandering beggar monk, and took a Vow of Silence for twelve years, not to utter a single word. He devoted his time to solitary thinking.

At the end of twelve years he began to teach the doctrine derived from his period of silence. He was known as a great speaker, and organized a Brotherhood of Monks and a Sisterhood of Nuns. As to his doctrine he, like Buddha, taught that the suffering of the world came from Desire. By giving up all desire, suffering ceases.

As a pupil of the Brahmin priests in the days of his youth, he reacted against the attitude of superiority and the vanity of priests, as they considered themselves superior even to kings and princes. He himself of course was a prince. He, like Buddha, was antagonistic to the caste system of Hinduism, and they both believed in Karma, Reincarnation, and Nirvana. Then too like Buddha, Mahavira believed that all living things had souls. Mahavira, however, went one step further and maintained that even trees, water and fire, and even certain vegetables, had souls. He asserted it was possible to be born again even as an onion or a beet.

Both Mahavira and Buddha were alike in their convictions that prayer and sacrifice were useless, and that the Vedas were not sacred books as they contained many errors.

However, whereas Buddha advocated a course of moderation in attaining freedom from suffering, Mahavira advocated self-torture and asceticism. Mahavira's teachings included the so-called Three Jewels of the Soul, Right Conviction, Right Knowledge, and Right Conduct. Right Conduct involved obedience to Five Commandments of the Soul, leading to the Good Life. These commandments were: Do not kill any living thing, or hurt any living thing by word, thought, or deed; Do not steal; Do not lie; Do not covet or desire anything; and Do not live an unchaste life and never become intoxicated.

Mahavira taught that when a soul sins it becomes heavy, the more sins the heavier the soul becomes. He provided for seven hells for the repose of the various sinners. Conversely, he taught that a soul becomes progressively lighter the more perfect its life, and maintained that there were twenty-six heavens for the different good souls, the twenty-sixth being Nirvana, a state of nothingness so far as the individual soul is concerned, becoming one with Brahma.

Mahavira taught a doctrine of salvation by good works. "Not in prayer, nor in idol-worship, will you find forgiveness and the way to the good life. Only by doing good can you reach Nirvana. Within yourselves lies salvation."

Mahavira's first commandment obviously made it impossible for Jainism to become a universal religion. It remains a religion in India as against that of Buddhism, as it advocated vegetarianism.

The followers of this religion are mostly all bankers and merchants along the Ganges, and especially in Calcutta. The wealthy Jainas have built thousands of beautiful temples in India, contrary to the teachings of their founder. They have also embraced the belief that twenty-three Jainas existed prior to Mahavira, who is considered the twenty-fourth and last. It is also maintained that the first Jainas appeared on earth many trillions of years ago. Idols to all the Jainas are found in their temples. The teachings and sermons of Mahavira are contained in the religion's sacred book Agamas (Precepts).

Hospitals have been established by the followers of Jainism for sick animals, old homes for cows, and wards for sick birds and insects. The Jainas number about 1,400,000, and are known as a kindly folk, a result apparently of their religious beliefs.

We shall now pass on to the consideration of two religions which originated in China proper, namely, Taoism and Confucianism, and one little-known religion, Mohism, which carries the hopes of many idealistic Chinese youth.

First let us briefly consider the main aspects of Taoism.

Taoism

The founder of Taoism, Lao-tze (The Old Philosopher), is reported to have been born 604 B.C. of poor parents residing in the District of Tsow; they named their son Li-Peh-Yang. The date of his death is given as 524 B.C.

As in the case of so many other religious leaders, there are some who question whether Lao-tze lived at all. Be that as it may, there is a book credited to him, a small book of about 5000 words, known as Tao-Teh-King, variously translated as The Book of Reason and Virtue, The Way and Its Power, and The Book of the Path of Virtue. It also contains some abracadabra. The author at an advanced age, becoming discouraged because of the increase in crime and the rottenness of government officials, gave up his position as Keeper of the Royal Archives in the city of Lo-yang, mounted a water-buffalo and rode to the border, apparently headed for Tibet. The border guard recognized him and would not permit him to pass through unless he put his philosophical teachings in writing. Whereupon, Lao-tze is said to have spent three days in hastily writing down his teachings and turned them over to the border guard. He and his water-buffalo then were allowed to pass on. Lao-tze was last seen heading west and was never heard from again. (This statement leaves us with the question of how the year of his death was determined.)

Confucius, as a young man, having heard of the famed Lao-tze, made up his mind to visit The Old Philosopher. While waiting to see him, Confucius devoted his time in the library reading. Suddenly Lao-tze entered and asked what he was reading. He replied he was reading The Book of the Changes, which teaches about humanity and justice. "Humanity and justice!" Lao-tze is reported to have exclaimed, "Does the pigeon bathe itself all day to make itself white? It does not. It is naturally white. And so with people. If they are good and just at heart you do not need to teach them justice."

At the conclusion of the heated debate which followed, Confucius is said to have summarized his own views: "I believe that people are born good, and that learning and knowledge will keep them good. But before we can have new knowledge, we must first know the old. That is why I think the wisdom of our forefathers should be studied carefully."

Lao-tze angrily replied: "The men of whom you speak, Sir, together with their bones have mouldered in the grave. Let go of your proud airs, and your big plans to teach the world justice. All this is of no use to you. That is what I have to tell you, and that is all!"

Confucius later likened Lao-tze to a dragon but apparently he had some respect for The Old Philosopher.

Tao is the central concept of Lao-tze's philosophy, the meaning of which has been variously interpreted. Even Lao-tze himself is quoted as having said: "The Tao that can be understood cannot be the real Tao."

One meaning of Tao as interpreted by certain authorities is "that of the way of ultimate reality." It is the very source of all existence from which all life springs and to which it eventually returns. It is life's "basic mystery, the mystery of mysteries, the entrance into the mystery of all life." . . . "How clear and quiet it is! It must be something eternally existing!" This was The Old Philosopher's emotional description of Tao. Though transcendent, yet it is immanent, and in this aspect it is the way of the universe, the principle of its rhythm and order, as well as its inexhaustible driving force. Thus, it is basically spiritual in nature. Man, according to Lao-tze, is a part of nature and should adjust himself to it, as water passing over rocks, or as a pugilist of modern times would say, "riding with the punches."

Lao-tze stated: "To those who are good to me I am good; and to those who are not good to me I am good. And thus all get to be good." The uniqueness of this basic moral principle is that it was asserted at about the same period that the very opposite principle was asserted among the Sumerians, the principle of an eye for an eye and a tooth for a tooth. Surely Lao-tze had experienced a nearness to Tao rare indeed in his part of the world, reflecting a conviction in his teachings of which Confucius became aware after his meeting with the famed philosopher.

One cannot help but entertain the suspicion that Wordsworth and Thoreau were both influenced by reading Lao-tze's Tao-Teh-King. The Zen Buddhist priests, too, have been apparently likewise influenced, especially in Lao-tze's teaching that we should not waste our time reading other people's philosophy, but that the individual should practice relaxation and meditation and personally learn to know Tao.

The teachings of Lao-tze fared no better than the teachings of other religious leaders after their death; they were mutilated beyond recognition by some of his followers. Innumerable sects arose, with their priests, temples, and idols. Nature became a world of magic and of spirit, mostly evil, which had to be placated. Such practices were instituted as building a house with a curved entrance corridor, and even painting a fake entrance on the side of the house to mislead the evil spirits, so they will crash against the wall of the curved entrance, or against the painted fake entrance, and so induce them to flee into the forest. Certain authorities suggest that Taoism has pretty much become a so-called "funeral racket."

As disappointing as these later developments have been, one cannot resist the feeling that The Old Philosopher lived very close to Tao, The Ultimate Reality.

The number of adherents of Taoism has been roughly estimated at 50,000,000, distributed mostly in China, Manchuria, and Korea.

We shall now proceed to the religion founded by Confucius, the personality whom we have already mentioned under Taoism.

Confucianism

The original name of its founder was Chiu K'ung, later known as K'ung-Fu-Tze (K'ung the Teacher), and later the latinized version Confucius, which name is said to have been given him by Jesuit priest missionaries in China during the 16th century. Although the exact dates of his birth and death are uncertain, some authorities give these dates as 551-479 B.C. He was born in the Province of Lu in the District of Tsow. His father was an old soldier, a man of powerful build and of the honorable family of K'ung. When his father was 70 years of age, he became concerned about not having anyone to worship him after his death. True, his wife had given him nine daughters but daughters worship the ancestors of the husbands they marry. True also, he had two sons by concubines, but they didn't count. So he divorced his wife and sought another from a gentleman of the House of Yen who had three eligible daughters. Only the youngest, an eighteen year old girl, was willing to marry the old man. A year later she presented the old soldier with a son, who became Confucius.

His father died when Confucius was three years old, leaving his wife and son in poor circumstances. Confucius' mother must therefore serve both as the boy's mother and father. She early realized her son was a precocious boy, and worked hard and encouraged him in his schooling. At fifteen he had "his mind bent on learning." He apparently was a healthy normal boy, too, for he helped support the family by hunting and fishing.

At nineteen years of age he married, and at the same time he was made Keeper of Granaries, for his learning and teaching ability had already become generally known. He apparently showed good administrative ability and was soon promoted to Superintendent of Fields of the District of Tsow. He was particularly happy in this position as it gave him time to devote to the study of the old classics.

Three years later his mother died, and he resigned his position to mourn her death for a period of twenty-seven months, for such was the old established Chinese custom. His wife, by whom he had one son, left him, some say because he left his position and went into mourning for his mother. During this time, however, he continued his studies in the old Chinese classics, history and poetry. He was soon able to make a good living by teaching, and eventually he is said to have had up to three-thousand pupils. Most of them were paying pupils, although he would not turn down a poor boy if he gave promise of becoming a good student.

At fifty-two years of age, he was made Chief-Magistrate of the town of Chung-tu. His administration apparently was so successful that the happiness of its citizens got around. This excited the curiosity of the Duke of the Province of Lu, who asked Confucius how he was able to get the loyalty and co-operation of the citizens. Confucius is reported to have explained: "I rewarded those who were good, and punished those who were bad. The people soon learned that it was good to be good and bad to be bad, and they became good and good people are loyal to each other and to the government." Thereupon the Duke offered him the position of Minister of Crime for the Province of Lu. Confucius readily accepted as it gave him an opportunity to test further his methods.

He started out in his new position like an efficiency engineer, and made a thorough survey of the crime problem in the province. He reported back to the Duke, "If we could do away with poverty and ignorance, then we would have no more crime in our land." The Duke's immediate question was, "How?" Confucius replied that the answer was education, that by educating the people in useful trades it would do away with poverty and crime. The Duke approved the suggested program. Within a comparatively short time the prisons were empty. The reputation of the Province of Lu spread and aroused the envy and concern of the governors of neighboring provinces. The envious governors quickly put an end to this embarrassing situation by presenting dancing girls and racehorses to the Duke. Between the dancing girls and the racehorses the Duke had no further time for Confucius' reform movement. Confucius thereupon resigned in disgust, and thereafter traveled around China in the hope of finding a head of government who was receptive to his ideas. He had no success and returned home to devote the remainder of his life to study, teaching, and writing.

The visit of Confucius with Lao-tze has already been mentioned under Taoism. Confucius realized that education and precepts are not in themselves motivations but must be attached to motivating forces, such as love of ancestors. Ancestor worship was an old established custom in China, derived from worship of spirits in nature and finally the worship of the spirits of ancestors. In Confucius' teachings the following words appeared a number of times—"What you do not want done to yourself, do not do to others." This is really the negative form of the teaching of Christ five centuries later, minus of course the first half of Christ's teaching of first loving God. While Lao-tze had counselled him to study in order to discover Tao, the central principle of all things, Confucius replied that he had studied it for twenty years. Lao-tze replied that the only way to obtain it is to give it room in one's heart.

Confucius, on the other hand, strongly advocated the practice of self-culture rather than dependence on supernatural beings for progress. He consistently discouraged his pupils in the efficacy of prayer and worship of God. On the other hand he taught them such precepts as:

> A gentleman has nine aims: To see clearly, to understand what he hears, to be warm in manner, dignified in bearing, faithful of speech, keen at work, to ask when in doubt, in anger to think of difficulties, and in sight of gain to think of right.

> Good is no hermit. It has many neighbors.

> To see what is right and not do it, that is cowardice.

> To love mankind, that is to love.

Confucius described a Superior Man as a noble and princely man who practiced the following virtues:

(1) Right attitude—co-operative and accommodating;

(2) **Right** procedure—known as rules of etiquette for all social situations;
(3) **Right** knowledge—correct moral habits from history, literature, and civics; proper words and actions;
(4) **Right** moral courage—necessary to be loyal to himself and charitable toward neighbors;
(5) **Right** persistence—unfailingly kind and helpful.

Confucius' associates have indicated certain aspects of his personality, namely, that he was a fussy individual, very conservative, cautious to the point of timidity, and very self-conscious. Thunderstorms and funeral processions considerably disturbed him, and he sidestepped all questions from his pupils on God and immortality.

Ten classical books in China are closely associated with Confucius, the first six of which being called kings:

The Shu King (Canon of History);
The Shi King (Canon of Poetry);
The I King (Canon of Changes or Prophecy);
The Chun Chiu King (Spring and Autumn)—the only one personally written by Confucius;
Li Ki King (Book of Etiquette);
Hsiao King (Book of Filial Piety).

The remaining four books are called "shu," and consist of reports of conversations between Confucius and various men living in his day. These four books are:

The Ta Hsio (Great Learning);
The Chung Yung (Doctrine of the Mean—against extremism);
Lun Yu (The Analects—maxims);
Meng-tsze (Mencius).

Mencius, who was born one hundred years after the death of Confucius, is the best known of his later disciples. In Mencius' essay on Benevolence he made, among other significant statements, the following:

Benevolence brings glory to an individual and its opposite brings disgrace.

> The feeling of commiseration is the principle of benevolence.

There was also another disciple, Confucius' grandson Keigh, who wrote The Doctrine of the Middle-Path, reflecting his grandfather's teachings. Also there was Chucius, who lived in the twelfth century A.D., and wrote commentaries on the classics.

About two hundred fifty years after Confucius, a new emperor came to the throne of China who decided to correct loose governmental systems which existed at that time. His name was Ts'in Shih Hwang-ti. He made up his mind to take over in his own hands the government of the whole of China. Of course, he faced opposition from the other governors, but by force of arms he got them all under his control and declared himself The First Emperor. A lackey adviser of the Emperor told him that the teachings in the classics went counter to his plans and therefore were misleading the people. The Emperor thereupon ordered all the old classics to be burned, which of course included the works of Confucius. However, certain scholars managed to hide his works, among others. This same emperor later had the Great Wall of China built. After the emperor's death, they had a great celebration and again brought out the works of Confucius along with the others.

From Emperor Ts'in the name China was derived. The emperor himself is now remembered as "The Criminal of Ten Thousand Generations."

Confucianism is unique among religions in that it has no sects. Confucius, who himself did not believe in God, has become a god to most of the Chinese people. It is interesting to note that much of the basic philosophy of Confucius has been adopted by the so-called humanists of today, a left-wing branch of Christianity.

Confucius was singularly inductive in his reasoning, and actually worshipped the Golden Age of the past.

Mohism

It would seem that if Confucianism is considered a religion, Mohism is even more entitled to be so considered because Mo-tzu, its founder, believed in a Supreme Being. Mo-tzu (estimated between 500 and 396 B.C.) became a good civil

297

administrator in the State of Sung after having served for a period as a victorious army general. It is said of him that he "skillfully carried out military defense and practical economy." He was known as a good logician, as well as a spiritually-minded thinker. After making a study of Confucianism, he repudiated it, particularly the doctrines of Fate and its elaborate rituals. He was known as "an apostle of brotherhood because he set purity of heart higher than formal correctness in fulfilling ceremonial laws." In this respect he deviated from the formalism of Confucius and advocated more the basic viewpoint of Lao-tze.

He was a vigorous defender of religious beliefs. His followers who founded religious groups, were later persecuted and branded as slaves. Whereas he was devoted to peace and credited with averting several wars, he allowed for defensive wars.

As best revealing his basic philosophy, the following quotations are taken from his statements on the subject of "Standard Patterns":

> Any one in the Great Society who takes any business in hand, cannot dispense with a standard pattern. For there to be no standard and the business to succeed, this just does not happen. Even the best experts who act as generals and councillors-of-state, all have standards (of action); and so also even the best craftsmen. They use a carpenter's square for making squares and compasses for making circles: a piece of string for making straight lines and a plumb line for getting the perpendicular. It makes no difference whether a craftsman is skilled or not; all alike use these five (devices) as standards, only the skilled are accurate. But, although the unskilled fail to be accurate, they nevertheless get much better results if they follow these standards in the work which they do.

He follows this statement up by eliminating as standards for rulers of the Great Society the human heartedness of fathers and mothers, the teachers and the princes, and proceeds with the following conclusion:

> That being so, what standard may be taken as suitable for ruling? The answer is that nothing is equal to imitating Heaven. Heaven's actions are all-inclusive and

298

not private-minded, its blessings substantial and unceasing, its revelations abiding and incorruptible. Thus it was that the Sage-kings imitated it. Having taken Heaven as their standard, their every movement and every action was found to be measured in relation to Heaven. What Heaven wanted, that they did; what Heaven did not want, that they stopped doing.

The question now is, what does Heaven want and what does it hate? Heaven wants men to love and be profitable to each other, and does not want them to hate and maltreat each other. How do we know that Heaven wants men to love and be profitable to each other? Because it embraces all in its love of them, embraces all in its benefits to them. How do we know that Heaven embraces all . . . ? Because it embraces all in its possession of them and in its gifts of food.

In the concluding paragraph he summarizes his thoughts in the following words:

Hence I say that Heaven is sure to give happiness to those who love and benefit other men, and is sure to bring calamities on those who hate and maltreat other men. I maintain that the man who murders an innocent person will meet with misfortune. What other explanation is there of the fact that when men murder each other, Heaven brings calamity on them? This is the way in which we know that Heaven wants men to love and benefit each other and does not want them to hate and maltreat each other.

Mencius, the most outstanding disciple of Confucius, was successful in discrediting the philosophy of Mo-Tzu.

Recently Mohism, as Mo-Tzu's religious philosophy is called, has been adopted by many of the younger generation of China as a way to China's salvation from its present turbulent and troublous times.

Zoroastrianism

The founder of Zoroastrianism was Zarathustra Spitama (660-583 B.C.). He was born in northwestern Persia, at or near

Azerbaijan. His father, Porushasp Spitama, was a land-owner and cattle-raiser, who apparently had five sons by three wives. Zarathustra is said to have been the middle son, by his wife Dughdova. The son apparently showed precocity, and his parents were determined to give him the best education in the land. At seven years of age the son was sent away to study under Burzin-kurus who was well-known in Iran for his wisdom. Besides religion, he also studied farming, cattle-raising, and healing. At the end of eight years he returned home to become confirmed at the age of fifteen into the religion of his people, putting on the so-called Sacred Shirt and the Sacred Girdle.

During this period Iran was attacked by the Turanians, their neighbors. Zoroaster volunteered immediately for service on the battle-field in the healing of wounded soldiers. A famine came after the end of the war, and again Zoroaster volunteered to work among the poor and sick of the land. After five years of such work, he again returned home. His father now wanted him to give up his social work, get married and settle down to become a land-owner and cattle-raiser. He followed his father's suggestion as regards marriage. However, he is said to have asked to see his bride's face before marrying her, thereby breaking a fixed custom of his people. After his marriage he would not agree to following his father's choice of a vocation for him, but continued in his work among the sick of his land. He appears to have forgotten himself in the work among the sick and needy.

After ten more years of social work, he could observe no visible improvement in the conditions of his people. This observation led him to wonder about the sources of good and evil. He felt that if he could learn this source, he could do something constructive to alleviate the suffering in the land. Finally he informed his wife of his decision to live like a hermit and meditate on the problem until he found a solution. His wife naturally felt he was foolish when he could have forgotten about the problems of other people and become a wealthy cattle-raiser. Zoroaster, however, stubbornly stuck to his decision and went up to Mount Sabalan.

After several months of solitary thinking on his problem without a solution, he was about ready to give up and return to his wife and children. Late one afternoon as he was sitting outside his cave on the mountain side and contemplating returning to his family, he witnessed a gorgeous sunset which was followed by darkness in the valley below. The correspondence between the physical phenomena of light and darkness, with the spiritual phenomena of good and evil, suddenly struck him. This sudden awareness made him jubilant. Now he had a basic thought to work with. As every day consists of light and darkness, so the world is made up of Good and Evil. "The Good must always be good, and the Evil must always be Evil," just as light and darkness can never change its nature. Thus he concluded that the magicians and idol-worshipping priests can never effectively pray that the good gods do evil or the evil gods do good. Hence, they are wrong. He further concluded that the world was ruled by two forces, one good, the other evil. He named the good force Ahura Mazda (the latter part of which name was later used by Edison) and the evil force Angra Mainyu. But he still was faced with the problem of why Good and Evil were created, and what people should do to eliminate evil with its suffering.

He remained on Mount Sabalan until he had reached the answers to these questions. "Now I shall go down and lead my people from darkness into light, from suffering to happiness, and from Evil to Good!"

His enthusiasm for his discovery was considerably dampened when the people apparently were unimpressed with his teaching. He failed to appreciate that an idol-worshipping people who were accustomed to believe only what they could physically see and touch as their physical idols, would naturally be skeptical about the God of Good and the Spirit of Evil which could not be seen or touched. However, he tenaciously went around preaching for ten years, and he ended up that initial period with only one convert, a cousin. However, he is reported to have experienced a theophany during this period which made an unforgettable impression on him. He is reported to have seen God in a wonderful vision on May 5, 630 B.C., during which certain spiritual truths were revealed to him. He is said to have had six subsequent visions, progressively revealing certain truths to him.

His cousin gave him a very fruitful criticism, and at the same time a constructive suggestion. The criticism was that he was talking over the heads of the people; that they simply did not understand him. At the same time his cousin suggested that

301

he get the attention of the most educated people in the land. And who were they? None other than the King and Queen, along with the remainder of the royal family.

Zoroaster must have been strongly impelled by his theophany to make his ideas known. As he was a man of action, he soon succeeded in getting an audience with King Vishtaspa, however not until indulging in a bit of sorcery with the gate-keeper at the King's palace. In the presence of King Vishtaspa, Zoroaster said in a firm voice: "I, Zoroaster Spitama, Prophet of the One Wise Lord, have come to you, Mighty King, to turn your heart from vain and evil idols towards the glory of the True and Wise and Eternal Lord!" The King challenged Zoroaster for proof. Thereupon Zoroaster offered to face the questioning of the king's wise men, priests, and magicians, and debate the matter with them.

Zoroaster won out in the debate and King Vishtaspa became a convert. The priests and magicians thereupon connived and surreptitiously set up a situation to support their charge that Zoroaster was nothing but a sorcerer. They succeeded and the irate king put him in prison. However, Zoroaster's subsequent success in putting the King's favorite but ailing horse back on its legs, restored Zoroaster again to the king's good graces. In short, Zoroaster succeeded in converting not only the king, but the king's whole court and eventually the entire country, yes even his own family.

In a subsequent war during which Iran was invaded again by the Turanians, Zoroaster was stabbed in the back while praying at the altar in the temple.

Zoroaster taught that Ahura Mazda (Lord Wisdom) created the universe and rules it. Angra Mainyu (Ahriman, the Spiritual Enemy or devil) invaded the world and disorders it. The power of evil, however, is limited in time. Although nature is divided by the two conflicting principles, light and darkness, good and evil, man as a free agent will bring about the final triumph of the right by his choosing of the right. In that manner he will be progressively extending the power of the good and gradually annihilating evil.

He enumerated six virtues: good thought, righteousness, wished-for kingdom, harmony on earth, salvation, and immortality. The hosts of the evil are legion, innumerable. Space primevally separated light and darkness, and time began with their conflict. The world first existed in a spiritual state, everything being represented by its heavenly prototype and in a transcendental form. The world and primitive man were later created in a material form to fight the powers of evil. Zoroaster also predicted the subsequent coming of a great prophet.

There is an obvious similarity between the teaching of Zoroaster and of Judaism and Christianity; uniquely all three relate theophanies. Influences of Zoroastrianism appear in Judaism and Christianity; for instance, the word "satan" first appeared in Hebrew writings after their captivity in Babylonia and their subsequent freedom effected by Cyrus, the Persian (Iranian) conqueror of the Babylonians.

The religions of Mithraism and Manicheism were also influenced by Zoroastrianism, and they in turn during the third and fourth centuries had their influence on Christianity.

Alexander the Great conquered Persia nearly three hundred years after the death of Zoroaster. He destroyed Avesta, the sacred book of the Zoroastrians and set up the religion of the Greeks of that day. However, the Persians secretly taught their religion to their children, and when the Persians were again free of foreign rule five hundred years later, they restored the teachings of Zoroaster. But approximately four hundred years later, the Arabs conquered Persia and forced a new religion, Muhammadanism, on the Persian people.

Today Zoroastrianism has left the smallest number of adherents of any other living religion, between 100,000 to 150,000. They reside mostly in Persia and in India. Those living in India, mostly around Bombay, are known as Parsees.

XXIV.

CURRENT HISTORICALLY DEVELOPED RELIGIONS

Judaism

As related in Genesis, Shem was the first-born of three sons of Noah, all of whom were with him in the ark along with their families.

Abraham was the first-born of three sons of Terah, who was a direct descendant of Shem.

Terah and his family resided in Ur of the Chaldees about the twentieth century B.C. Terah subsequently left Ur with his family to go to Canaan. The question is naturally raised why he should make such a move. Legend has it that Terah conducted a flourishing idol manufacturing business at Ur, and during busy periods his sons, who were shepherds, would assist the father. Abram reacted against idol-worship, especially when brought so close to the industry of making them. One day out of disgust he smashed all his father's idols except one, beside which he placed the axe he had used. Abram's action became known and as a result Terah thought it best for him and his family to leave Ur. They settled for a period in Haran, where Terah, Abram's father, died.

At this point we shall quote from Chapter 12 of Genesis:

Now the Lord had said unto Abram, Get thee out of thy country, and from thy kindred, and from thy father's house, unto a land that I will shew thee; and I will make of thee a great nation, and I will bless thee, and make thy name great; thou shalt be a blessing; and I will bless them that bless thee, and curse him that curseth thee: and in thee shall all families of the earth be blessed.

Abram did as the Lord had spoken, took Sarai, his wife, and his household, left Haran, and was led westward to the land of Canaan. When he arrived at Canaan, "the Lord appeared unto Abram, and said, Unto thy seed will I give this land: and there builded he an altar unto the Lord who appeared unto him."

Subsequently a severe famine occurred in Canaan which led Abram to take his household and live-stock to Egypt. As he felt that the Egyptians might kill him to get his beautiful wife Sarai, he arranged with her to say that she was his sister. Actually she was his half-sister for their father was Terah. It turned out that his wife Sarai did attract the attention of the pharaoh, who wanted to arrange with Abram for her to become his possession. When it finally was revealed that she was really Abram's wife, the pharaoh became wrought up and drove Abram and his group out of Egypt. Abram then returned to Canaan.

Abram as a cattle-raiser became very wealthy, but he was yet to have a son by Sarai. "And Abram said, Lord God, what wilt thou give me seeing I go childless?", at the same time suggesting that he might make someone in his household his heir. However, the Lord assured him he would have an heir by his own seed, and told him,

Look now toward heaven, and tell the stars if thou be able to number them: and he said unto him, So shall thy seed be. And he (Abram) believed in the Lord; and and he counted it to him for righteousness.

The Lord subsequently foretold in a dream which Abram had of the future slavery of his people in Egypt, saying:

And he said unto Abram, Know of a surety that thy seed shall be a stranger in a land that is not theirs, and shall serve them; and they shall afflict them four hundred years. And also that nation, whom they shall serve, will I judge: and afterward shall they come out with great substance.

At the same time the Lord assured Abram that his people would again return to Canaan after their period of slavery.

Because Sarai apparently was still unable to bear a son to Abram, she suggested to her husband that he have a child by her Egyptian handmaiden Hagar. The suggestion was followed and subsequently Hagar bore Abram a son, who was named Ishmael.

From Chapter 17 of Genesis, we quote:

> And when Abram was ninety years old and nine, the Lord appeared to Abram, and said unto him, I am the Almighty God; walk before me, and be thou perfect. And I will make a covenant between me and thee, and will multiply thee exceedingly. And Abram fell on his face: and God talked with him, saying, As for me, behold, my covenant is with thee, and thou shalt be a father of many nations. Neither shall thy name any more be called Abram, but thy name shall be Abraham; for a father of many nations have I made thee. And I will make thee exceeding fruitful, and I will make nations of thee and kings shall come out of thee . . . And I will give unto thee, and to thy seed after thee, the land wherein thou art a stranger, all the land of Canaan, for an everlasting possession, and I will be their God.

Thereupon, the rite of circumcision was instituted as a token of the covenant. Abraham became circumcised, as also did his son Ishmael who was then thirteen years of age. The Lord God at the same time changed Sarai's name to Sarah:

> And I will bless her, and give thee a son also of her: yea, I will bless her, and she shall be a mother of nations, kings of people shall be of her.

Because of their age, both Abraham and Sarah laughed at this incredible promise:

> And Abraham said unto God, O that Ishmael might live before thee! And God said Sarah thy wife shall bear thee a son indeed; and thou shalt call his name Isaac: and I will establish my covenant with him for an ever-

lasting covenant and with his seed after him. And as for Ishmael, I have heard thee: Behold, I have blessed him, and will make him fruitful, and will multiply him exceedingly; twelve princes shall he beget, and I will make him a great nation. But my covenant will I establish with Isaac, which Sarah shall bear unto thee at this set time in the next year.

This seemingly incredible promise of the Lord was fulfilled, and Sarah bore a son at her advanced age, who was given the name Isaac.

Later Abraham's faith was subjected to a severe test by the Lord, when he requested Abraham to sacrifice his only son Isaac upon an altar. This Abraham reluctantly proceeded to do. From the 22nd Chapter of Genesis we shall quote:

And Abraham stretched forth his hand, and took the knife to slay his son. And the angel of the Lord called unto him out of heaven, and said, Abraham, Abraham: and he said, Here am I. And he said, Lay not thine hand upon the lad, neither do thou any thing unto him: for now I know that thou fearest God, seeing thou has not withheld thy son, thine only son from me. . . . And the angel of the Lord called unto Abraham out of heaven the second time, And said, By myself have I sworn, saith the Lord, for because thou hast done this thing, and hast not withheld thy son, thine only son: That in blessing I will bless thee, and in multiplying I will multiply thy seed as the stars of the heaven, and as the sand which is upon the sea shore; and thy seed shall possess the gate of his enemies; and in thy seed shall all the nations of the earth be blessed; because thou hast obeyed my voice.

In Canaan Abraham was known as Ibri (Hebrew), and his family Ibris, which means "from across"—the Euphrates. The characteristic difference between the Hebrews and the other tribes in Canaan was that the Hebrews did not worship idols as did the others.

To settle a later dispute between Sarah and Hagar, Abraham sent Hagar and her son Ishmael away into the desert. However, as foretold by the Lord, Ishmael later had twelve sons, all of whom became princes.

Isaac, Abraham's only son by Sarah, later married, and we now quote from the 25th Chapter of Genesis:

> And Isaac was forty years old when he took Rebekah to wife, the daughter of Bethuel the Syrian of Padanaram, the sister of Laban the Syrian. And Isaac entreated the Lord for his wife, because she was barren: and the Lord was entreated of him, and Rebekah his wife conceived. And the children struggled together within her; and she said, If it be so, why am I thus? And she went to enquire of the Lord. And the Lord said unto her, Two nations are in thy womb, and two manner of people shall be separated from thy bowels; and the one people shall be stronger than the other people; and the elder shall serve the younger. And when her days to be delivered were fulfilled, behold, there were twins in her womb.

And Esau was the first twin to be delivered, hence the first-born, and Jacob the twin brother.

Esau became a great hunter, and because Isaac loved the venison which Esau brought home to him, he became partial to his son Esau. Jacob, on the other hand, was the favorite son of his mother Rebekah. Again we shall quote from Genesis, the 25th Chapter:

> And Jacob sod (stewed) pottage: and Esau came from the field, and he was faint: and Esau said to Jacob, Feed me, I pray thee, with that same red pottage; for I am faint: Therefore was his name called Edom. And Jacob said, Sell me this day thy birthright. And Esau said, Behold, I am at the point to die: and what profit shall this birthright do to me? And Jacob said, Swear to me this day; and he sware unto him; and he sold his birthright unto Jacob. Then Jacob gave Esau bread and pottage of lentils; and he did eat and drink, and rose up, and went his way; Thus Esau despised his birthright.

Isaac did not want his sons to marry a Canaanite, for

Canaanites were idol-worshippers. Therefore, Esau married a daughter of Ishmael, his uncle.

Jacob later managed by deceit to get his now-blind father's blessing by seeming to be Esau. When Esau learned of this he planned in anger to kill his twin-brother Jacob. Rebekah learned of Esau's intentions and arranged with Isaac to send Jacob away to Padan-aram, ostensibly to seek a wife from among her brother Laban's daughters, and at the same time give Esau's wrath time to assuage.

One night on the way to Padan-aram Jacob had a dream, and here we quote from the 28th Chapter of Genesis:

> And he dreamed, and behold a ladder set up on the earth, and the top of it reached to heaven: and behold the angels of God ascending on it. And, behold the Lord stood above it, and said, I am the Lord God of Abraham thy father, and the God of Isaac, the land whereupon thou liest, to thee will I give it, and to thy seed; and thy seed shall be as the dust of the earth; and thou shalt spread abroad to the west, and to the east, and to the north, and to the south: and in thee and in thy seed shall all the families of the earth be blessed. And, behold, I am with thee, and will keep thee in all places whither thou goest, and will bring thee again into this land; for I will not leave thee until I have done that which I have spoken to thee of.

Jacob continued on to Laban, his uncle, and remained with him a number of years, first to give his brother Esau's anger time to cool off, and secondly, to serve his uncle Laban for seven years for his daughter Rachel for his wife. Through his uncle's subterfuge, his service was extended to seven years more, for he wanted Rachel and not Leah, the elder daughter whom Laban offered at the end of the first seven years' service.

Jacob brought prosperous times for Laban who became very rich in livestock as well as in other valuables. Jacob served six years more to earn cattle. When Jacob finally left Laban to return to Canaan, he took with him Laban's daughter Leah as well as Rachel, along with eleven sons and one daughter named Dinah, all born of Leah, Rachel and their handmaids. He also took with him a large number of servants with their families, and a great herd of livestock.

Jacob sent representatives ahead with gifts to arrange for a reconciliation with Esau. Before Jacob met Esau and during a period when he was alone, he wrestled at night with what he at first thought was a man but who turned out to be an angel. Jacob would not let him go until he received a blessing from him, and the angel said unto him:

> What is thy name? And he said, Jacob. And he said, Thy name shall be called no more Jacob, but Israel; for as a prince hast thou power with God and with men, and hast prevailed.

Reconciliation was accomplished with Esau without even the acceptance of Jacob's tendered gifts. Esau, too, had prospered after Jacob's flight to Laban, and had become wealthy.

Subsequently Rachel died during the birth of her second son, Benjamin, and Jacob's twelfth son, apparently his only child born in Canaan. The first-born of Rachel, Joseph, was the favorite son of Jacob, which favoritism caused jealousy among the other brothers. This jealousy was further aggravated by Joseph's dream that the brothers would at some future time bow down before him. They therefore connived to kill him by putting him at the bottom of a dry well in the desert. Judah finally dissuaded them, and as a compromise Joseph's brethren sold him to a passing Ishmaelite caravan enroute to Egypt.

Famine in Canaan later led Jacob to send his sons to Egypt to purchase corn, where he learned it was plentiful. To the great shock and embarrassment of the brothers, they discovered that their brother Joseph was now the equivalent of prime minister of Egypt and to whom they now found themselves bowing down as predicted in Joseph's prior dream. To shorten the story, this initial contact with Joseph eventually brought the Israelites to Egypt where they settled in Goshen on the Nile, first as a free people, at least while Joseph was alive.

The tendency of the Israelites to keep apart and not become integrated with the Egyptians and worship their gods, made the King suspicious of them, especially after they rapidly increased in population, even to the point of threatening to outnumber the Egyptians. This suspicion eventually led the King to make the Israelites slaves, thus keeping them under his firm control.

Moses, an Israelite of the tribe of Levi, escaped being killed when a baby as a decree had been issued that all Israelite male babies should be killed. He had by the subterfuge of his real parents been adopted by the daughter of the King. Moses subsequently received the best education of that time, and had finally become a general in the Egyptian army. As he had been made aware of his early ancestry, he was naturally sympathetic to the plight of his people and their abuse as slaves. One day he witnessed the cruelty of an Egyptian taskmaster toward one of his people, lost his temper, and killed the Egyptian. This forced him to flee to Midian in Arabia. There he served as a shepherd for Jethro, a Midianite priest, and he eventually married Zipporah, one of Jethro's daughters.

One day while serving as a shepherd on a lonely mountainside and brooding over the slavery of his people in Egypt, he experienced a theophany. He first saw an angel in a burst of flame. Then he noticed the flame came from a burning bush that was not consumed. We shall at this point quote from the third chapter of Exodus:

And when the Lord saw that he turned aside to see, God called unto him out of the midst of the bush, and said, Moses, Moses. And he said, Here am I. And he said, Draw not nigh hither; put off thy shoes from off thy feet, for the place whereon thou standest is holy ground. Moreover he said, I am the God of thy father, the God of Abraham, the God of Isaac, and the God of Jacob. And Moses hid his face; for he was afraid to look upon God. And the Lord said, I have surely seen the affliction of my people which are in Egypt, and have heard their cry by reason of their taskmasters; for I know their sorrows; and I am come down to deliver them out of the hand of the Egyptians, and to bring them up out of that land unto a good land and a large, unto a land flowing with milk and honey; unto the place of the Canaanites, and the Hittites, and the Amorites, and the Perizzites, and the Hivites, and the Jebusites. Now, therefore, behold, the cry of the children of Israel is come unto me: and I have also seen the oppression wherewith the Egyptians oppress them. Come now therefore, and I will send thee unto Pharaoh, that thou mayest bring forth my people the children of Israel out of Egypt.

311

Moses was very reluctant to accept the gigantic task to which God wanted to assign to him, saying that he was no speaker. God's answer to this excuse was: "Thy brother Aaron shall be thy prophet (speaker)." Moses then asked the Lord what name to give if the Israelites should inquire who gave him authority. "And God said unto Moses, I AM THAT I AM: and he said, Thus shalt thou say unto the children of Israel, I AM hath sent me unto you."

Moses was finally persuaded, and he returned to Egypt. He first revealed God's significant message and purpose to his brother Aaron.

There subsequently ensued considerable dickering, with Aaron as spokesman, with the new pharaoh (the former pharaoh having died since Moses' flight). Using sorcery and the threat of various plagues as persuaders, Moses was finally given permission from the pharaoh to take the Israelites to Midian, ostensibly to worship. The pharaoh later reneged on his promise as he had on prior ones, and sent his great army consisting of some six-hundred chariots after the fleeing Israelites. But to no avail, for the God of Israel had enabled his chosen people to cross the Red Sea which later engulfed the pursuing Egyptian army. It was a miracle how over sixty-thousand slave people could elude the greatest army of that time. From the twelfth chapter of Exodus we now quote:

> Now the sojourning of the children of Israel, who dwelt in Egypt was four hundred and thirty years. And it came to pass at the end of the four hundred and thirty years, even the selfsame day it came to pass, that all the hosts of the Lord went out from the land of Egypt . . . And Moses took the bones of Joseph with him: for he (Joseph) had straitly sworn the children of Israel, saying, God will surely visit you; and ye shall carry up my bones away hence with you.

These happenings, according to recent authorities, occurred about the thirteenth century B.C.

Moses' troubles had just begun, for he faced a very difficult time in keeping the Israelites pacified during their trials in the wilderness. They continually blamed him for having brought them out of Egypt where things were much better for them even as slaves than they were now as free men in the wilderness. First they ran out of water and thereafter food. Moses, with God's help, miraculously obtained water for them, and manna as food, and later quail.

Three months after their flight from Egypt, the Israelites came into the wilderness of Sinai, and camped before the Mount. At this point we shall quote from the nineteenth chapter of Exodus:

> And Moses went up unto God, and the Lord called unto him out of the mountain, saying, Thus shalt thou say to the house of Jacob, and tell the children of Israel; Ye have seen what I did unto the Egyptians, and how I bare you on eagles' wings, and brought you unto myself. Now therefore, if you will obey my voice indeed, and keep my covenant, then ye shall be a peculiar treasure unto me above all people; for all the earth is mine: And ye shall be unto me a kingdom of priests, and a holy nation. These are the words which thou shalt speak unto the children of Israel.

Moses passed on God's message to the elders, "And all the people answered together, and said: All that the Lord hath spoken we will do. And Moses returned the words of the people unto the Lord." To this acceptance by the people God said:

> And the Lord said unto Moses, Lo, I come unto thee in a thick cloud, that the people may hear when I speak with thee, and believe thee for ever. And Moses told the words of the people unto the Lord. And the Lord said unto Moses, Go unto the people, and sanctify them to-day and to-morrow, and let them wash their clothes, And be ready against the third day: for the third day the Lord will come down in the sight of all the people upon Mount Sinai. And thou shalt set bounds unto the people round about, saying, Take heed to yourself, that ye go not up into the mount, or touch the border of it: whosoever toucheth the mount shall be surely put to death.

Moses followed God's instructions. We shall now quote further from the nineteenth chapter as follows:

> And it came to pass on the third day in the morning,

that there were thunders and lightnings, and a thick cloud upon the mount, and the voice of the trumpet exceeding loud; so that all the people that was in the camp trembled. And Moses brought forth the people out of the camp to meet with God; and they stood at the nether part of the mount. And Mount Sinai was altogether on a smoke, because the Lord descended upon it in fire: and the smoke thereof ascended as the smoke of a furnace, and the whole mount quaked greatly. And when the voice of the trumpet sounded long, and waxed louder and louder, Moses spake, and God answered him by a voice. And the Lord came down upon Mount Sinai, on the top of the mount; and the Lord called Moses up to the top of the mount: and Moses went up.

From the twentieth chapter of Exodus, we shall continue quoting:

And God spake all these words, saying. I am the Lord thy God, which have brought thee out of the Land of Egypt, out of the house of bondage.

Thou shalt have no other gods before me.

Thou shalt not make unto thee any graven image, or any likeness of anything that is in heaven above, or that is in the earth beneath, or that is in the water under the earth:

Thou shalt not bow down thyself to them, nor serve them: for I the Lord thy God am a jealous God, visiting the iniquity of the fathers upon the children unto the third and fourth generation of them that hate me; And shewing mercy unto thousands of them that love me, and keep my commandments.

Thou shalt not take the name of the Lord thy God in vain, for the Lord will not hold him guiltless that taketh his name in vain.

Remember the sabbath day, to keep it holy. Six days shalt thou labor, and do all thy work: But the seventh day is the sabbath of the Lord thy God: in it thou shalt not do any work, thou, nor thy son, nor thy daughter, thy manservant, nor thy maidservant, nor thy cattle, nor thy stranger that is within thy gates: For in six days the Lord made heaven and earth, the sea, and all that in

314

them is, and rested the seventh day: wherefore the Lord blessed the sabbath day, and hallowed it.

Honor thy father and thy mother: that thy days may be long upon the land which the Lord thy God giveth thee.

Thou shalt not kill. (Actual original meaning "slay—murder.")

Thou shalt not commit adultery.

Thou shalt not steal.

Thou shalt not bear false witness against thy neighbor.

Thou shalt not covet thy neighbor's house, thou shalt not covet thy neighbor's wife, nor his manservant, nor his maidservant, nor his ox, nor his ass, nor any thing that is thy neighbor's.

And all the people saw the thunderings, and the lightnings, and the noise of the trumpet, and the mountain smoking: and when the people saw it, they removed, and stood afar off.

And they said unto Moses, Speak thou with us, and we will hear, but let not God speak with us, lest we die.

And Moses said unto the people, Fear not: for God is come to prove you, and that his fear may be before your faces, that ye sin not.

And the people stood afar off, and Moses drew near unto the thick darkness where God was. And the Lord said unto Moses, thou shalt say unto the children of Israel, Ye have seen that I have talked with you from heaven. Ye shall not make with me gods of silver, neither shall ye make unto you gods of gold. An altar of earth thou shalt make unto me, and shalt sacrifice thereon thy burnt offerings, and thy peace offerings, thy sheep, and thine oxen: in all places where I record my name I will come unto thee, and I will bless thee.

And if thou wilt make me an altar of stone, thou shalt not build it of hewn stone: for if thou lift up thy tool upon it, thou hast polluted it. Neither shalt thou go up by steps unto mine altar, that thy nakedness be not discovered thereon.

Thus the Israelites were the first people to make a covenant with God. The immensity of their responsibility was far beyond their imagination. Moses alone perhaps appreciated somewhat

the importance and significance of that responsibility. In biological terms it might be stated that the Israelites were to become
the nucleus of a new living cell, with the ten commandments
as its basic chromosomes, and the cytoplasm representing the
rest of mankind.

It was during this period that judges were to render judgments on the basis of: "Eye for eye, tooth for tooth, hand for
hand, foot for foot," etc., which meant—let the punishment fit
the crime.

To re-emphasize to the children of Israel the importance of
resisting the temptation to idol-worship, we quote from the
twenty-third chapter of Exodus:

> Behold, I send an Angel before thee, to keep thee in
> the way, and to bring thee into the place which I have
> prepared. Beware of him, and obey his voice, provoke
> him not; for he will not pardon your transgressions: for
> my name is in him. But if thou shalt indeed obey his
> voice, and do all that I speak; then I will be an enemy
> unto thine enemies, and an adversary unto thine adver-
> saries. For mine Angel shall go before thee, and bring
> thee in unto the Amorites, and the Hittites, and the
> Perizzites, and the Jebusites: and I will cut them off.
> Thou shalt not bow down to their gods, nor serve them,
> nor do after their works; but thou shalt utterly over-
> throw them, and quite break down their images.

And from the twenty-fourth chapter we quote:

> And Moses wrote all the words of the Lord, and
> rose up early in the morning, and builded an altar under
> the hill, and twelve pillars, according to the twelve tribes
> of Israel.

From the same chapter we shall further quote:

> And the Lord said unto Moses, Come up to me into
> the mount, and be there: and I will give thee tables of
> stone, and a law, and commandments which I have writ-
> ten; that thou mayest teach them. And Moses rose up,
> and his minister Joshua: and Moses went up into the
> mount of God. And he (Moses) said unto the elders,

Tarry ye here for us, until we come again unto you: and, behold, Aaron and Hur are with you: if any man have any matters to do, let him come unto them. And Moses went up into the mount, and a cloud covered the mount. And the glory of the Lord abode upon Mount Sinai, and the cloud covered it six days: and the seventh day he called unto Moses out of the midst of the cloud. And the sight of the glory of the Lord was like devouring fire on the top of the mount in the eyes of the children of Israel. And Moses went into the midst of the cloud, and gat him up into the mount: and Moses was in the mount forty days and forty nights.

During this second meeting on the mount, the Lord commanded Moses, apparently with Joshua in attendance, to have built a tabernacle (a sort of portable synagogue), and issued through Moses minute instructions as to how it was to be constructed, together with its appurtenances. As to the so-called "mercy seat" to be located in the most holy place, we quote from the twenty-fifth chapter:

And thou shalt put the mercy seat above upon the ark; and in the ark thou shalt put the testimony that I shall give thee. And there I will meet with thee, and I will commune with thee from above the mercy seat, from between the two cherubim which are upon the ark of the testimony, of all things which I will give thee in commandment unto the children of Israel.

It was also at this second meeting with the Lord on the Mount that the Lord emphasized the importance of the children of Israel keeping the sabbath for a perpetual covenant, as:

It is a sign between me and the children of Israel for ever: for in six days the Lord made heaven and earth, and *on the seventh day he rested,* and *was refreshed.*

During the forty-day meeting with the Lord, the people became impatient because of Moses' delay in returning to them. They said to Aaron, as recorded in the thirty-second chapter of Exodus: "Up, make us gods, which shall go before us; for as for this Moses, the man that brought us up out of the land of Egypt, we wot not what is become of him." To keep them pacified, Aaron built a molten calf of gold from the earrings contributed by the people, and upon its completion the people said: "These be thy gods, O Israel, which brought thee up out of the land of Egypt." So they danced and feasted around the golden calf.

The Lord was fully aware of what was going on and so informed Moses on the mount:

> And the Lord said unto Moses, I have seen this people, and, behold, it is a stiffnecked people; Now therefore let me alone, that my wrath may wax hot against them, and that I may consume them: and I will make of thee (Moses) a great nation.

How many wouldn't have seized this opening for self-aggrandizement. But Moses pleaded with the Lord and finally persuaded Him from His threatened action. Moses thereupon went down the mountain carrying with him the tables of stone on which the Lord had written, accompanied by Joshua. The sight which greeted Moses and Joshua aroused Moses' anger to such an extent that he threw the stone tables down, breaking them. "And he took the calf which they had made, and burnt it in the fire, and ground it to powder, and stewed it upon the water, and made the children of Israel drink of it." (Apparently for purposes of roughage to get idolatry out of their system.)

Further quoting from the thirty-second chapter of Exodus:

> And it came to pass on the morrow, that Moses said unto the people, You have sinned a great sin: and now I will go up unto the Lord; peradventure I shall make an atonement for your sin. And Moses returned unto the Lord, and said, Oh, this people have sinned a great sin, and have made them gods of gold. Yet now, if thou wilt forgive their sin—; and if not, blot me, I pray thee, out of thy book which thou hast written. And the Lord said unto Moses, Whosoever hath sinned against me, him will I blot out of my book. Therefore now go, lead the people unto the place of which I have spoken unto thee: behold, mine Angel shall go before thee; nevertheless in the day when I visit I will visit their sin upon them. And the

Lord plagued the people, because they made the calf, which Aaron made.

Moses repeated to the people what the Lord had said: "for I will not go up in the midst of thee; for thou art a stiffnecked people; lest I consume thee in the way." When they heard this they did not put on their ornaments and went into mourning.

Moses finally succeeded after a meeting with God in persuading Him to forgive the Israelites and restore them to the status of being his chosen people. During his pleading Moses had even offered himself up to God as atonement for his people. God finally relented, and we quote here from the thirty-third chapter of Exodus:

> For wherein shall it be known here that I (Moses) and thy people have found grace in thy sight? Is it not in that thou goest with us? so shall we be separated, I and thy people, from all the people that are upon the face of the earth. And the Lord said unto Moses, I will do this thing also that thou hast spoken: for thou hast found grace in my sight, and I know thee by name.
>
> And he (Moses) said, I beseech thee, shew me thy glory, and he said, I will make all my goodness pass before thee, and I will proclaim the name of the Lord before thee, and will be gracious to whom I will be gracious, and will shew mercy on whom I will shew mercy. And He said, Thou canst not see my face; for there shall no man see me, and live. And the Lord said, Behold, there is a place by me, and thou shalt stand upon a rock: And it shall come to pass, while my glory passeth by, that I will put thee in a cleft of the rock, and will cover thee with my hand while I pass by: And will take away mine hand, and thou shalt see my back parts: but my face shalt not be seen.

Moses was thereupon instructed to hew two more tables, on which the following morning on the Mount God wrote the same words written on the first tables.

We shall now quote from the thirty-fourth chapter of Exodus:

And the Lord passed by before him, and proclaimed,
The Lord, the Lord God, merciful and gracious, long-
suffering, and abundant in goodness and truth, Keeping
mercy for thousands, forgiving iniquity and transgression
and sin, and that will by no means clear the guilty; visiting the iniquity of the fathers upon the children, and
upon the children's children, unto the third and to the
fourth generation.

(This would seem to suggest that while the sins of the individual may be forgiven, yet the consequences of those sins
continue on to following generations, on a sort of Mendelian
basis of inheritance.)

The tables of stone were thereupon placed by Moses in
the Ark of the Covenant, which was later kept in the Most Holy
Place in the tabernacle.

The codified laws of Moses appear in Exodus and Deuteronomy. These were later expanded by the later decisions and
interpretations by rabbis. These expanded laws are now known
as the Talmud.

After spending many years in the wilderness, during which
time they became a hardy people, the Israelites finally arrived
opposite the promised land. Thereupon God said to Moses
according to the following quotation taken from the thirty-
fourth chapter of Deuteronomy:

And the Lord said unto him, This is the land which
I sware unto Abraham, unto Isaac, and unto Jacob,
saying, I will give it unto thy seed: I have caused thee
to see it with thine eyes, but thou shalt not go over
thither. So Moses the servant of the Lord died there in the
land of Moab according to the word of the Lord. And he
buried him in a valley in the land of Moab, over against
Beth-peor; but no man knoweth of his sepulchre unto
this day.

And the Lord then commissioned Joshua, Moses' minister,
quoting from the first chapter of the Book of Joshua:

Now after the death of Moses the servant of the Lord
it came to pass, that the Lord spake unto Joshua the son
of Nun, Moses' minister, saying, Moses my servant is

dead, now therefore arise, go over this Jordan, thou, and all this people, unto the land which I do give to them, even to the children of Israel. . . .

There shall not any man be able to stand before thee all the days of thy life: as I was with Moses, so I will be with thee: I will not fail thee, nor forsake thee. Be strong and of a good courage; for unto this people shalt thou divide for an inheritance the land, which I sware unto their fathers to give them.

And thereupon, the Israelites under Joshua's leadership, occupied and settled the promised land "with great vigor."

After Joshua's death, the Israelites were ruled by six so-called "great" and six "minor" judges. During the rule of Samuel, their old respected priest and the last of the great judges, the Israelites appealed to him that they be given a king like their neighboring nations. Samuel was very reluctant to acquiesce to this appeal but finally anointed Saul as their first king. He reminded them that the Lord alone was their king and that only trouble could come from anointing a worldly king.

After Saul came King David. Under David's son Solomon, whose mother was Bathsheba, the Israelic nation reached its highest glory. Solomon during his reign built the First Temple in Jerusalem, a magnificent structure. As Solomon was a tolerant, broadminded king he also built so-called "cult sites" to the gods of his many pagan wives. But, the Israelitic covenant with God had been broken, and the consequences thereof were soon to develop.

Solomon's death marked the beginning of the division of the Israelitic nation. First it was divided into the Northern Kingdom, composed of ten tribes, and the Southern Kingdom, composed of the tribes of Benjamin and Judah. The Northern Kingdom eventually was conquered by the Assyrians in 722 B.C., and its ten tribes were carried off into captivity, never to be heard from again. The Kingdom of Judea (the Southern Kingdom), however, continued until about 600 B.C., when Nebuchadnezzar conquered it, and led the Judeans into Babylonian captivity. In 537 B.C. they were freed by the decree of Cyrus II, the Persian, after Babylonia was conquered by the Medes and Persians under the leadership of Cyrus II. Incidentally, the Babylonian captivity of the Israelites, as well as the subsequent freeing by Cyrus II, was foretold by the Prophet Isaiah around

722 B.C., over a hundred years prior to their actual occurrence.

The temple was rebuilt in Jerusalem with the assistance of Cyrus II, and under the inspiration and leadership of both Ezra, the scribe, and Nehemiah, the governor. Ezra tried diligently to re-establish the purity of the "holy seed" which had become quite mixed during their captivity. The Maccabees then ruled as kings until 37 B.C., when Herod usurped the throne with Roman assistance. The abortive revolt against the Romans in 70 A.D. led to the total destruction of Jerusalem, along with its second temple, by the Roman general Titus, later to become Roman Emperor Titus.

During the period of the kings, numerous prophets of God tried to warn the kings and their people against their continual disobedience of the laws of God revealed to Moses, all to no avail. Isaiah, especially, warned his people against forsaking their reliance on Jehovah for reliance on princes. When they failed to heed his warnings, he foresaw nothing but woe and gloom for his people.

There is no question of the fulfillment of God's promise to Abraham concerning the great number of his seed and their influence among the nations of the world.

The sacred scriptures of Judaism are The Old Testament, consisting of the Five Books of Law, called Torah, the historical books, the Prophets, and other miscellaneous writings.

There are about 12,000,000 adherents to Judaism, about 2,500,000 in Israel, 3,000,000 in Europe, mostly in Russia and Poland, and about 6,500,000 in North and South America, mostly in the United States.

They are today divided into three main branches, Orthodox, Conservative, and Reform, each with numerous sects.

As a parting word on Judaism we cannot resist quoting the words of Martin Buber (1878-1965), an outstanding exponent of Hasidic philosophy, on the subject of Judaism, taken from a speech delivered in 1937 on "The Prejudices of Youth":

> "As regards its actual form, Judaism also is a mixture of the false and the genuine, but as regards its genuine character, we find a great unity of everything genuine and original and pure which we need to overcome our unjustified prejudices; the meaningfulness of history, the sovereignty of spirit, the verifiability of truth, the power of decision ensuing from personal responsibility, the

spontaneity between men and—finally—faith as the engagement of one's entire life to the Lord of the one voice, who wishes to be recognized in each of his manifestations."

Islam

Islam means "submission to the will of God." This is the name of the religion founded in 622 A.D. by Muhammad ibn Abdullah (580-632 A.D.) in the City of Mecca, Arabia. The religion is most commonly called Muhammadanism, but its adherents, known as Muslims (true believers), desire it to be called Islam.

Their basic confession of faith is: "There is no God but Allah, and Muhammad is His prophet."

The Muslims trace the roots of their religion back to Terah, and his son Abraham, some even back to Adam. The source of their beliefs is based upon "The Book," the same as Judaism and Christianity.

The Muslims are the descendants of Ishmael, Abraham's son by Hagar, the Egyptian. Ishmael's descendants became the Arabians, and their capital city was Mecca. This is also where the so-called Black Stone, said to be from Adam's time, is located, as well as the Kaaba, the temple, and the famous well which Ishmael as a baby is said to have brought into being by his kick.

Subsequently, Mecca became a prosperous city of merchants who, as a side-line, sold water from the sacred well for profit. The Arabians eventually became doubtful about the sacredness of water sold for profit, and gradually became cynical of all beliefs. In their place they sought out fortune-tellers to solve their personal problems, and also indulged in gambling, excessive drinking, and of course women. The manufacture and sale of idols proved to be a profitable industry for the merchants. The pilgrims regularly visiting Mecca, the sacred city, could be counted on to keep the idol industry flourishing.

Muhammad was born of aristocratic parents in Mecca, but he became an orphan at the age of six, and was brought up by an uncle. He apparently had very little, if any, schooling, for he was unable personally to put his later teachings into writing but depended on his secretary, Abu Bekr. Muhammad began working as an assistant to shepherds and finally became a full-fledged shepherd. Later he became a camel-driver in caravans.

As Muhammad proved very trustworthy and efficient, he finally was placed in charge of the caravans of a very wealthy widow, named Kadijah, in Mecca. She was much impressed by Muhammad, not only with his services but also with his personality, for while he was short in stature, he was broad-shouldered and powerfully built, possessed of heavy black hair, and a dynamic personality. Eventually through intermediaries, the suggestion was passed on to Muhammad that Kadijah would be receptive to him as a husband. He had been likewise impressed with her. The subsequent marriage turned out to be a very happy one in spite of the variance in ages, she being forty and he twenty-five at the time of their marriage. Needless to say, their caravan business continued to prosper.

The continual scenes of drunkenness, gambling, and idol-worshipping among his fellow Arabians troubled Muhammad; in fact he would go out into the hills and brood over the disgusting state of affairs. During his travels he had been impressed by what he had heard and seen of the religions of Judaism and Christianity. In fact, a cousin of his wife was a convert to Judaism and would read to him from the Old and New Testaments.

On one of his lonely visits to the countryside he reported a meeting with the Angel Gabriel. At first he was fearful about his mental balance and confided his experience to his wife. She surprisingly became interested and encouraged him to continue his meditations. Another meeting with the Angel Gabriel assured him of his calling—to convert his people away from their idol-worship. He began preaching in Mecca, at first with much fear and trepidation.

From the very beginning he would assert to the people, "There is no God but Allah, and Muhammad is His prophet." The people subjected him to much ridicule and would challenge him for proof. They had many gods, in fact one for every day of the year; their prevailing religion was one of animistic polytheism. True, Allah Taala was one of their many gods, but Muhammad now proclaimed that he was the only god.

The challenge of proof at first embarrassed him, and finally as proof he told them to observe the wonders of creation, the earth and the sky; here was the proof of the existence of Allah as the one and only true god, for he and he alone was the creator of those wonders. Still they refused to take his preaching seriously. Muhammad did succeed in converting part of his family, as well as Abu Bekr, his first follower and who later as his secretary recorded Muhammad's speeches.

The merchants paid no attention to his activity until he began to criticize them for capitalizing on the superstition of the people, selling Idols, as well as selling water from the sacred well to pilgrims. This potential threat to their flourishing industry led them eventually to force Muhammad to flee Mecca to save his own life. This flight took place when Muhammad was forty-three years of age, and the Muslims count time from the year of Muhammad's flight Anno Hegira from Mecca to Yathrib. At Yathrib the people were sympathetic to his teachings as they had previously sent delegations to Mecca to inquire into them. Yathrib, incidentally, had a small Jewish community from whom the Arabs had become acquainted with the one-god idea.

As he became convinced that the only way to convert the people of Mecca was by force, he began robbing the caravans out of Mecca, not only to get money to buy arms for the army he was organizing but also to needle the merchants to send out a force to engage his army. The merchants reacted sooner than Muhammad anticipated and his unprepared army was overwhelmed. However, he was not discouraged but reorganized and enlarged his army, and was finally able to march on Mecca with a force of ten thousand men. Word of their march soon spread to Mecca, and the people in fear fled to the hills. Muhammad's army entered Mecca without any resistance. At Muhammad's instructions, all the idols were systematically destroyed but nothing else in the city was damaged. When the people finally ventured back to their city and found things as they had left them except for the idols, they willingly embraced the religion of Muhammad.

The death of his faithful wife Kadijah was a great blow to Muhammad, but he tenaciously continued his efforts to spread his religion among all the tribes of Arabia, as well as to some foreign tribes. To them Muhammad said:

> My teachings are simple;
> Allah is the One God, and Muhammad is His prophet;
> Give up idolatry;
> Do not steal;
> Do not lie;

Do not slander;
And never become intoxicated.
If you follow these teachings, then you follow Islam.

Muslims claim that God's revelation to man has proceeded through four great stages: first, through Abraham monotheism was revealed; second, through Moses the Ten Commandments of God were given; third, through Jesus the Golden Rule was revealed, and finally through Muhammad, the last prophet, the question was answered as to how specifically the love of neighbor was to be carried out. "The glory of Islam consists in having embodied the beautiful sentiment of Jesus into definite laws." The first important rules of true believers according to Islam are:

Believe in Allah, and Muhammad, His Prophet;
Pray five times each day;
Be kind to the poor and give alms;
Keep the Fasts during the Month of Fasts;
And make the yearly pilgrimage to Mecca, the Holy City.

In addition there are certain social laws.

Following Muhammad's death at sixty-two years of age, his loyal follower and secretary Abu Bekr, took over the leadership of the movement. Later, by the sword, the Muslims spread north to Syria, east to India and China, and west to northern Africa, and even up to Spain. There, however, they met defeat and retreated back to Africa. The promise of a percentage of the plunder and the assurance of immediate entrance to heaven to those killed on the battlefield, naturally improved the fighting spirit of their armies.

The religion of Islam appears to be particularly popular and attractive to the colored people of Africa, possibly because of its simplicity and lack of stringent requirements.

The Muslims have given us such great philosophers and thinkers as Avicenna and Averroës. A great Muslim philosopher has written: "This inexplicable finite centre of experience (man) is the fundamental fact of the universe. All life is individual; there is no such thing as universal life. God Himself is an individual: He is the most unique individual."

The adherents of Islam number around 400,000,000, which

are distributed mainly in Arabia, Pakistan, Africa, part of China, Indonesia, and Asiatic Russia. The Muslims are divided into two main divisions: the Sunnites, who believe the Caliph should be selected, and the Shi'ites, who believe the Caliphate should be made up of descendants of Muhammad. Each division is comprised of many sects.

The sacred book of Islam is the Koran.

Christianity

"But when the fulness of the time was come, God sent forth his Son, made of a woman, made under the law."

Gal. 4:4

Like Judaism and Islam, Christianity is an historical religion, progressively revealed, in fact it is most closely intermeshed by prophecy with Judaism, and carries on where Judaism left off.

For the chronological sequence of the life of Jesus, we shall rely on the Gospel According to Luke rather than on the other three gospels according to Matthew, Mark, and John.

According to most biblical scholars, Luke, the author of the third gospel, was a physician by profession, a gentile Christian, apparently of Greek cultural background. He later became a co-worker and personal physician of Apostle Paul, accompanying him on many of his missionary journeys. Luke also personally met Peter and John, and others who had been associated personally with Jesus. From all the information he gathered of Jesus' activities from these eyewitnesses, as well as from other sources, including the gospel of Mark, he wrote the only gospel following a strictly historically chronological sequence. He addressed this account to his friend Theophilus, an apparently distinguished friend, "that you mightest know the certainty of those things wherein thou hast been instructed." (This assertion by Luke is refreshing and would have pleased Goethe who once said, "Tell me of your certainties: I have doubts enough of my own.")

In the first chapter of this gospel Luke cites the events leading up to the birth of John the Baptist as well as the birth of Jesus. Briefly, they are as follows:

There lived in the days of Herod (the king of Judea), a

righteous priest named Zacharias, and his wife Elizabeth. Although they had prayed for an offspring, they at an advanced age were still childless. One day while Zacharias was performing his priestly functions in the privacy of the altar within the temple, he was frightened by the sudden appearance of an angel who said, "Fear not, Zacharias: for thy prayer is heard; and thy wife Elizabeth shall bear thee a son, and thou shalt call his name John." . . . "And many of the children of Israel shall he turn to the Lord their God." . . . "to make ready a people prepared for the Lord."

In the sixth month of the subsequent pregnancy of Elizabeth, the same angel, who was Gabriel, appeared in Nazareth of Galilee to a virgin espoused to a man whose name was Joseph, both of the house of David; and continuing from the first chapter of Luke:

> And the virgin's name was Mary. And the angel came in unto her and said, Hail, thou that art highly favored, the Lord is with thee: blessed art thou among women. And when she saw him, she was troubled at his saying, and cast in her mind what manner of salutation this should be. And the angel said unto her, Fear not Mary, for thou hast found favor with God, And, behold, thou shalt conceive in thy womb, and bring forth a son, and shalt call his name Jesus. He shall be great, and shall be called the Son of the Highest: and the Lord God shall give unto him the throne of his father David: And he shall reign over the house of Jacob for ever; and of his kingdom there shall be no end. Then said Mary unto the angel, How shall this be, seeing I know not a man? And the angel answered and said unto her, The Holy Ghost shall come upon thee, and the power of the Highest shall overshadow thee: therefore also that holy thing which shall be born of thee shall be called the Son of God. And behold, thy cousin Elizabeth, she hath also conceived a son in her old age; and this is the sixth month with her, who was called barren. For with God nothing shall be impossible. And Mary said, Behold the handmaid of the Lord; be it unto me according to thy word. And the angel departed from her.

Mary immediately followed her first impulse, to visit her

cousin Elizabeth and confide in her the visit of the angel and his astounding message. Mary was greeted with open arms by her cousin, who not only confirmed what the angel had stated as to her pregnancy, but that she had also been foretold of the angel's visit and message to Mary.

In due time a son was born to Zacharias and Elizabeth, who was named John by his parents according to the angel's instruction.

Mary's subsequent pregnancy almost resulted in a separation from Joseph, her espoused. However, as mentioned in the gospel of Matthew, Joseph had a dream in which an angel revealed to him God's purpose with Mary, and this dissuaded him from his contemplated action.

A subsequent decree from Caesar Augustus (Palestine then being under Roman rule) that all should go to their home city to be taxed, necessitated that Joseph take his pregnant wife with him from Nazareth, Galilee, to Bethlehem, Judea, his home city, as he was of the house and lineage of David. While in Bethlehem, Mary gave birth to her first-born son, and named him Jesus as the angel had instructed. Certain shepherds, watching over their flock by night, had a sudden visitation by an angel, as brought out in the second chapter of Luke as follows:

And, lo, the angel of the Lord came upon them, and the glory of the Lord shone round about them: and they were sore afraid. And the angel said unto them, Fear not; for, behold, I bring you good tidings of great joy, which shall be to all people. For unto you is born this day in the city of David a Saviour, which is Christ the Lord. And this shall be a sign unto you; Ye shall find the babe wrapped in swaddling clothes, lying in a manger. And suddenly there was with the angel a multitude of the heavenly host praising God, and saying, Glory to God in the highest, and on earth peace, good will toward men.

After the visitation the shepherds went to Bethlehem and found Joseph and Mary with the babe Jesus where the angel had stated.

Eight days after its birth, the babe was circumcised and given the name Jesus as the angel had instructed. He was subsequently brought to Jerusalem by the parents to be presented to the Lord according to the law of Moses which applies to first-born male children. There Simeon, a devout old man, approached the parents and took the child in his arms, happily asserting that he had been promised that he would see the Lord's Christ before he died. He went on to say:

> Lord, now lettest thou thy servant depart in peace, according to thy word: For mine eyes have seen thy salvation, Which thou hast prepared before the face of all people; A light to lighten the Gentiles, and the glory of thy people Israel.

Both parents naturally marvelled at Simeon's statement.

It is brought out in the gospel of Matthew that King Herod, because of a visit of three magis from the East seeking Jesus "the newborn king," put out a decree that all male children two years old and under should be killed. Herod's purpose was revealed to Joseph in a dream, in which he was instructed by an angel to flee with the mother and child to Egypt. Upon the subsequent death of Herod, the angel instructed Joseph to take his wife and child back to Israel. Joseph thereupon took his wife and child to Nazareth, Galilee, where they had formerly resided. "And he came and dwelt in a city called Nazareth: that it might be fulfilled which was spoken by the prophets, He shall be called a Nazarene," as quoted from Matthew 2:23. So it was at Nazareth that Jesus spent his childhood.

The parents would go down to Jerusalem every year at the feast of the passover. On one of these trips, when Jesus was twelve years of age, he became separated from his parents and ended up in the midst of some learned doctors in the temple. He plied them with questions and noted carefully their replies; he apparently impressed them with his precocity. The parents who had started on their way back to Nazareth thinking their son was with the group, suddenly discovered his absence and rushed back to Jerusalem to find him. They finally found him in the temple. His mother immediately reproached him for causing his parents sorrow. "And he said unto them, How is it that ye sought me? wist ye not that I must be about my Father's business?"

In the fifteenth year of the reign of Tiberius Caesar, John, the son of Zacharias, began preaching in the valley of the

Jordan "the baptism of repentance for the remission of sins."
We shall continue quoting from the third chapter of Luke:

> As it is written in the book of the words of Esaias the
> prophet, saying, The voice of one crying in the wilder-
> ness, Prepare ye the way of the Lord, make his paths
> straight. Every valley shall be filled, and every mountain
> and hill shall be brought low; and the crooked shall be
> made straight, and the rough ways shall be made smooth;
> And all flesh shall see the salvation of God. Then said he
> to the multitude that came forth to be baptized of him,
> O generation of vipers, who hath warned you to flee from
> the wrath to come? Bring forth therefore fruits worthy of
> repentance, and begin not to say within yourselves, We
> have Abraham to our father; for I say unto you, That
> God is able of these stones to raise up children unto
> Abraham. And now also the axe is laid unto the root
> of the tree: every tree therefore which bringeth not forth
> good fruit is hewn down, and cast into the fire.

Many people, as the result of John's preaching, repented their
sins and were baptized. Some wondered whether John was the
promised Messiah and they finally asked him directly, and as
quoted from the third chapter:

> John answered, saying unto them all, I indeed baptize
> you with water; but one mightier than I cometh, the
> latchet of whose shoes I am not worthy to unloose; he
> shall baptize you with the Holy Ghost and with fire;
> Whose fan is in his hand, and he will thoroughly purge
> his floor, and will gather the wheat into his garner; but
> chaff he will burn with fire unquenchable.

Jesus was about thirty years of age when he himself came
down to the Jordan to be baptized by John:

> Now when all the people were baptized, it came to
> pass, that Jesus also being baptized, and praying, the
> heaven was opened, and the Holy Ghost descended in a
> bodily shape like a dove upon him, and a voice came from
> heaven, which said, Thou art my beloved Son; in thee
> I am well pleased.

Thereafter Jesus went into the wilderness to think through his powerful spiritual experience and was subjected to many temptations. These temptations apparently involved the use of the power now given him over the so-called natural laws to impress the people of his own greatness. He overcame these temptations and subsequently used his higher powers only in healing the sick and for the welfare of his fellow-man and not for his own glorification.

He returned to Nazareth after his baptism in the Jordan, and on the sabbath day stood up in the synagogue to read from the Book of Isaiah handed to him, as recorded in Chapter four of Luke:

> And when he had opened the book, he found the place where it was written, The spirit of the Lord is upon me, because he hath anointed me to preach the gospel to the poor; he hath sent me to heal the broken-hearted, to preach deliverance to the captives, and recovering of sight to the blind, to set at liberty them that are bruised. To preach the acceptable year of the Lord.
>
> And he closed the book, and he gave it again to the minister, and sat down. And the eyes of all them that were in the synagogue were fastened on him. And he began to say unto them, This day is this scripture fulfilled in your ears.

This formal announcement in the synagogue initiated Jesus' ministry of "going about doing good" (in the words of Simon Peter), healing the sick, the blind, and crippled, teaching God's purpose with mankind—the coming kingdom of God, the significance and necessity of being born again, and instructing his disciples of their future mission. This activity gradually led up to his crucifixion and subsequent resurrection. All this took place in the short period of three years, but it created a leaven among mankind which was to change the course of its history.

He chose his disciples from among the common people, especially from among fisher folk, and made them all "fishers of men." He directed his preaching and teaching among what the pharisees called "sinners and publicans." In fact the pharisees asked Jesus' disciples, "Why do ye eat and drink with publicans and sinners? And Jesus answering said unto them, They that are whole need not a physician; but they that are sick. I came not to call the righteous, but sinners to repentance. And they said unto him," as recorded in Chapter five of Luke:

> Why do the disciples of John fast often, and make prayers, and likewise the disciples of the Pharisees; but thine eat and drink? And he said unto them, Can ye make the children of the bridechamber fast, while the bridegroom is with them? But the days will come, when the bridegroom shall be taken away from them, and then shall they fast in those days,
>
> And he spake also a parable unto them, No man putteth a piece of new garment upon an old; if otherwise, then both the new maketh a rent, and the piece that was taken out of the new agreeth not with the old.
>
> And no man putteth new wine into old bottles; else the new wine will burst the bottles, and be spilled, and the bottles shall perish. But new wine must be put into new bottles; and both are preserved. No man also having drunk old wine straightway desireth new; for he said, The old is better.

Jesus healed many during this period, including the man sick with the palsy and the leper. Naturally these healings amazed the people and they glorified God. The crowds increased to the extent that on the shore of the Sea of Galilee he was forced to borrow Simon Peter's fishing boat from which to preach to the crowds on shore. It was after such an occasion that he suggested to Peter that he throw out his net which resulted in a catch both amazing and humbling to Simon Peter. He now more than ever before realized that Jesus was no ordinary man.

Periodically Jesus felt wearied from his efforts and departed to the mountain to pray. On one of these periods of rest he chose from among his disciples twelve whom he named apostles. When Jesus returned to the plain, a multitude of people from all over Judea, Jerusalem, and from the seacoast of Tyre and Sidon were waiting to hear him and be healed. It was then that he made his famous sermon on the mount, which gives the core of his message to mankind. The most complete account of this sermon appears in the fifth, sixth, and seventh chapters of Matthew's gospel. In this sermon he makes many significant statements, among which are the following:

> Ye are the salt of the earth; but if the salt have lost his savor, wherewith shall it be salted? it is thenceforth good for nothing, but to be cast out, and to be trodden under foot of men. (Matthew 5:13)

> Let your light so shine before men, that they may see your good works, and glorify your Father which is in heaven. (Matthew 5:16)

> But seek ye first the kingdom of God, and his righteousness, and all these things shall be added unto you. (Matthew 6:33)

> Not every one that saith unto me, Lord, Lord, shall enter into the kingdom of heaven; but he that doeth the will of my Father which is in heaven. (Matthew 7:21)

"And it came to pass, when Jesus had ended these sayings, the people were astonished at his doctrine: For he taught them as one having authority, and not as the scribes."

It was during this period that he healed the centurion's servant simply by his word, which word was accepted implicitly by the centurion. In fact the centurion's faith led Jesus to remark to the people, "I say unto you, I have not found so great faith, no, not in Israel."

During this period also it is recorded that Jesus met a funeral procession in which the dead man was the only son of a sorrowing widow. Jesus had compassion on her,

> And said unto her, Weep not. And he came and touched the bier: and they that bore him stood still. And he said, Young man, I say unto thee, Arise, And he that was dead sat up, and began to speak. And he delivered him to his mother.

(How differently Jesus assuaged this widow's sorrow from that of Buddha in a similar situation some five or six hundred years prior.)

In the meantime John the Baptist no doubt had been observing Jesus' activity with great interest and later with great concern. It was John's anticipation that the promised Messiah would assert his judgeship immediately rather than at a subsequent period. John apparently could not reconcile this expectation with the behavior of Jesus before his enemies the pharisees. Finally, John could not bear the doubt any longer and sent two of his disciples to ask Jesus point-blank whether he was the promised Messiah. This incident is quoted from the seventh chapter of Luke in part as follows:

> When the men was come unto him, They said, John the Baptist hath sent us unto thee, saying, Art thou he that should come? or look we for another?
> And in that same hour he cured many of their infirmities and plagues, and of evil spirits; and unto many that were blind he gave sight. Then Jesus answering said unto them, Go your way, and tell John what things ye have seen and heard; how that the blind see, the lame walk, the lepers are cleansed, the deaf hear, the dead are raised, to the poor the gospel is preached. And blessed is he, whosoever shall not be offended in me.

Some will here question why he did not unequivocally reply, Yes, I am the promised Messiah. But he chose rather to refer back to prophecy and its fulfillment, which he further re-emphasized in the following:

> And when the messengers of John were departed, he began to speak unto the people concerning John. What went ye out into the wilderness for to see? A reed shaken with the wind? But what went ye out for to see? A man clothed in soft raiment? Behold, they which are gorgeously apparelled, and live delicately, are in kings' courts. But what went ye out for to see? A prophet? Yes, I say unto you, and much more than a prophet. This is he, of whom it is written, Behold, I send my messenger before thy face, which shall prepare thy way before thee. For I say unto you, Among those that are born of women there is not a greater prophet than John the Baptist; but he that is least in the kingdom of God is greater than he.

In the same chapter it is recorded that a pharisee invited Jesus to his home to eat with him. The pharisee failed to extend to Jesus the customary courtesies of a guest. At the same occasion an unknown woman washed Jesus' feet and anointed his head. "Now when the Pharisee which had bidden him saw it, he spake within himself, saying, This man, if he were a prophet, would have known who and what manner of woman this is that toucheth him; for she is a sinner." In the subsequent summation of Jesus' comments to Simon, the pharisee, he stated: "Wherefore I say unto thee, Her sins, which are many, are forgiven; for she loved much: but to whom little is forgiven, the same loveth little. And he said unto her, Thy sins are forgiven."

In the eighth chapter it is recorded:

> And it came to pass afterward, that he went throughout every city and village, preaching and shewing the glad tidings of the kingdom of God: and the twelve were with him, And certain women, which had been healed of evil spirits and infirmities, Mary called Magdalene, out of whom went seven devils, and Joanna the wife of Chuza Herod's steward, and Susanna, and many others, which ministered unto him of their substance.

Jesus, in his preaching, effectively used parables, such as the parable of the sower, the prodigal son, and the like. These he invariably interpreted to his disciples whenever they requested it.

Jesus' parable of the vineyard, and His mention of the "stone which the builders rejected," which became the cornerstone, both appearing in the 21st Chapter of Matthew, particularly excited the anger of the chief priests and Pharisees for "they perceived that he spake of them." Their anger was further aggravated when Jesus related the parable of the king's marriage feast for his son, which parable appears in the first part of the 22nd Chapter of Matthew. However, at that time Jesus' popularity with the people was so high that the priests and the Pharisees dared not touch Jesus.

During one of the crossings of the Sea of Galilee a storm arose while Jesus was asleep in the boat. His disciples became fearful and awakened their master. After Jesus quieted the storm, "he said unto them, Where is your faith?"

Subsequently he healed a demented man who had been troubled with evil spirits for a long time. This was the incident where the evil spirits coming out of the man were reported to have entered a herd of swine, who as a result ran into the sea and drowned. (Incidentally, this occurrence is often cited by present-day critics of Jesus, which critics maintain that Jesus' action led to the owner of the swine suffering an unjust material loss; in other words, it is a case involving the relativity of values.)

Finally the time came when Jesus considered his twelve disciples were ready to go out on their own. He gave them power to cure diseases, and sent them out to preach the kingdom of God and to heal the sick. Their preaching and healing activity, along with that of their master, raised the concern of Herod. At first Herod feared that John the Baptist, whom he had beheaded, had come back to haunt him.

Upon the return of the disciples from their first preaching effort, Jesus naturally was keenly interested in their report; and, as recorded in the ninth chapter of Luke, Jesus asked them:

> Whom say the people that I am? They answering said, John the Baptist; but some say, Elias (Elijah); and others say, that one of the old prophets is risen again. He said unto them, But whom say ye that I am? Peter answering said, The Christ of God. And he straitly charged them, and commanded them to tell no man that thing: Saying, The Son of man must suffer many things, and be rejected of the elders and chief priests and scribes, and be slain, and be raised the third day.

Jesus' so-called transfiguration took place after this discussion with his disciples, the account of which is given in this same chapter of Luke, as follows:

> And it came to pass about an eight days after these sayings, he took Peter and John and James, and went up into a mountain to pray. And as he prayed, the fashion of his countenance was altered, and his raiment was white and glistering. And, behold, there talked with him two men, which were Moses and Elias: Who appeared in glory, and spake of his decease which he (Jesus) should accomplish at Jerusalem. But Peter and they that were with him were heavy with sleep: and when they were awake, they saw his glory, and the two men that stood with him. And it came to pass, as they departed from him, Peter said unto Jesus, Master, it is good for us to be here: and let us make three tabernacles; one for thee, and one for Moses, and one for Elias: not knowing what he said.
>
> While he thus spake, there came a cloud, and overshadowed them: and they feared as they entered into the cloud. And there came a voice out of the cloud,

saying, This is my beloved Son: hear him. And when the voice was past, Jesus was found alone. And they kept it close, and told no man in those days any of those things which they had seen.

When Jesus and his disciples returned to the plain, many people were waiting for him. Among them was a man with his demented son; about which we quote from Chapter nine:

And I besought thy disciples to cast him (evil spirit) out; and they could not. And Jesus answering said, O faithless and perverse generation, how long shall I be with you, and suffer you? Bring thy son hither. And as he was yet a coming, the devil threw him down, and tare him. And Jesus rebuked the unclean spirit, and healed the child, and delivered him again to his father. And they were all amazed at the mighty power of God, But while they wondered every one at all things which Jesus did, he said unto his disciples, Let these sayings sink down into your ears: for the Son of man shall be delivered into the hands of men.

It will be noted that Jesus was gradually preparing his disciples for his future passion.

The disciples subsequently sent messengers to a village in Samaria to prepare for a visit by Jesus but the Samaritans refused to receive him. To the suggestion of James and John that they command fire to come down from heaven to them as Elijah did, Jesus turned and rebuked them with these words:

Ye know not what manner of spirit ye are of. For the Son of man is not come to destroy men's lives but to save them.

And they went to another village. (Luke 9:55-6)

Jesus later appointed seventy additional workers to go two by two into Perea, across the Jordan to the east. They were to prepare the people for a later visit by Jesus. In other words, they were Jesus' advance agents so to speak. Before they started out for the trip Jesus had this, among other things, to say, as brought out in Chapter 10:2-3 of Luke's account:

Therefore said he unto them, The harvest truly is great, but the laborers are few: pray ye therefore the Lord of the Harvest, that he would send forth laborers into his harvest. Go your ways: behold I send you forth as lambs among wolves.

The seventy eventually returned very enthusiastic about their reception, and they were especially pleased of the power of Jesus' name. Their report pleased Jesus. From Chapter 10:21-24, we quote:

In that hour Jesus rejoiced in spirit, and said, I thank thee, O Father, Lord of heaven and earth, that thou hast hid these things from the wise and prudent, and hast revealed them unto babes; even so, Father; for so it seemed good in thy sight.

All things are delivered to me of my Father; and no man knoweth who the Son is, but the Father; and who the Father is, but the Son, and he to whom the Son will reveal him.

And he turned him unto his disciples, and said privately, Blessed are the eyes which see the things that ye see: For I tell you, that many prophets and kings have desired to see those things which ye see, and have not seen them; and to hear those things which ye hear, and have not heard them.

It was during this period that a certain lawyer questioned Jesus, asking what he should do to inherit eternal life. As regards this incident we quote from Chapter 10:26-9:

He (Jesus) said unto him, What is written in the law? how readest thou?

And he (the lawyer) answering said, Thou shalt love the Lord thy God with all thy heart, and with all thy soul, and with all thy strength and with all thy mind; and thy neighbor as thyself.

And he said unto him, Thou hast answered right: this do, and thou shalt live.

But he, willing to justify himself, said unto Jesus, And who is my neighbor?

In answer to this last question Jesus cited the famous parable of the Good Samaritan.

Among other significant sayings of Jesus during this period cited by Luke in Chapter 11 was:

> And when the people were gathered thick together, he began to say, This is an evil generation: they seek a sign; and there shall no sign be given it, but the sign of Jonas the prophet. For as Jonas was a sign unto the Ninevites, so shall also the Son of man be to this generation. The queen of the south shall rise up in the judgment with the men of this generation, and condemn them: for she came from the utmost parts of the earth to hear the wisdom of Solomon; and, behold, a greater than Solomon is here.
>
> The men of Nineveh shall rise up in the judgment with this generation, and shall condemn it: for they repented at the preaching of Jonas; and, behold, a greater than Jonas is here.

During a visit in the home of a pharisee, Jesus reacted against the concern of giving physical cleanliness primary attention while overlooking the importance of inner cleanliness, as quoted from Luke 11:39-52:

> And the Lord said unto him, Now do ye Pharisees make clean the outside of the cup and the platter; but your inward part is full of ravening and wickedness. Ye fools, did not he that made that which is without make that which is within also?
>
> But rather give alms of such things as ye have; and, behold all things are clean unto you. But woe unto you, Pharisees! for ye love the uppermost seats in the synaagogues, and greetings in the markets. Woe unto you, scribes and Pharisees, hypocrites! for ye are as graves which appear not, and the men that walk over them are not aware of them.
>
> Then answered one of the lawyers, and said unto him, Master, thus saying thou reproachest us also.
>
> And he said, Woe unto you also, ye lawyers! for ye lade men with burdens grievous to be borne, and ye yourselves touch not the burdens with one of your fingers.

Woe unto you! for ye build the sepulchres of the prophets, and your fathers killed them.

Truly ye bear witness that ye allow the deeds of your fathers: for they indeed killed them, and ye build their sepulchres.

Therefore also said the wisdom of God, I will send them prophets and apostles, and some of them they shall slay and persecute:

That the blood of all the prophets, which was shed from the foundation of the world, may be required of this generation; From the blood of Abel unto the blood of Zacharias, which perished between the altar and the temple: verily I say unto you, it shall be required of this generation.

Woe unto you, lawyers! for ye have taken away the key of knowledge; ye entered not in yourselves and them that were entering in ye hindered.

"And as he said these things unto them, the scribes and the Pharisees began to urge him vehemently, and to provoke him to speak of many things: Laying wait for him, and seeking to catch something out of his mouth, that they might accuse him."

Later Jesus said to his disciples as recorded in part in Luke 12:1-7:

Beware ye of the leaven of the Pharisees, which is hypocrisy. For there is nothing covered, that shall not be revealed; neither hid, that shall not be known. Therefore whatsoever ye have spoken in darkness shall be heard in the light; and that which ye have spoken in the ear in closets shall be proclaimed upon the housetops.

And I say unto you my friends, Be not afraid of them that kill the body, and after that have no more that they can do. But I will forewarn you whom ye shall fear: Fear him, which after he hath killed hath power to cast into hell; yea, I say unto you, Fear him.

Are not five sparrows sold for two farthings, and not one of them is forgotten before God? But even the very hairs of your head are all numbered. Fear not therefore: ye are of more value than many sparrows.

Even during this period, Jesus gave indications to his disciples of his return, apparently during a subsequent period for he was still with them. He stated after giving a parable of the return after a wedding of the master of a house, "Be ye therefore ready also for the Son of man cometh at an hour when ye think not."

After completing this particular message to his disciples, he said to the crowd of people who gathered to hear him, the following:

> When ye see a cloud rise out of the west, straightway ye say, There cometh a shower; and so it is. And when ye see the south wind blow, ye say, There will be heat; and it cometh to pass. Ye hypocrites, ye can discern the face of the sky and of the earth; but how is it that you do not discern this time?

In the thirteenth chapter, Luke records Jesus' parable of the fig tree, as follows:

> A certain man had a fig tree planted in his vineyard; and he came and sought fruit thereon, and found none. Then said he unto the dresser of this vineyard, Behold, these three years I come seeking fruit on the fig tree, and find none: cut it down; why cumbereth it the ground?
>
> And he answering said unto him, Lord, let it alone this year also, till I shall dig about it, and dung it; And if it bear fruit, well; and if not, then after that thou shalt cut it down.

While speaking in a synagogue on a sabbath day, Jesus healed a woman as recorded by Luke in Chapter 13:11-3:

> And, behold, there was a woman which had a spirit of infirmity eighteen years, and was bowed together, and could in no wise lift up herself. And when Jesus saw her, he called her to him, and said unto her, Woman, thou art loosed from thine infirmity. And he laid his hand on her; and immediately she was made straight, and glorified God.

For this act Jesus raised the indignation of the ruler of the synagogue because he performed the act of healing on the sabbath.

Concerning the kingdom of God, Jesus is quoted by Luke in the same chapter thirteen as saying:

> Unto what is the kingdom of God like? and whereunto shall I resemble it?
>
> It is like a grain of mustard seed, which a man took, and cast into his garden; and it grew, and waxed a great tree; and the fowls of the air lodged in the branches of it.
>
> And again he said. Whereunto shall I liken the kingdom of God? It is like leaven, which a woman took and hid in three measures of meal, till the whole was leavened.

Jesus reached the height of his popularity with the people after his miracle of feeding the five thousand. After the feeding Jesus and his disciples disappeared, and the crowds eagerly sought him. When they found him on the other side of the Sea of Galilee at Capernaum, they said to him, "Rabbi, when comest thou hither?" From the sixth chapter of John, we quote Jesus' answer:

> Verily, verily, I say unto you, Ye seek me, not because ye saw the miracles, but because ye did eat of the loaves, and were filled.
>
> Labor not for the meat which perisheth, but for that meat which endureth unto everlasting life, which the Son of man shall give unto you; for him hath God the Father sealed.
>
> Then said they unto him, What shall we do, that we might work the works of God?
>
> Jesus answered and said unto them. *This is the work of God, that ye believe on him whom he hath sent.*
>
> They said therefore unto him, What sign shewest thou then, that we may see, and believe thee? What dost thou work? Our fathers did eat manna in the desert; as it is written, He gave them bread from heaven to eat.
>
> Then Jesus said unto them, Verily, verily, I say unto you, Moses gave you not that bread from heaven; but my Father giveth you the true bread from heaven. *For the bread of God is he which cometh down from heaven, and giveth life unto the world.*
>
> Then said they unto him, Lord, evermore give us this bread. And Jesus said unto them, I am the bread of life:

he that cometh to me shall never hunger; and he that believeth on me shall never thirst.

After these sayings Jesus' popularity took a sudden drop. (Here Jesus tried to put over the real purpose of His incarnation, but the purpose was far too abstract for the people to grasp. Even unto this day only a minority of people have grasped Jesus' real significance.)

The pharisees were worried about the success of Jesus' healings and preachings, and apparently tried to frighten him away by saying Herod would kill him. To this threat Jesus replied: "Go ye, and tell that fox, Behold, I cast out devils, and I do cures to-day and to-morrow, and the third day I shall be perfected."

In the 15th chapter, Luke records the parable of the Lost Sheep as well as that of the Prodigal Son. The parable of the Lost Sheep is recorded as follows:

> And he spake this parable unto them, saying,
> What man of you, having a hundred sheep, if he lose one of them, doth not leave the ninety and nine in the wilderness, and go after that which is lost, until he find it? And when he hath found it, he layeth it on his shoulders, rejoicing. And when he cometh home, he calleth together his friends and neighbors, saying unto them, Rejoice with me; for I have found my sheep which was lost.
> I say unto you, that likewise joy shall be in heaven over one sinner that repenteth, more than over ninety and nine just persons, which need no repentance.

The parable of the Prodigal Son likewise emphasizes the concern of the Lord for the individual man gone astray in sin.

In the 16th chapter, among other items, the incident of the rich man and Lazarus is cited, a part of which is quoted from Chapter 16:27-31:

> Then (the rich man) said, I pray thee therefore, father (Abraham) that thou wouldest send him (Lazarus) to my father's house: For I have five brethren; that he may testify unto them, lest they also come into this place of torment. Abraham saith unto him, They have Moses

and the prophets; let them hear them. And he said, Nay, father Abraham: but if one went unto them from the Dead, they will repent.

And he said unto him, If they hear not Moses and the prophets, neither will they be persuaded though one rose from the dead.

Jesus from time to time made some very significant statements, one of which will be mentioned at this time, as recorded in John 8:56-58:

Your father Abraham rejoiced to see my day: and he saw it, and was glad.

Then said the Jews unto him, Thou are not yet fifty years old, and hast thou seen Abraham?

Jesus said unto them, Verify, verily, I say unto you, Before Abraham was, I am.

In Chapter 17:1-2, Jesus is quoted by Luke in part as saying the following to his disciples:

It is impossible but that offenses will come: but woe unto him, through whom they come! It were better for him that a millstone were hanged about his neck, and he be cast into the sea, than that he should offend one of these little ones.

Jesus apparently was now on his way to Jerusalem. He met a group of ten lepers who pleaded to Jesus to have mercy on them. Jesus thereupon instructed them to appear before the priests, as clearance by a priest was necessary to vouch for a leper's cure. Of the ten that were cleaned, only one returned to give thanks and glorify God. Jesus is then quoted as saying:

Were there not ten cleansed? but where are the nine? There are not found that returned to give glory to God, save this stranger. And he said unto him, Arise, go thy way; thy faith hath made thee whole.

The pharisees demanded of Jesus to know when the kingdom of God would come, to which Jesus answered:

The kingdom of God cometh not with observation: Neither shall they say, Lo here! or, lo there! for, behold, the kingdom of God is within you.

In the remainder of chapter seventeen Luke records Jesus' description of world conditions at the time of his so-called second advent or coming.

Jesus instructs his disciples of the necessity of being persistent in prayer, citing as example the occasion of the judge and the widow's pleadings, as recorded by Luke in the eighteenth chapter. Also in this chapter appears Jesus' saying: "Verily I say unto you. Whosoever shall not receive the kingdom of God as a little child shall in no wise enter therein."

As they neared Jericho on their way to Jerusalem, the following prophecy was made to his disciples, recorded in Luke 18:31-34:

Behold, we go up to Jerusalem, and all things that are written by the prophets concerning the Son of man shall be accomplished. For he shall be mocked, and spitefully entreated, and spitted on: And they shall scourge him, and put him to death: and the third day he shall rise again.

(In connection with the foregoing prophetic references made by Jesus, added significance thereto will be given if we re-read Psalm 22 and Isaiah 53rd chapter.)

In Jericho Jesus ate at the home of Zaccheus, a rich publican and so-called "sinner." Zaccheus on this occasion was converted, Jesus saying to him in Luke 19:9-10:

This day is salvation come to this house, forsomuch as he also is a son of Abraham. For the Son of man is come to seek and to save that which was lost.

In the latter part of this same chapter is recorded the triumphal entry of Jesus into Jerusalem. From Chapter 19:29-48, we quote the following:

And it came to pass, when he was come nigh to Bethpage and Bethany, at the mount called the mount of

Olives, he sent two of his disciples, saying, Go ye into the village over against you; in the which at your entering ye shall find a colt tied, whereon yet never man sat: loose him, and bring him hither. And if any man ask you, Why do ye loose him? thus shall ye say unto him, Because the Lord hath need of him.

And they that were sent went their way, and found even as he had said unto them. And as they were loosing the colt, the owners thereof said unto them, Why loose ye the colt? And they said, The Lord hath need of him. And they brought him to Jesus: and they cast their garments upon the colt, and they set Jesus thereon. And as he went, they spread their clothes in the way.

And when he was come nigh, even now at the descent of the mount of Olives, the whole multitude of the disciples began to rejoice and praise God with a loud voice for all the mighty works that they had seen; saying, Blessed be the King that cometh in the name of the Lord; peace in heaven, and glory in the highest.

And some of the Pharisees from among the multitude said unto him, Master, rebuke thy disciples. And he answered and said unto them, I tell you that, if these should hold their peace, the stones would immediately cry out.

And when he was come near, he beheld the city, and wept over it, Saying, if thou hadst known, even thou, at least in this thy day, the things which belong unto thy peace! but now they are hid from thine eyes. For the days shall come upon thee, that thine enemies shall cast a trench about thee, and compass thee round, and keep thee in on every side, and shall lay thee even with the ground, and thy children within thee; and they shall not leave in thee one stone upon another; because thou knowest not the time of thy visitation.

And he went into the temple, and began to cast out them that sold therein, and them that bought; Saying unto them, It is written, My house is the house of prayer: but ye have made it a den of thieves.

And he taught daily in the temple. But the chief priests and the scribes and the chief of the people sought to destroy him, and could not find what they might do: for all the people were very attentive to hear him.

(The foregoing occasion becomes especially significant in the light of the prophecy of Zechariah found in Zech. 9:9:

> Rejoice greatly, O daughter of Zion; shout, O daughter of Jerusalem: behold, thy King cometh unto thee: he is just, and having salvation; lowly, and riding upon an ass, and upon a colt the foal of an ass.

From a census taken by Roman authorities there were some 2,700,000 Jews present in Jerusalem at the time of the Passover, attracted apparently by the rumor that Jesus would be there. Thus we can surmise that the priests and the pharisees became even more deeply concerned about Jesus' rising popularity with the people.)

After his arrival in Jerusalem and while preaching to the people in the temple, the chief priests and scribes demanded of him by what authority he did these things. He silenced them by asking them: "The baptism of John, was it from heaven, or of men?" They after consultation stated they could not answer, and Jesus said, "Neither tell I you by what authority I do these things."

Jesus then turned to the people and related to them the following most significant parable, as recorded in Luke: 20:9-18:

> A certain man planted a vineyard, and let it forth to husbandmen, and went into a far country for a long time. And at the season he sent a servant to the husbandmen, that they should give him of the fruit of the vineyard: but the husbandmen beat him, and sent him away empty.
>
> And again he sent another servant: and they beat him also, and entreated him shamefully, and sent him away empty.
>
> And again he sent a third: and they wounded him also, and cast him out.
>
> Then said the lord of the vineyard, what shall I do? I will send my beloved son: it may be they will reverence him when they see him.
>
> And when the husbandmen saw him, they reasoned among themselves, saying, This is the heir: come, let us kill him, that the inheritance may be ours. So they cast him out of the vineyard, and killed him.
>
> What therefore shall the lord of the vineyard do unto

them? He shall come and destroy these husbandmen, and shall give the vineyard to others.

And when they heard it, they said, God forbid. And he beheld them, and said, What is this then that is written, The stone which the builders rejected, the same is become the head of the corner? Whosoever shall fall upon that stone shall be broken; but on whomsoever it shall fall, it will grind him to powder.

(Here Christ reveals in parable form God's progressive attempts to initiate the so-called kingdom of God among mankind—the psycho-social stage of man as an evolutionary biologist would term it.)

It was now quite obvious that the leaders of the temple were determined to end Jesus' ministry before he had won all the people away from their control. They subsequently tried to get him to make seditious statements while answering their catch questions. To the question regarding the widow married seven times, which involved Moses' laws, Jesus gave the following answer, recorded in Luke 20:34-44:

The children of this world marry, and are given in marriage. but they which shall be accounted worthy to obtain that world, and the resurrection from the dead, neither marry nor are given in marriage: Neither can they die any more: for they are equal unto the angels; and are the children of God, being the children of the resurrection.

Now that the dead are raised, even Moses shewed at the bush, when he calleth the Lord the God of Abraham, and the God of Isaac, and the God of Jacob. For he is not a God of the dead, but of the living:

Then certain of the scribes answering said, Master, thou has well said, and after that they durst not ask him any question at all.

And he said unto them, How say they that Christ is David's son? and David himself saith in the book of Psalms, The Lord said unto my Lord, Sit thou on my right hand, Till I make thine enemies thy footstool. David therefore calleth him Lord, how is he then his son?

The people questioned him about when his predicted second

advent for purposes of judgment would occur. Jesus' recorded answer to this question is given in the twenty-first chapter of Luke.

A description of the so-called Last Supper, attended by Jesus and his twelve apostles, appears in the twenty-second chapter of Luke. Verses fifteen through twenty-two thereof will be here quoted:

> And he said unto them. With desire I have desired to eat this passover with you before I suffer: For I say unto you, I will not any more eat thereof, until it be fulfilled in the kingdom of God.
>
> And he took the cup, and gave thanks, and said, Take this, and divide it among yourselves: For I say unto you, I will not drink of the fruit of the vine, until the kingdom of God shall come.
>
> And he took bread, and gave thanks, and brake it, and gave unto them, saying, This is my body which is given for you: this do in remembrance of me.
>
> Likewise also the cup after supper, saying, This cup is the new testament in my blood, which is shed for you. But, behold, the hand of him that betrayeth me is with me on the table. And truly the Son of man goeth, as it was determined: but woe unto that man by whom he is betrayed.

Jesus here has reference to his betrayal by his apostle Judas Iscariot, which betrayal was soon to occur. Jesus at this time said in part to his apostles as quoted from Chapter 22:29-34:

> And I appoint unto you a kingdom, as my Father hath appointed unto me: That ye may eat and drink at my table in my kingdom, and sit on the thrones judging the twelve tribes of Israel.
>
> And the Lord said, Simon, Simon, behold, Satan had desired to have you, that he may sift you as wheat: But I have prayed for thee, that thy faith fail not: and when thou art converted, strengthen thy brethren.
>
> And he said unto him, Lord, I am ready to go with thee, both into prison, and to death.
>
> And he said, I tell thee, Peter, the cock shall not crow this day, before that thou shalt thrice deny that thou knowest me.

After the Last Supper with his apostles, Jesus went to the Mount of Olives, as recorded in Luke 22:41-46:

> And he was withdrawn from them about a stone's cast, and kneeled down, and prayed, Saying, Father, if thou be willing, remove this cup from me: nevertheless not my will, but thine be done.
>
> And there appeared an angel unto him from heaven, strengthening him. And being in an agony he prayed more earnestly: and his sweat was as it were great drops of blood falling down to the ground.
>
> And when he rose up from prayer, and was come to his disciples, he found them sleeping for sorrow. And said unto them, Why sleep ye? rise and pray, lest ye enter into temptation.

At this point Judas appeared with the servant of the high priest with a multitude with swords and staves, whereupon Judas bestowed the betrayal kiss on Jesus' cheek. Jesus then asked them, "Whom seek ye? And they said Jesus of Nazareth." Jesus thereupon replied, according to Apostle John's gospel, Chapter 18:8, "I have told you that I am he: if therefore ye seek me, let these (his apostles) go their way." Peter wanted to give battle but Jesus told him, according to Apostle John, "Put up thy sword into the sheath: the cup which my Father hath given me, shall I not drink it?"

Luke records in Chapter 22:52-53:

> Then Jesus said unto the chief priests, and captains of the temple, and the elders, which were come to him, Be ye come out, as against a thief, with swords and staves? When I was daily with you in the temple, ye stretched forth no hands against me: but this is your hour, and the power of darkness.

Jesus was led away "and Peter followed afar off." In about one hour's time Peter denied on three different occasions that he knew Jesus, and after the third time "the cock crew." Thereupon Jesus turned around and looked toward Peter, and Peter remembered the word of the Lord. Luke in addition records in Chapter 22:62-71 the following:

And Peter went out, and wept bitterly.

And the men that held Jesus mocked him, and smote him. And when they had blindfolded him, they struck him on the face, and asked him, saying, Prophesy, who is it that smote thee? And many other things blasphemously spake they against him.

And as soon as it was day, the elders of the people and the chief priests and the scribes came together, and led him into their council, saying, Art thou the Christ? tell us.

And he said unto them, If I tell you, ye will not believe: And if I also ask you, ye will not answer me, nor let me go. Hereafter shall the Son of man sit on the right hand of the power of God.

Then said they all, Art thou then the Son of God? And he said unto them, Ye say that I am.

And they said, What need we any further witness? for we ourselves have heard of his own mouth.

Thereupon Jesus was led to Pontius Pilate, the Roman governor. After considerable questioning, Pilate said to the chief priests and to the people: "I find no fault with this man. And they were the more fierce, saying, He stirreth up the people, teaching throughout all Jewry, beginning from Galilee to this place (Jerusalem). When Pilate heard of Galilee, he asked whether the man were a Galilean. And as soon as he knew that he belonged unto Herod's jurisdiction, he sent him to Herod, who himself also was at Jerusalem at that time."

Herod was completely unsuccessful in getting any response from Jesus. Whereas Pilate's questions Jesus had readily answered, Herod's questions were simply ignored by Jesus. This no doubt enraged Herod, "and Herod with his men of war set him at naught, and mocked him, and arrayed him in a gorgeous robe, with a crown of thorns, and sent him again to Pilate."

Jesus was then led back to Pilate. Pilate's judgment is recorded in Luke 23:13-15:

And Pilate, when he had called together the chief priests and the rulers and the people, Said unto them,

Ye have brought this man unto me, as one that perverteth the people: and, behold, I, having examined him before you, have found no fault in this man touching those things whereof ye accuse him; No, nor yet Herod: for I sent you to him; and, lo nothing worthy of death is done unto him.

Eventually in trying to satisfy the mob leaders, he compromised by saying he would chastise Jesus and release him, "for of necessity he must release one unto them at the feast. And they cried out all at once, saying, Away with this man, and release unto us Barabbas (a murderer)." Pilate again indicated he preferred to release Jesus, "But they cried, saying Crucify him, crucify him." In Apostle Matthew's gospel it is recorded in Chapter 27:24-25:

> When Pilate saw that he could prevail nothing, but that rather a tumult was made, he took water, and washed his hands before the multitude, saying, I am innocent of the blood of this just person: see ye to it.
> Then answered all the people, and said, His blood be on us, and on our children.

After Jesus' physical beating and lack of sleep, he apparently was not strong enough to carry the cross to Calvary, so one Simon, a Cyrenian, carried it behind Jesus. On the way to Calvary, women "bewailed and lamented him," causing Jesus to turn to them and say, as quoted from Luke 23:28-31:

> Daughters of Jerusalem, weep not for me, but weep for yourselves, and for your children. For, behold, the days are coming, in which they shall say, Blessed are the barren, and the wombs that never bare, and the paps which never gave suck. Then shall they begin to say to the mountains, Fall on us; and to the hills, Cover us. For if they do these things in a green tree, what shall be done in the dry?

Jesus was crucified between two malefactors. He prayed for those who nailed him to the cross with the words; "Father, forgive them; for they know not what they do. And they parted his raiment, and cast lots." Luke continues the account in Chapter 23:35-47:

> And the people stood beholding. And the rulers also

with them derided him, saying, He saved others; let him save himself, if he be Christ, the chosen of God. And the soldiers also mocked him, coming to him; and offering him vinegar, And saying, If thou be the king of the Jews, save thyself.

And a superscription also was written over him in letters of Greek, and Latin, and Hebrew. This is the King of the Jews.

And one of the malefactors which were hanged railed on him, saying, If thou be Christ, save thyself and us, But the other answering rebuked him, saying, Dost not thou fear God, seeing thou art in the same condemnation? And we indeed justly; for we receive the due reward of our deeds: but this man hath done nothing amiss. And he said unto Jesus, Lord, remember me when thou comest into thy kingdom.

And Jesus said unto him, Verily I say unto thee, To-day shalt thou be with me in paradise.

And it was about the sixth hour, and there was a darkness over all the earth until the ninth hour. And the sun was darkened, and the veil of the temple was rent in the midst. And when Jesus had cried with a loud voice, he said, Father into thy hands I commend my spirit, and having said thus, he gave up the ghost.

Now when the centurion saw what was done, he glorified God, saying, Certainly this was a righteous man.

Apostle John records in Chapter nineteen of his gospel that Jesus while on the cross turned over his mother to John's care. Mark, in his gospel, records in Chapter 15:34, the additional item that "at the ninth hour Jesus cried with a loud voice, saying, My God, my God, why hast thou forsaken me?"

From the latter section of Apostle John's gospel, we quote from Chapter 19:31-36:

The Jews therefore, because it was the preparation, that the bodies should not remain upon the cross on the sabbath day, (for that sabbath day was a high day,) besought Pilate that their legs might be broken, and that they might be taken away,

Then came the soldiers, and brake the legs of the first, and of the other which was crucified with him, But when they came to Jesus, and saw that he was dead already, they brake not his legs: But one of the soldiers with a spear pierced his side, and forthwith came there out blood and water.

And he that saw it bare record, and his record is true: and he knoweth that he saith true, that ye might believe. For these things were done that the scripture should be fulfilled, A bone of him shall not be broken.

In this connection Psalm 34:20 is quoted: "He keepeth all his bones: not one of them is broken." Reference also made thereto in Exodus 12:46.

Joseph of Arimathea, known as a good and just man and counsellor, begged and received permission from Pilate to take down the body of Christ, which he along with Nicodemus prepared for burial in a sepulchre "that was hewn in stone, wherein never man before was laid. And that day was the preparation, and the sabbath drew on. And the women also, which came with him from Galilee, followed after, and beheld the sepulchre, and how his body was laid. And they returned, and prepared spices and ointments; and rested the sabbath day according to the commandment." (Luke 23:53-56)

The various gospels differ as to the sequence of those who saw Jesus after his resurrection. It appears he was first seen by Mary Magdalene and later by Mary, Jesus' mother, and other women, all of whom rushed to inform the apostles. Peter was the first to rush into the sepulchre to find it empty. Subsequently two men, walking toward Emmaus just outside of Jerusalem and discussing the event of the crucifixion, reported to the apostles that Jesus suddenly appeared beside them and interpreted the eventful happenings in the light of prophecy from Moses and all the prophets. The eleven apostles and they that were with them stated, as quoted from Luke 24:34-49:

The Lord is risen indeed, and hath appeared to Simon, And they told what things were done in the way, and how he (Jesus) was known of them in breaking of bread. And as they thus spake, Jesus himself stood in the midst of them, and saith unto them, Peace be unto you. But they were terrified and affrighted, and supposed that they had seen a spirit.

And he said unto them, Why are ye troubled? and why

do thoughts arise in your hearts? Behold my hands and my feet, that it is I myself: handle me, and see for a spirit hath not flesh and bones, as ye see me have.

And when he had thus spoken, he shewed them his hands and his feet. And while they yet believed not for joy, and wondered, he said unto them, Have ye here any meat?

And they gave him a piece of broiled fish, and of a honeycomb, And he took it, and did eat before them.

And he said unto them, These are the words which I spake unto you, while I was yet with you, that all things must be fulfilled, which were written in the law of Moses, and in the prophets, and in the psalms, concerning me.

Then opened he their understanding, that they might understand the scriptures, and said unto them, Thus it is written, and thus it behooved Christ to suffer, and to rise from the dead on the third day: And that repentance and remission of sins should be preached in his name among all nations, beginning at Jerusalem. And ye are witnesses of these things.

And he led them out as far as to Bethany, and he lifted up his hands, and blessed them. And it came to pass, while he blessed them, he was parted from them, and carried up into heaven. And they worshipped him, and returned to Jerusalem with great joy: And were continually in the temple, praising and blessing God.

John in his gospel account records that the following incident occurred in a meeting between Apostle Thomas and Jesus, as quoted from Chapter 20:24-29:

But Thomas, one of the twelve, called Didymus, was not with them when Jesus came. The other disciples therefore said unto him, We have seen the Lord. But he said unto them, Except I shall see in his hands the print of the nails, and put my finger into the print of the nails, and thrust my hand into his side, I will not believe. And after eight days again his disciples were within, and Thomas was with them: then came Jesus, the doors being shut, and stood in the midst, and said, Peace be unto you.

Then saith he to Thomas, Reach hither thy finger, and behold my hands; and reach hither thy hand, and

356

thrust it into my side; and be not faithless, but believing.

And Thomas, answered and said unto him, My Lord and my God. And Jesus saith unto him, Thomas, because thou hast seen me, thou hast believed: blessed are they that have not seen, and yet have believed.

John further states at the very close of his gospel, Chapter 21:24-25:

This is the disciple which testifieth of these things, and wrote these things: and we know that his testimony is true. And there are also many other things which Jesus did, the which, if they should be written every one, I suppose that even the world itself could not contain the books that should be written.

In the first chapter of "The Acts of the Apostle," Luke has this to say to his friend Theophilus:

The former treatise have I made, O Theophilus, of all that Jesus began both to do and teach, Until the day in which he was taken up, after that he through the Holy Ghost had given commandments unto the apostles whom he had chosen: To whom also he shewed himself alive after his passion by many infallible proofs, being seen of them forty days, and speaking of the things pertaining to the kingdom of God:

And being assembled together with them, commanded them that they should not depart from Jerusalem, but wait for the promise of the Father, which, saith he, ye have heard of me. For John truly baptized with water; but ye shall be baptized with the Holy Ghost not many days hence.

When they therefore were come together, they asked of him, saying, Lord, wilt thou at this time restore again the kingdom of Israel? And he said unto them,

It is not for you to know the times or the seasons, which the Father hath put in his own power. But ye shall receive power, after that the Holy Ghost is come upon you: and ye shall be witnesses unto me both in Jerusalem, and in all Judea, and in Samaria, and unto the uttermost part of the earth.

And when he had spoken these things, while they beheld, he was taken up; and a cloud received him out of their sight. And while they looked steadfastly toward heaven as he went up, behold, two men stood by them in white apparel; Which also said, Ye men of Galilee, why stand ye gazing up into heaven? this same Jesus, which is taken up from you into heaven, shall so come in like manner as ye have seen him go into heaven.

Obedient to Jesus' instructions, the apostles gathered in Jerusalem in an upper room, during which Peter rose up in their midst and called attention to the necessity of choosing another apostle to fill the vacancy created by Judas' betrayal. Speaking of Judas he said:

Now this man (Judas) purchased a field with the reward of iniquity; And falling headlong, he burst asunder in the midst, and all his bowels gushed out. For it is written in the book of Psalms, Let his habitation be desolate, and let no man dwell therein: and his bishopric let another take.

Matthias was thereupon chosen to replace Judas.

In the second chapter of "The Acts," Luke relates the very significant event on the Day of Pentecost, when the so-called "comforter" promised by Jesus came. The first part of Chapter 2:1-2 is quoted here:

And when the day of Pentecost was fully come, they were all with one accord in one place. And suddenly there came a sound from heaven as of a rushing mighty wind, and it filled all the house where they were sitting.

The power of the Holy Spirit, with which the apostles were baptized on the Day of Pentecost, changed the formerly timid and frightened group of Jesus' disciples into a fearless, aggressive missionary group, made of martyr stuff as later events testified. Many on the day of Pentecost had the experience of what Jesus meant by being born again, from being motivated by strictly selfish desires as inherited from the so-called first Adam, to the powerful spiritual motivation as was initiated by the so-called second Adam, Jesus Christ. The effect on the disciples of this baptism of the Holy Spirit led some of the observers to consider that they were all intoxicated.

Subsequently Saul of Tarsus (Paul), a previously fanatic persecuter of the Christians, experienced a dramatic conversion when Jesus suddenly revealed himself to Paul on his way to Damascus on a mission of persecution of Christians. From the standpoint of educational background, he was ideally suited for the mission Christ assigned to him, namely, to carry the gospel of the kingdom of God to the gentiles. It was he who convinced Peter that it was necessary, as was previously suggested by Jesus, "to put new wine in new bottles," for Peter at first considered that the Christians should also be good Jews and obey the law of Moses. A confirming dream which Peter had convinced him that Paul was correct in this matter.

Today it is estimated there are about 800,000,000 adherents to Christianity in all parts of the world. However, Jesus had carefully emphasized that "the kingdom of God is within you," and that it is by their works that the members of this invisible kingdom are known. Hence, the reliance on the number from so-called church membership records is a rather doubtful source of the true adherents.

The unbelievably horrible crimes committed in the name of the Christian church, such as the Inquisition (started against the so-called Waldensians), the killing of the Anabaptists, the wholesale burning of witches at the stake are, of course, absolutely foreign to Jesus' teaching, as appears in Matthew 7:1-5 as follows:

> Judge not, that ye be not judged. For with what judgment ye judge, ye shall be judged; and with what measure ye mete, it shall be measured to you again.
>
> And why beholdest thou the mote that is in thy brother's eye, but considerest not the beam that is in thine own eye? Or how wilt thou say to thy brother, Let me pull out the mote out of thine eye; and, behold, a beam is in thine own eye?
>
> Thou hypocrite, first cast out the beam out of thine own eye, and then shalt thou see clearly to cast out the mote out of thy brother's eye.

Also in this connection, we quote again from Luke 9:55-6 Jesus' rebuke of his disciples for suggesting that He call down fire from heaven when a certain Samaritan village refused to receive Jesus:

> Ye know not what manner of spirit ye are of. For the Son of man is not come to destroy men's lives but to save them.
> And they went to another village.

The atrocities committed in the name of religion is living proof that evil is endemic to man and to his institutions especially when much power is placed in the hands of a few individuals.

Christianity has become divided into three main branches: the Roman Catholics; the Orthodox Eastern Church; and the Protestants. Luther, a Roman Catholic priest during the latter part of the sixteenth century, broke away from the Roman Church during the dispute initially caused by the sale of indulgences, a practice initiated by Pope Leo X to defray the cost of building St. Peter's Cathedral in Rome. We recall that the cost of building the Temple at Jerusalem under Solomon's reign resulted in burdensome taxes on the Jews, also causing dissension leading to divisions among the Jews.

There are now some two hundred and fifty sects among the Protestants. The tendency today, however, appears to be one of merging of the sects.

The sacred book of Christianity is The Bible, made up of the Old and New Testaments.

PART FOUR

PINPOINTING THE WHITHER AND THE WHY VIA SUMMATIONS, ABSTRACTIONS, COMMENTS, AND CONCLUSIONS

XXV.

BRIEF GENERAL SUMMARY

Up to this point in our thesis we have attempted, first, in Part I, to analyze the nature of the personality, the conscious entity which poses our original problem. Secondly, in Part II, we have reviewed the progressive attempts of men in various cultures, to understand the natural environment in which they found themselves, all presented in an historical and chronological order. We have also reviewed their efforts to apply as much of that knowledge as possible toward improving their adjustment to that particular environment. In the latter section of Part II, a progressive recapitulation is made of the so-called evolutionary background of the human personality, which represents evolution's present maximum development. Thirdly, in Part III, a review is made of the attempts of man in various current cultures to arrive at the value-determining beliefs by which they may live and guide themselves, not only in their present behavior but also to enable them to project a future behavior pattern consistent with such beliefs. Such value-determining beliefs are for the guidance of the individual man and for mankind as a society.

In short, up to now we have been principally occupied with the so-called natural history stage of our problem.

Now, let us first mention a few of the main inferences we may draw from our attempt at self-analysis in Part I. The personality, a conscious entity, appears to possess both a physical and a psychical aspect. The physical aspect is governed by the laws of mass-energy, and the psychical aspect by the laws of psychic energy, which is in some respects controlling over the physical. Both aspects appear to work progressively and coincidentally toward a created entity. The physical aspect starts with the zygote, the initial physical living form which contains in its so-called chromosomal structure the determiners of the physical characteristics of the personality, contributed by the dominant genes of the respective parents. One might consider the genes (bipolar dominants and recessives) in the chromosomal structure as the "pre-programmed" developmental sequence of the future organization of the physical body. After the initial conjugation of the two parental germ cells, the environment of the resulting zygote is within the womb of the mother, where it gradually develops for a period of approximately nine months during its early development stage. During this early phase the developing foetus appears to recapitulate the progressive creative steps of the general so-called evolutionary stages. After birth the living physical body in its subsequent development must make continual adjustments to its external physical environment from babyhood, through adulthood, and finally to physical death, under the guidance of the psychical directing factor which we have chosen to call the RI.

So much for the physical aspect of the personality. We shall now move on to the so-called psychical aspect. This aspect appears to have its roots and sustenance in the brain of the physical body. From this source, via its organs of sense, the psychical cognitive aspect (the mind) receives not only its sense-data but also its innate motivating forces, the so-called instincts, both data sources supplying the raw materials for its continuing cogitation and overt action.

The functioning of the psychical aspect was pictured as a sort of progressively growing tree over which lead branch hovers the RI, the postulated cogitating and directing factor of the personality. The RI was pictured as the responsible entity, stationed at the so-called stream of consciousness. We further determined that its initial decisions, arrived at by the reflection of its sense-data against its prism of logic, as well as by its choice of love objects in conjunction with its instincts, laid the basis for the formation of the sentiments, attitudes, beliefs and subsequent habits of the personality entity. With these data the RI determined its reaction to the various situations in which it found itself.

The RI, we further concluded, has the capacity of imagination. With this imaginative capacity, in conjunction with its prior experience and current knowledge stored in memory, all reflected against its prism of logic, the RI is enabled to create not only on a physical level such as an automobile or a computer, but also on an artistic, social and intellectual level. Such creations on an intellectual level would be social institutions, works of art, theories of science and systems of philosophy. The joint creations of all men within a particular group constitutes the culture of that group, generally with a form of religion at its core.

What enables man to create a culture?—something no other living creature can do. He is so enabled by reason of the possession of a three-fold capacity: namely, to invent, to communicate, and to transmit to future generations such inventions and experience. This last-mentioned capacity is technically known as "social habituation." (Warden) The creations of mankind, in short, their cultures, reflect and in fact evidence a purposive and progressive intelligence in man.

We shall now direct our attention to Part II in the light of our findings in Part I. All of Part II represents a brief account of the progressive cultural development of man, not only his attempts to interpret the environment of nature in which he finds himself, or more accurately, of which he himself is a part, but to apply or translate the knowledge coming out of such interpretive endeavor for his own welfare and environmental adaptation.

By what techniques does he go about this task? Basically he must have faith both in his sense-data from the external world and in his sense of logic, which includes its sense of causality. Yes he must proceed by faith, for the faithless and the absolute sceptic would not even get started in the task. Strange as it may seem, the very existence of the external world must be accepted by faith in sense-data. In this connection we should recall that Greek philosophy came to an abrupt standstill because of scepticism, the lack of faith in sense-data.

Faith in the existence of the external world is vital for it is the only common meeting ground, along with the sense of logic, that man has with his fellow-man. For instance, what would man do without this common meeting ground and the subject of weather as a check before initiating more serious conversation? The inner world of thought is a relatively private world, and it is good that it is so.

From observation and introspection we conclude that the

factor of intelligence, plus a conscious directing entity (the RI), is required to conceive, design, and produce a "non-living" useful form. At least these two factors are the minimal requirement for creation of the non-living culture of man. Then we may fairly infer and postulate at least these two factors of intelligence and a directing entity for the existence of a living culture, of which man himself is the highest form.

Scientists have discovered, as our review indicates, that the universe is rational; in fact they rely on its rationality in all their progressive research. This observed rationality, order and apparent coherent design point toward an intelligence factor. From the existence of this intelligence factor in all nature, it seems reasonable to infer the existence also of a conscious directing entity. An undirected and free-floating intelligence appears to our sense of logic as incredible. We can, of course, postulate that the factor of chance, if given sufficient time, would produce a living form such as man. However, Dr. Lecomte du Noüy, a highly rated and respected mathematician and biologist now deceased, gave rather convincing proof in his book "Human Destiny" that it is practically infinitely improbable that chance alone produced such a living form as man.

We could, of course, maintain that nature did not come into being by chance but in accordance with natural laws; but then how would we account for the existence of natural laws?

Descartes, Spinoza, and Berkeley attributed the functional harmony in nature to God. Today's physicists, however, are reluctant to solve their problems by bringing in the so-called supernatural. Their approach, however, is becoming increasingly difficult. The physicists prefer to emphasize that nature can be explained by mathematical principles, and point to Einstein's accomplishments. But this approach is increasing rather than narrowing the gap between man's observation and the world as scientifically and mathematically conceived. Then, too, we would be faced with the question—from whence came this mysterious ability to think mathematically?

After considering these possibilities, we shall tentatively postulate that the apparent rational structure in nature reflects a conscious directing entity. With the intelligence factor heretofore evidenced, together with this postulated directing entity, we possess the necessary basic factors to account for the existence of the rational structure of the natural world. We look forward, in our further search, to find various epistemic correlations to support our postulate of such a conscious directing entity.

Many intellectuals will charge that we are here guilty of gross anthropomorphic thinking in drawing this conclusion. Quite true, we are undeniably guilty, but after all what other recourse has man? Basically, the "supreme court" of all of man's judgments is his prism of logic. Dr. Einstein created a mathematical structure of the Universe from his prism of logic. The rationality thus revealed in the structure of the physical world led him to believe in a "supreme intelligence." Does he thus escape the charge of anthropomorphic thinking? No, because he has arrived at the belief of the existence of the "supreme intelligence" through introspection of his own and observation of his fellow-man's behavior.

Let us further consider the processes of intelligent thought. Julian Huxley conjectures that there has been no biological improvement in the brain of man since that of the man living approximately 40,000 years ago. Accordingly, we may infer that the only factor accounting for the difference of beliefs between early and present-day scholars is the difference in total sense-data. The early scholars apparently were possessed of the same relatively comparable mental equipment, brain cells, imaginative capacity, and prism of logic as present-day scholars. They did not, however, have the benefit of the accumulated knowledge and culture possessed by modern scholars upon which to cogitate and reflect.

The basic process of constructing scientific theories and philosophical systems was essentially the same for the scholars of all periods. The early scholars were forced to rely more on their imaginative capacity to compensate for their limited knowledge. They also were blind to the possibilities of analysis and objective experimentation; they seemed to shy away from subjecting their constructed theories and systems to objective verification and validation. Some present-day scientists and scholars have even suggested that the early Greek scholars were lazy, for logical analysis and experimentation requires hard work and infinite patience, and also, work was then only for slaves. The present-day scientific method would never have fitted into their city-state social organization.

As we have reviewed the progressively modified and changing theories of former scholars, we have occasionally noticed with disappointment how they have at times ignored certain possible theories because they conflicted with basic conceptions of earlier or current authorities, witness Aristotle's established principles or the value-determinations of the Church fathers. It would appear, then, that in the search for truth all possibilities should be freely and continually subjected to critical study, proof, and attempted verification. From our review of past situations we have found that no one authority, be he a scientist, philosopher, theologian or politician, dispensed truth only with no error. There is therefore always in current so-called knowledge an intermixture of both truth and error. It is the responsibility of the searcher for truth to sift out the error where he finds it. We like to believe, however, that there is more truth than error in current knowledge.

As we have proceeded in our review, we have been encouraged to discover that, in the apparent conglomerate mass of nature, certain so-called natural laws function. It is faith in the continued functioning of these laws that enables man to make appropriate adjustments to his environment. It is basically a matter of faith, for just because the sun has risen every morning in our memory is no absolute guarantee that it will rise tomorrow. However, on the basis of inductive reasoning we may reasonably expect and plan for the sun's rising tomorrow. Thus, we do unawaredly plan ahead by faith. We function under the law of causality, which is faith that a certain considered cause will currently produce a certain effect based upon prior knowledge and experience. That is the very faith which gives significance to choice, the freedom to will. Bertrand Russell has stated, "The conception of 'cause'—however loath we may be to admit the fact—is derived from the conception of 'will'."

The physicist, the chemist, the biologist, and the psychologist have all, via inductive and deductive reasoning, uncovered laws in nature, which laws they use for purposes of predictability. Scientists are eager seekers of predictability. The mathematician starts out with axioms, so-called self-evident truths accepted on the faith in the sense of logic, and his proofs are deductively arrived at. Why? Because pure mathematics is the creative product of pure logic. Point and instant exists only in pure logic. Strangely, two ones can occur in a pure form only in logic, for there are no two things exactly alike in nature— no, not even a molecule or a hydrogen atom according to the chemist and physicist. It is true that the axioms of mathematics are self-evident. However, the science of mathematics is a creation of the human mind; and it would never have been developed if it were not for the problems presented to man in his attempts to adapt and adjust himself to his external environment—in other words, in his attempts to "subdue" nature.

It may come as a surprise to some individuals that there are many systems of mathematics by which man attempts to explain natural phenomena. Yet mathematics appears, for the present at least, to be the most effective technique for discovering and understanding the miracle of nature, both in its macrocosm and in its microcosm.

Thus as we survey the numerous and varied laws unearthed by scientists in nature, we may inductively conclude from objective evidence that a "supreme intelligence" actually functions in nature, both in its creation and in its perpetuation.

A brief review at this point of the subject of causality now appears appropriate.

XXVI.

REVIEW OF THE SUBJECT OF CAUSALITY

Aristotle broke down the classical conception of causality to four types: (1) the material cause, such as for example the rough granite rock of the subsequent statue; (2) the formal cause, the conceived form in the mind of the sculptor; (3) the efficient cause, the sculptor himself; and (4) the final cause, the completed statue.

Aenesidemus of Cnossus, a Greek sceptic of the sensationalistic school, influenced Pyrrho to question the possibility of any certain knowledge, mainly because of the differences between the constituents of causal relationships. He maintained that because of these differences, the causal relation was inconceivable, not only for the corporeal but for the incorporeal world as well; nor can it exist between bodies and minds. The efficient cause of a body cannot be a body, nor can it be an immaterial entity. With regard to objects which we call causes, he asserted that only bodies and immaterial beings exist. Hence, he concludes there are no causes in the proper sense of the term. But Anesidemus must have had some faith in the principle of cause and effect or he would not have spent the time to convince others of his views. In other words he must have believed in the effectiveness of his argumentative efforts to bring about a change in the opinions of others.

David Hume also contributed ideas on the subject of causality. Hume maintained that the idea of causality is not the product of reasoning but that it is an idea in the sense in which sensationalism attaches to it. He maintained that we could not determine any single event, or infer any cause or effect, without the assistance of observation and experience.

Hume defines cause as "an object precedent and continuous to another, and so united with it, that the idea of the one determines the mind to form the idea of the other, and the impression of the one to form a more lively idea of the other." He goes on to state, "I turn my eye to two objects supposed to be placed in that relation; and examine them in all the situations, of which they are susceptible. I immediately perceive that they are continuous in time and place, and that the object we call cause precedes the other we call effect. In no one instance can I go any farther, nor is it possible for me to discover any third relation betwixt these objects."

To the ordinary layman the immediately foregoing impresses him as so much "gobbledygook," for he sees the situation quite plainly as when the toe of one man makes sudden contact with the seat of another.

If a miracle may be defined as an event which cannot be explained within a cause and effect relationship, it would appear that Hume has succeeded in creating many miracles which are not ordinarily considered as such.

Hume asserts further, "Cause and effect are relations, of which we receive information from experience, and not from any abstract reasoning or reflection." He apparently overlooked that the determination of "relations" as in natural laws, requires considerable "abstract reasoning or reflection." Hume, of course, is right in one sense, namely, that we could not have predicted from our prior knowledge of the individual qualities of oxygen and hydrogen that their proportionate mixture of one atom of oxygen and two of hydrogen would produce water; but once we acquired that knowledge, we could proceed with this knowledge as a cause in future action.

Immanuel Kant, on the contrary, maintained that the law of causality was a pure, innate, a priori element of the understanding. He stated that from the standpoint of relations, all phenomena are united by the tie of causality. This principle would exclude the hypothesis of chance. Furthermore, there is a reciprocal action between effects and their causes, which excludes the idea of fate. From the standpoint of modality he goes on to maintain that every phenomenon is possible that conforms to the laws of space and time, and furthermore every phenomenon is necessary, the absence of which would imply the suspension of these laws. Hence miracles are excluded.

Georg Hegel had still another conception of causality. He

maintained that the cause is inseparable from its effect, and that the effect is indissolubly connected with its efficient cause. Therefore, the causal series is not an indefinite series in which each effect produces a new effect without reacting upon the cause that produced it. Hegel asserted that every effect is the cause of its cause, and every cause the effect of its effect. As an example, rain is the cause of moisture and moisture, in turn, is a cause of rain. He goes on to assert that the causal series in nature is not a straight line prolonged to infinity, but a curved line which returns to its starting point, in short, a circle. According to his conception then, a creator caused or created Georg Hegel and Hegel in turn caused or created the creator. He would, undoubtedly, rationalize this situation by asserting that the existence of Hegel as an effect caused the cause to become a cause.

Such absolute idealism would, of course, discourage scientific endeavor. This, in fact, it actually did, temporarily at least, in Germany. We can be reasonably certain, however, that from a practical standpoint Hegel did not govern his daily living on his philosophical conception of causality.

Schopenhauer asserted that the mind understands only what is subject to the law of causality, that it is fatally dependent on this law. His reasoning was more down-to-earth than Hegel's.

Bertrand Russell states in his book 'Human Knowledge' that: "Everything that we believe ourselves to know about the physical world depends entirely upon the assumption that there are causal laws."

In his 'Age of Reason,' Thomas Paine asserts: "The only idea man can affix to the name of God is that of first cause, the cause of all things. And incomprehensible and difficult as it is for a man to conceive what a first cause is, he arrives at the belief of it from the tenfold greater difficulty of disbelieving it."

Thomas Aquinas used causality as one of his five proofs of the existence of God, the creator. He maintained that in the world of sense, the connection or coherence between the past, present, and future is intelligible only on the principle of efficient causation. As a thing cannot be the efficient cause of itself, everything has an efficient cause distinct from itself. This efficient cause again has its own cause, and so on, and thus there is a sequence of efficient causes. As the sequence cannot be infinite, it must of necessity lead back to an ultimate efficient cause, an uncaused cause so-to-speak, namely, God.

372

This form of proof can be likened to a chain process. Therefore, we could ask, what is to prevent a re-entrant link resulting in a closed chain? Edmund Whittaker, in his book "Space and Spirit," (published by Henry Regnery Co. N.Y.) has some rather interesting comments in this connection. He states that St. Thomas made provision against re-entry by applying Aristotle's physics of different spheres of influence; thus his links of causes were logically so-called monotonic. However, Whittaker goes on to say that whereas Aristotle's physics has since been replaced, St. Thomas' "second-way" would not be applicable today, and must be reworded.

Whittaker states, in this connection, that modern physics enables one to prove that the relation of cause and effect is a strictly monotonic relation. The proof of this is furnished by referring to the present law of physics that no physical influence can be transmitted faster than the speed of light in vacuo. This law, enunciated by Dr. Einstein, ensures that where one body causes an effect of any kind in another body not coincident with it, the cause precedes in time the effect. The breakdown of the argument through the coincidence of bodies is also eliminated by the doctrine that molar bodies are built up of elementary particles separated from one another by empty space. Thus, the cause-effect relation must be extended indefinitely as an open chain in time of antecedents and successors.

Does this chain, then, possibly continue backward to negative eternity, or does it terminate at some definite time in the past? In answering this question, Whittaker brings out that science automatically eliminates the possibility of a negative eternity as it is now generally agreed among reputable scientists, based on sound and many-sided evidence, that the universe had a beginning in time.

Whittaker further asserts that under the argument of St. Thomas, the chains of causation may be both branched and have junctions with one another without essentially affecting the proof. In addition, St. Thomas' argument does not require, when tracing backward, that chains of causation should terminate on the same ultimate point. Thus, the argument does not necessarily lead to the conclusion that the universe acquired its so-called entire "stock-in-trade" in a single consignment at the beginning of creation but permits a continual succession of intrusions or new creations.

Furthermore, Whittaker states that rational science is possible only over a field where there is regularity, where there is a connection between past, present, and future; but, he concedes, this regularity is not universal and exhaustive. In this connection he cites the belief of C. S. Peirce, an American mathematician and philosopher, that the laws of nature have resulted from an evolutionary process, the fixing of ineradicable habits, so-to-speak, in the world of inanimate matter.

Edmund Whittaker in conclusion significantly states that however this may be, the way in which regularity and novelty are simultaneously ensured in both the physical and the psychical spheres "compels our wonder and exaltation." "The universe," he asserts, "is far from being a mere mathematical consequence of the disposition of the particles at the Creation, and is a much more interesting and eventful place than any determinist imagines."

Application of the Law of Causality in Science

With this brief review of some of the principal interpretations given the law of causality, let us now continue on where we left off as regards John's practical problems in attaining predictability. However, as a scientist John's problems become much more complex and abstract. He now discovers that the process in determining predictability involves many axiomatic faiths. Axioms he has learned are basic in mathematics, but for the other sciences predictability requires the determination of natural laws from sense-data. But to accumulate such required sense-data requires more faith on his part than the very primary faith in the existence of the Creator which is based on free choice alone. We shall enumerate a few of the faiths forced upon a researcher in the field of science:

First, he must have faith in the axioms of mathematics, and in his sense of logic;

Second, he must have faith that the external world actually exists even when he is not observing it, for he has learned from Berkeley and Kant that it cannot be objectively proved;

Third, he must have faith in the persistence of the specific properties of forms, for he has learned that all nature is in a constant state of flux; even an apparently "lifeless" rock is a body whose particles are in a constant state of vibration;

Fourth, he must have faith in the persistence of established

374

sequences of observed natural phenomena, i.e., the law of causality;

Fifth, he must have faith in the persistence of the established relations and interacting relationships of forms, i.e., coherence.

And after he has subscribed to these faiths, either consciously or unconsciously, knowingly or unknowingly, he must be prepared at any time to modify, change, or even entirely revamp his overall conception of the universe upon the failure to verify and validify his hypotheses. This is a very painful experience, as Newtonian physicists will agree as when forced to revamp classical physics to agree with Einstein's revolutionary theories. Even Einstein himself admits that he too is vulnerable, as he stated at one time: "No amount of experimentation can ever prove me right; a single experiment may at any time prove me wrong."

The scientist, however, has been encouraged that so far his faith in the rationality of nature has not been in vain; so logical analysis and logical synthesis confidently go on. Yes, the universe and life itself for John is beginning to take on exciting form and meaning.

But we are getting ahead of our discussion, for we must now briefly review some of the techniques and forms of logic which a scientist must follow in order to arrive at the factors of predictability. As concerning logic, even though we may know the meaning of each word in a sentence, we will not necessarily understand the meaning of the whole sentence until we understand the relations between the words. As a simple example, let us quote a sentence contained in a non-sense letter sent by a "Met" baseball fan to the management: "As for the infield, once they're used to it, he'll do better." Here, while we understand the meaning of each word making up the sentence, we can make no sense out of their coherence. Why? Because the stated relations lack self-consistence and meaningful sequence; in short, it is non-sense. Another sentence, however, in this same letter makes more sense: "Pitching's no problem once it is solved." In other words, he predicts the non-existence of the problem once it is solved, although an obvious tautology.

Likewise, scientists and philosophers must not only have meaningful concepts, propositions and theories to explain all phenomena of nature, but these concepts, propositions, and theories must be consistently meaningful and coherent in explaining such phenomena. Certain phenomena must not be ignored if they should not fit into a particular scientific theory or philosophy.

Both scientists and philosophers have been working on the problem of making sense out of the various phenomena of the universe for what seems a long time from the standpoint of history. However, when considered in relation to the time from the beginning of creation, it is a relatively brief time. True, they have made progress in its solution, but Einstein states: "Science is not and will never be a closed book. Every important advance brings new questions. Every development reveals, in the long run, new and deeper difficulties."

So let the scientist and philosopher relax—they apparently will never be unemployed. There is only one danger that would put a stop to their labor, and that would be the sudden discovery that the structure of nature is irrational. This danger too, they have so far happily discovered, is remote indeed.

Now, with respect to the meaning of relations, Earl Russell in his treatise, "Our Knowledge of the External World," has classified relations in two different ways. One classification includes the so-called symmetrical relation, as when a relation holds between say A and B, also holds between B and A; for example, if A is a brother or sister of B, then B would also be a brother or sister of A. A non-symmetrical relation, on the other hand, would be one where say A is a brother of B and B turns out to be a sister of A. An asymmetrical relation, however, is one when if it is true as between A and B, is never true of B and A; thus father would be true as between A and B, but never true of B and A; the words before, after, greater, etc., immediately suggest an asymmetrical relation; and all series are relations of this type.

The second way of classifying relations is according to whether they are transitive, non-transitive, or intransitive. A transitive relation would be one which if it holds between A and B and also between B and C, also holds between A and C. Before, after, greater, and the like, suggest transitive relations. A non-transitive relation, on the other hand, is one which is not transitive in the sense above indicated, such as "brother" in the non-symmetrical relation previously cited. Non-transitive relations include all kinds of dissimilarity. An intransitive relation, however, is one where it holds for A and B and B and

C, but never has it to A. "Father" would be an example of an intransitive relation.

Earl Russell asserts that traditional logic (Aristotelian) maintains that all propositions have the subject-predicate form and that all relations must be reduced to properties of the apparently related terms. Thus, traditional logic is unable to admit the reality of relations. Russell further asserts that when the reality of relations is admitted, all logical bases for supposing the world of sense to be illusory are eliminated. He goes on to state that whereas the axioms of mathematics are used in philosophical logic, higher mathematics belongs essentially to mathematical logic alone.

F. S. C. Northrup in his treatise, "The Logic of the Sciences and the Humanities," brings out that in determining "the relation between diverse things it is necessary to express each in terms of a common denominator." He states that scientific or philosophic theory of any kind is a body of propositions, and a body of propositions is a set of concepts. He defines a concept as a term to which a meaning has been assigned. He classifies concepts into two basic types, namely, concepts by (1) intuition and concepts by (2) postulation. A concept of intuition (1) denotes the immediacy of the purely empirically apprehended so-called pure fact. This concept is divided into two groups, namely, concepts of sensation or inspection, such as the color blue; and concepts by introspection, such as an immediately felt pain.

Northrup defines a concept by postulation (2) as "one the meaning of which in whole or part is designated by the postulates of the deductive theory in which it occurs." A postulate, incidentally, is an indemonstrable practical hypothesis. "Blue" in the sense of the number of a wave-length in electromagnetic theory is an example of a concept of postulation. Concepts of postulation are classified by Northrup as:

(1) Concepts of intellection, designating factors which can be neither imagined nor sensed, as the space-time continuum of Einstein's field physics;

(2) Concepts by imagination, designating factors which can be imagined but cannot be sensed, such as the ether concept of classical prerelativistic physics, and the atoms and molecules of classical particle physics;

377

(3) Concepts of perception, designating factors which are in part sensed and in part imagined, such as the public space of daily life, other persons, tables, chairs, and the like;

(4) Logical concepts of intuition, designating factors, the content of which is given through the senses or by mere abstraction from the totality of sense awareness, and whose logical universality and immortality are given by postulation. Examples of such concepts would be the "Unmoved Mover" in Aristotle's philosophy, and Whitehead's "eternal objects."

Northrup also summarizes the main stages in solving a problem of physical science as follows:

The first stage is the analysis of the problem—"the problematic situation must be reduced to the relevant factual situation."

The second stage is the natural history stage of the problem. This stage involves the inspection of relevant factors designated by the analysis of the problem made in the first stage. The inductive method of Bacon is appropriate in this stage. It begins with immediately apprehended fact and ends with described fact. Described fact, incidentally, is fact brought under concepts as heretofore previously classified and to this extent under theory. Described fact takes on the form of propositions.

The third stage of the inquiry involves the method of hypothesis, its deductively formulated theory and its concepts by postulation. It involves the projection of relevant hypotheses suggested by the observed relevant facts. It also involves the deduction of logical consequences from each hypothesis, which permits it being put to experimental test.

The fourth stage involves the clarification of one's initial problem in the light of the verified hypothesis. It also involves the generalization of the solution by means of a pursuit of the logical implications of the new concepts and theory with respect to other subject matter and applications.

Northrup, incidentally, calls attention to the fact that the mathematical physicist in his efforts to verify his theory commits the logical fallacy of the hypothetical syllogism, also called the fallacy of affirming the consequent. For example, to quote Northrup: "Let (A) represent the primitive concepts and postulates of the deductive theory which designate the unobserved

378

entities and structures of the scientific theory. Let (B) designate the deduced theorems together with the epistemic correlation joining the concepts by postulation of these theorems to their corresponding concepts by inspection referring to directly inspectable items. It is to be noted that upon this basis a theory is shown to be false when the epistemic, inspectable correlates of its deduced consequences differ from what is naturally or experimentally observed, and the theory is said to be confirmed when the inspected correlates of the deduced theorems are naturally or experimentally observed. The logic of these two cases is as follows: (1) If A then B; B is not the case; therefore, A is not the case. (2) If A then B; B is the case; therefore A is the case."

From the foregoing it will be seen that the logic is sound if the theory is not confirmed, as under (1). However, it is invalid in the case of its confirmation, as it commits the logical fallacy of affirming the consequent, for there is the possibility of another theory affirming the facts as well or even better. One way of avoiding some of this danger as suggested by Northrup is that physicists should carefully consider other possible theories as well as their own in their verification procedure.

Dr. Einstein realized the tentative nature of the physicists' reasoning, for he at one time made the statement: "The belief in an external world independent of the perceiving subject is the basis of all natural science. Since, however, sense perception only gives information of this external world or of 'physical reality' indirectly, we can only grasp the latter by speculative means. It follows from this that our notions of physical reality can never be final. We must always be ready to change these notions—in order to do justice to perceived facts in the most logically perfect way. Actually a glance at the development of physics shows that it has undergone far-reaching changes in the course of time."

From the foregoing it is obvious that the task of scientists and philosophers in solving the mysteries of the universe is indeed a complex one. It represents steps by the process of logical analysis of scientists who seek predictability, and logical synthesis by philosophers who seek a coherent picture of all phenomena. The source material required by the philosophers to do a half-way respectable effort at synthesis is staggering to say the least. That fact is undoubtedly the reason "whole philosophies" are few and far between. Theme "scores" are plentiful but there is an absence of professionals who will

XXVII.

EVOLUTION OF PHYSICS LEADING UP TO
RELATIVITY THEORIES

Einstein spent a life-time in serious mathematical research to establish a theory which would encompass all the physical phenomena of nature. In relating his steps of reasoning through his problem, he cites the progressive attempts made by previous investigators in this field.

He begins with the rise of the mechanical view, citing Aristotle's statement in his Mechanics during the latter part of the fourth century B.C. that "the moving body comes to a standstill when the force which pushes it along can no longer so act to push it." This apparently common-sense conclusion was not questioned until Galileo put it to test almost two thousand years later. He found Aristotle's conclusion wrong. From experimentation Galileo concluded that if no external forces act on a body, it moves uniformly, i.e., with the same velocity along a straight line. Galileo's conclusion was formulated by Newton a generation later as the law of inertia. This law reads: "Every body perseveres in its state of rest, or of uniform motion in a right line, unless it is compelled to change that state by forces impressed thereon."

This was Newton's first law of motion. The second and third laws were: "Change of motion is proportional to the force that acts on a body and takes place in the direction of this force;" and "to every action there is an equal and opposite reaction." The first two of these three laws, of course, were stated informally by Galileo. Newton applied these laws to demonstrate that there is a force of gravity acting between any two bodies in the universe that is directly proportional to the product of their masses and inversely proportional to the square of the distance between them.

These laws were derived by speculative thinking consistent with observation of natural phenomena. They can be subjected only to so-called "idealized experiment." The first law applied to rectilinear motion. By the application of vectors it was also adapted to curved motion, such as that occurring in the orbits of the moon, the planets, the sun, and the stars. The term vector was formulated by the recognition that a number alone is insufficient for describing certain physical concepts. For instance, in the characterization of a velocity, a direction as well as a number is needed.

Einstein considered mathematics as a tool of reasoning if it is desired to draw conclusions which may be compared with experiment. Algebraic equations were his favorite reasoning tools.

The elliptical construction of a vector diagram of the change in velocity revealed that the force on the earth is directed toward the sun. Astronomers wished to be able to predict the position of the earth and the other planets of the sun at any set instant of time, the date and duration of a solar eclipse, and so on. For this predictability it was necessary not only to know the direction of the force but also its magnitude.

We owe it to Newton to make the successful guess. In accordance with his law of gravitation, the forces of attraction between two large bodies depends on a simple relation to their distance from each other. It becomes smaller as the distance increases, such as two times two or four times smaller if the distance is doubled, or three times three or nine times smaller if the distance is trebled, and so on. His law of gravitation, as previously indicated, was the product of his application of his two laws of motion.

The significance of one of the fundamental concepts of mechanics, that of mass, was unnoticed for many years. The physicists finally took note that if the same force acts on a body, the velocity of a body on a horizontal plane depends on its mass, being smaller if the mass is greater, and so on. This is known as inertial mass. The fact that the inertial mass and the gravitational mass, as determined by scales, were identical was for many years considered accidental by classical physics. The force of gravitation, of course, made possible scales for determining so-called weight. To modern physics, however, the identity of inertial and gravitational mass is considered most significant. In fact, the identity of these two masses furnished the clew from which Einstein developed his general theory of relativity. It will be recalled that under Aristotle's principles of mechanics the speed of fall of objects varied in proportion to their weight. Galileo by actual experiment determined that the speed of fall was identical regardless of weight. In other words the gravitational force varied in proportion to the weight of each object; hence, their speeds were the same. Their similar accelerations were determined as 32.2 ft. per second.

The subject of heat served as another clew for Einstein. For a long time science considered temperature and heat to be interchangeable terms. Heat was at first considered a weightless substance. Count Rumford, an American adventurer, while superintending the boring of cannon in a Munich military arsenal, casually observed that considerable heat was generated by friction, and apparently the amount of heat generated in this manner seemed inexhaustible. The chips resulting from the boring operation were very hot, in fact hotter than boiling water. However, in placing an equal weight of chips and of thin slips taken from the same block of metal into equal quantities of cold water of like temperature, he observed that the water into which the chips were placed was not heated any more than the water in which the thin slips of metal were placed. He concluded that anything which any insulated body or bodies can continue to furnish without limitation, cannot possibly be a "material substance." He speculated that it might be motion.

With the combined contributions of Rumford, Black, a versatile Scotsman, and Mayer, a German physician, heat was finally considered as energy.

It was left for Joule, an English brewer, to conduct the crucial experiment. With the use of a simple apparatus in which the gradual fall of two weights caused a paddle wheel to turn in water, the raised temperature of the water reflected the heat created by the fall of the weights. He determined that the potential energy of 772 pounds raised one foot above the ground is equivalent to the quantity of heat necessary to raise the temperature of one pound of water from 55° F to 56° F.

The physicists of the nineteenth century finally concluded that heat and mechanical energy were only two of the many forms of energy. There was the radiation energy of the sun, which in part was transformed to heat on the earth's surface.

An electric current possesses energy as it heats a wire and runs an electric motor. There was also chemical energy, as that resulting from the burning of coal and thus producing heat. In a closed isolated system energy is conserved, and though weightless behaves like a substance. Hence, there were two conservation laws, that of matter and that of energy.

The forces of attraction and repulsion are the most easily conceived forces. The force between two particles depends, like gravitational forces, only on the distance between them, along with their velocities. In the middle of the nineteenth century, Helmholtz believed that it would be possible to describe all natural phenomena in terms of simple forces between unalterable objects. Hence the problem of physical material science was to refer natural phenomena back to unchangeable attractive and repulsive forces whose intensity depends only upon distance. Helmholtz considered that the solution of this problem would result in the complete comprehensibility of nature. The very thought of the possibility of the complete understanding of nature was frightening, especially so for physicists. However, the fear of this possibility proved to be rather premature, at least for the physicists of the late nineteenth and early twentieth century.

The mechanical view led to the development of the kinetic theory of matter and this altered the picture. It was understandable that the application of heat to a closed vessel containing gas resulted in increased heat; but how is this heat connected with motion? If every problem is a mechanical one, heat must be mechanical energy. The object of the kinetic theory is to account for all phenomena of nature as mechanical in nature. Hence, under the kinetic theory a gas is considered a congregation of an enormous number of moving particles or molecules colliding with each other, and thereby changing direction with each collision. Each molecule was assumed to have an average kinetic energy.

It was observed that when two different gases were put in similar vessels, with a moving piston inserted at the top of each vessel, that equal weights placed on each piston would result in the same degree of compression. Therefore, it was assumed that all gas molecules occupied the same space. It was further assumed that by increasing the gravitational force, the proportional resistance of the gas to the force resulted from increasing the number of collisions between molecules.

In this connection, a botanist named Brown in the first half of the nineteenth century, observed through a microscope the streaming of particles in both organic and inorganic matter. This phenomena was subsequently called Brownian movement. About eighty years thereafter this observation, to which the kinetic theory of matter was applied, resulted in the conclusion that this so-called Brownian movement was caused by the continual collision of molecules. From this theory the number of molecules in one gram of hydrogen was determined as 303,000,-000,000,000,000,000,000, and the mass of one hydrogen molecule as 0.000,000,000,000,000,000,000,0033 grams. Hence, the kinetic theory of matter enabled physicists to explain heat under the mechanical view.

However, the interpretation of electrical and magnetic phenomena within the mechanical view ran into difficulty. In the case of electrical energy, the attempt was made to interpret its phenomena in mechanical terms, similar to that of a flow of water. The difference of electrical charge between the positive and negative poles in a series of voltaic batteries was considered the potential energy. When the poles were connected, causing a flow of electrical energy from the positive to the negative poles, kinetic energy was produced. If the wire was thin enough, the density of the electrical energy caused heat.

The attempt to interpret magnetism in mechanical terms was likewise made. But then the prior experiments by Oersted and later by Rowland revealed phenomena that could not be fitted into the mechanical view. Oersted found that an electrical current deflected a magnetic needle. Rowland later discovered that magnetism could produce an electric current; also that the degree of deflection of the magnetic needle varied with the velocity of the electrical charge. In other words, an electric current created a magnetic field perpendicular to the direction of the current; also it was observed that a magnetic field in certain situations could cause a flow of electric current in a wire circling it. Thus it was found that the two phenomena of a magnetic field appearing perpendicular to the flow of an electric current and of the magnetic effect not only varying with the distance but also with the velocity of the electrical charge, could not be explained under the mechanical view. Hence, another theory must be attempted.

The phenomena of light also could not be explained under the mechanical view. Newton had postulated a flow of light corpuscles to explain light phenomena. However, Huygens had postulated a wave-in-the-ether theory of light. Certain experiments appeared to support the corpuscle theory and others the wave theory. Both theories could be made to explain the phenomena of color and refraction. Experiments also appeared to support the existence of a transverse rather than a longitudinal wave.

Young's experiment in passing a light beam alternately through two small adjacent holes produced an effect on the screen which could be explained by either theory. However, when passing the light through both holes simultaneously, parallel lines appeared between the two screen effects. The appearance of the parallel lines could only be explained by the wave theory. Therefore, Newton's corpuscular theory went temporarily into eclipse.

The contributions of Oersted and Faraday in the early part of the nineteenth century and later by Maxwell and Rowland, led to a new concept in physics, considered the most significant since Newton's time. It was the concept of the field. Surprisingly, it was found that it is not the charges nor the particles but the field in the space between the charges and particles which is needed to describe properly physical phenomena. In other words, the unseen was found necessary to explain the seen, a most revolutionary departure from the mechanical view.

Maxwell formulated his famous mathematical equations from the concept of the field. These equations describe the structure of the electromagnetic field, and govern both electrical and optical phenomena. The inconsistencies of the old theories constructed from the mechanical view necessitated that new properties be ascribed to the space-time continuum, and thus alter the scene of all events in the physical world.

Einstein developed the relativity theory in two stages. The first stage led to what is known as the *special theory of relativity* which applied only to inertial co-ordinate systems in which Newton's law of inertia is valid. Two basic assumptions are involved in the special theory of relativity. The first assumption is that physical laws are the same in all co-ordinate systems moving uniformly relative to each other. The second assumption is that the velocity of light always has the same value, 186,324 miles per second. From these assumptions, all confirmed by experiment, the properties of idealized moving rods and clocks changing in length and rhythm respectively, depending on velocity, are deductively determined.

Under this revolutionary theory, the old laws became invalid if the velocity of a moving particle approached that of light. For instance, a rod would shrink to half its length at about ninety per cent of the speed of light, and a clock would also slow down proportionately. However, the mass would increase rather than decrease. The new laws for a moving body reformulated by this theory have been experimentally confirmed. Also under these laws it has been determined that mass is energy and energy has mass. It will be recalled that Einstein's famous equation of $E = MC^2$ was involved in the conception of the atomic bomb, his theory being most dramatically confirmed thereby. Thus, the two conservation laws now became united into the conservation law of mass-energy.

The *general theory of relativity* involves the space-time continuum, and is not restricted to inertial co-ordinate systems. It formulates new structure laws for the gravitation field, and forces us to consider the part played by geometry in the description of the physical world. The fact that gravitational and inertial mass are equal is considered essential to the theory, rather than accidental as under the classical mechanics.

The general theory differs only slightly in experimental consequences from those of the classical theory. Its inner consistency and the simplicity of its basic assumptions constitute its strength.

While the importance of the concept of the field in physics is stressed in the theory of relativity, a pure field physics is yet to be formulated. Therefore, for the present the existence of both field and matter must be assumed.

The problem of the determination of continuity and discontinuity in natural phenomena will now be briefly considered in the light of Einstein's review of physics. This, of course, is emphasized in the *quantum theory,* which assumes that some physical quantities so far regarded as continuous are now composed of elementary quanta.

It will be recalled that from the observation of the phenomena of the Brownian movement, a kinetic theory of matter was formulated. From that theory the mass of a hydrogen molecule was determined. The so-called electric fluid also was determined as a stream of discontinuous quanta known as electrons.

In this theory, formulated by J. J. Thomson, the atom was pictured as being made up of a central core called the nucleus, around which circled electrons representing negative charges corresponding in number to the positive charges in the nucleus. The hydrogen atom was pictured as made up of a nucleus consisting of one proton (a positive charge) and one electron (a negative charge) which circled around the nucleus. It turned out that the mass of the electron was almost two thousand times smaller than the mass of the proton nucleus. It was at one time considered that an atom of any element was its smallest elementary quantum. Now this has been found untrue, that an atom is a very complex unit made up of many different quanta within its nucleus.

It is recalled that Rutherford was one of the early contributors, along with Thomson and others, to the development of nuclear physics.

With the development of the electron theory, electrical phenomena were found to possess a granular structure. Surprisingly, light phenomena were determined also to be granular in structure, reverting to Newton's corpuscles. They are now called photons (a word coined by Einstein), the energy quanta of light. Bohr's theory of the construction of the atom explained light spectra, although it failed to explain other phenomena.

The questions of whether light rays are waves or a shower of photons, and also whether electrons are waves or a shower of elementary particles, are yet to be definitely determined. At present it might be said they are energy quanta stored in magnetic waves. To answer these problems it is necessary to retreat further from the mechanical view, for quantum physics formulates laws governing crowds and not individuals. As Einstein stated: "Not properties but probabilities are described, not laws disclosing the future of systems are formulated, but laws governing the changes in time of the probabilities and relating to great congregations of individuals."

It is quite evident from the present trend of physics, especially in the analysis of the microcosm, that mathematics and the theories derived from mathematics are indispensable to arrive at experimental "gestalts" amenable to verification by direct observation of nature.

Einstein made considerable progress in constructing theories tending toward the explanation and unification of the science of physics. His theories are now in the stage of the verification process.

The fact that Einstein's relativity theories are based largely on mathematical equations intrigues us to speculate on a possible physical basis for his equations. These speculations have led us to the deductively formulated Theory of Latent Energy which will be developed within the next chapter of our thesis.

XXVIII.

THEORY OF LATENT ENERGY
(DEDUCTIVELY FORMULATED)

Introduction to Specific Problems

An old retired school teacher with failing eyesight wrote to the science editor of a Metropolitan newspaper to ask what happened to the "ether" concept, as she had recently been informed by a young science student that "ether was out." The editor called for assistance from an outstanding physics authority of a large university, and was informed that with the new field theory, the ether concept was no longer necessary.

The information was passed on to the inquiring old lady, to which she remarked incredulously—"That can't be!" Her implied common-sense belief in the existence of an ether doesn't necessarily make her belief a fact, for in the light of present scientific hypotheses, her belief becomes highly improbable. Yet again improbability does not necessarily mean impossibility. Thus it is still possible that her belief is a fact.

Einstein acknowledged the phenomena of light as consisting of both particles (which he named photons) and magnetic waves. However, as to the medium through which the photons passed he suggested that we try not to use the word "ether" but just "take for granted that space has the physical property of transmitting electromagnetic waves and not to bother too much about the meaning of this statement."

Alfred Whitehead in a chapter of his "Science and the Modern World" speaks of the "enormous permanences" of nature, especially that of ordinary matter. He cites that the molecules contained in the oldest rocks may have been in existence unchanged for over a thousand million years, not only in themselves but in their relative position to one another. "In that length of time," he goes on to say, "the number of pulsations of a molecule vibrating with the frequency of yellow sodium light would be about $16.3 \times 10^{22} = 163,000 \times (10^6)^3$."

Now vibrations involve movements and movements require energy. The question is naturally raised, from whence came the energy for this tremendous activity?

A man once bought a car, a compact so-called, and would boast to his friends about the wonderful gas mileage it was delivering. Then mysteriously his fuel gauge registered at full and remained so regardless of his driving. The owner brought his car to the garage to have the gauge checked. The mechanic after checking assured the owner the gauge was registering correctly. This naturally left the car owner completely baffled, until he surprised one of his friends surreptitiously pouring gasoline into the tank of his car.

It does seem that the phenomena cited by Whitehead should at least excite the curiosity of physicists. From whence comes the energy for all the pulsations within the enumerable atoms of inorganic and organic nature?

Bertrand Russell, writing on the subject of "The World of Physics," states in part: "The new theory (of the atom) takes over from Bohr the doctrine that the energy in an atom must have one of a discrete series of values involving h; each of these is called an 'energy level.' But as to what gives the atom its energy the theory is prudently silent."

At one time it was thought by physicists that the energy of the Universe was continually running down from its initial potential, through kinetic, and toward "maximal entropy," the term used by Clausius. Yet, it is now generally acknowledged that the earth is increasing in mass instead of decreasing as formally believed. Also, the phenomena of growth in organic nature appear to run counter to Clausius' theory of maximal entropy. The question may also be raised, from whence comes the progressively increasing mass, cited by Einstein, of bodies in relation to the speed of light? Einstein himself suggests kinetic energy as the source. In other words, their acceleration creates mass; but from what?

It would also seem that Descartes made a logical observation in his statement "that the mere separation of bodies by distance proved the existence of a medium between them"; at least if we are to assume that we are living in a physical world.

Moreover, there would appear certain problems in physics which have more or less resisted satisfactory solutions. These problems on closer inspection may be inter-related; in fact, they may all revolve around the basic problem of the phenomena of light. This basic problem, along with some of the suggested inter-related problems, involve the explanation of the following phenomena:

I. The phenomena of light—the basic problem. Is it an ether wave phenomena as suggested by Huygens, a shower of corpuscles as suggested by Newton, an electromagnetic wave as under the current field theory, or a composite of the wave and a particle, in other words, a "wavicle"?

II. The loss of mass in Beta-decay Processes, and Packing Loss in Helium Nuclei Formation;

III. The Force of Gravitation;

IV. The Earth's Magnetic Field;

V. The Phenomena of Heat;

VI. The magnetic field co-existing with the flow of an electric current;

VII. The differentiation between Magnetic Waves;

VIII. Planck's Unit Constant in his Quantum Energy Theory.

Prior History and/or Current Theories Relating to the Problems

I. The Phenomena of Light

Huygens, during the first half of the seventeenth century, observed that light travels through a so-called vacuum. He also observed that light split into two rays in passing through a crystal of Iceland spar. From the observation of light passing through a vacuum he concluded that this so-called vacuum is not actually so, and this led him to reinstate Aristotle's concept of ether. Thus light was considered by Huygens as an undulation within the ether in transversal waves.

Newton's theory, on the other hand, held that "light was an emission of fine corpuscles ejected from a glowing source," and thus did not involve waves. Faraday was reluctant to accept the ether concept, and naturally favored his concept of the magnetic field.

The negative result of the famous Michelson-Morley experiment with the use of the interferometer proved fatal, temporarily at least, to Huygens' undulation in ether theory.

Einstein proposed abandoning the ether theory as it would require a substance, according to him, finer than any gas and at the same time more elastic than the hardest steel. Both of these qualities, of course, would appear irreconcilable. Therefore Einstein suggested, as mentioned heretofore, that we try not to use the word "ether." In the meantime, of course, we are living so to speak in an interregnum.

The wave theory of light was accepted in favor of Newton's corpuscular theory, especially after Faraday's concept of the electromagnetic field was substantiated by Maxwell's mathematical equations. The experiment of Young and Fresnel also appeared to support the wave theory. These men passed a light beam first through one pin hole and immediately thereafter through an adjoining pin hole. This produced two series of light and dark rings on a screen, which effect could be interpreted by the advocates of either the corpuscular or the wave theory. However, when light was passed through both holes simultaneously, stripes appeared between the two rings. This phenomena could be explained only by the wave theory.

Young and Fresnel's experiments appeared to clinch the argument for the wave theory of light. However, recent experiments involving photo-electric phenomena, and also the so-called "bullet" effect of a beam of light, point again to the quantum or corpuscular theory.

II. (1) *The Loss of Mass in Beta-decay Processes and* (2) *Packing Loss in Helium Nuclei Formation*

(1) The loss of mass in radioactive or so-called beta-decay processes, such as occurs during the disintegration of a free neutron into a proton and an electron, has been observed. This loss of mass has resulted, by a process of elimination, in the postulation of a hypothetical particle not directly observable, which ghost particle has been named the "neutrino." This phenomenon was first suggested by Wolfgang Pauli but the idea was later developed by Enrico Fermi into his beta-decay theory. The charge of the neutrino is zero, and the mass is considered

by some authorities as zero also, yet according to George Gamow the latest experimental evidence has determined this mass to be no more than one-tenth as much as that of an electron. This mass apparently must have been arrived at by a process of elimination, for the neutrino has not yet been found.

(2) A helium nucleus is made up of two protons and two neutrons, the total sum of the individual mass units of which is 4.03302 MU. Yet the helium nucleus as a unit weighs 4.00280. In other words, by packing the four particles together there is a resulting loss of .03022 MU. This is the startling discovery of modern physics.

How explain these losses?

III. The Force of Gravitation

A Leipzig professor is said to have opened his physics classes by cutting a string from which was suspended a metal ball, and then making the observation: "This is the greatest miracle I can show you in all my lectures."

Here is a phenomenon which is taken for granted by the majority of people, except when they were babies. The physicist and philosopher, however, are alike challenged to supply an explanation of it.

Dr. Einstein stated, "Physics really began with the invention of mass, force, and an inertial system." From the inertial system came the concept of inertial mass, and from mass (scale weight) came the idea of gravitational force. The two masses were considered as separate phenomena by classical physics, and it was only by observation that the ratio between the two was seen to be identical. It was Galileo's experimentation that surprisingly revealed that the gravitational so-called "calling" force of the earth was equal to the so-called "answering" force of an object. In other words, objects of differing weights fall at the same rate of speed; and thus their acceleration is independent of mass.

To classical physics the identity of the two masses was considered as accidental, but to Einstein and modern physics the equivalence of the two masses is considered fundamental and essential to the development of Einstein's general theory of relativity.

Newton considered gravitation as a fundamental force between all bodies. While he did not attempt to describe the nature of this force, he did proceed to describe the relationship of events under its influence. These relationships are embodied in his law of gravitation. This law states that the force is directly proportional to the product of the masses and inversely proportional to the square of the distance. Newton believed that this force acted through empty space without delay over unlimited distances.

Einstein, who incidentally doubted the existence of ether, could not agree with Newton on the immediacy of the reaction of the force at all distances because of the limitations set on it by the speed of light. Consistent with the modern quantum physics, Einstein considered that gravitation travels in waves and also forms fields as does light. The gravitational waves appear in strong gravitational fields, and the particles formed are called gravitons by Einstein. Gravitons are thus comparable to photons, another concept postulated within Einstein's theory.

Whereas Newton considered the universe as empty space in which celestial bodies are subject to a number of forces, the most significant of which is that of gravitation, Einstein viewed the universe as mass-energy with space identical with such mass-energy. Einstein, incidentally, applied Vogt's theory of pycnosis in his reasoning.

G. F. Fitzgerald (1851-1901), a British scientist born in Dublin, wrote: "Gravity is probably due to a change in structure of aether, produced by the presence of matter."

IV. The Earth's Magnetic Field

The existence of a magnetic field around the earth is another observed phenomenon still awaiting adequate explanation. The north magnetic pole of the earth is near the south geographic pole. Conversely, the south magnetic pole is near the north geographic pole. Thus the earth is a large dipole, with magnetic lines of force existing between them. The location of both magnetic poles will vary over periods of time and do not remain stationary. Eleasser has suggested that electric currents are generated in the earth's molten center, set in circulation by the rotation of the earth, and simultaneously generating a magnetic field. As the central core of the earth is considered to be composed of iron-nickel, this theory appears to be the most promising one at present.

V. Heat Phenomena

Heat and temperature at one time were considered synonymous terms. Black, however, made an observation that led to the realization that they are two distinct concepts, each having different meanings. Black brought out the idea that different substances possess different "heats." Later the term was changed to temperature. For instance, if three unlike substances of different temperature are placed together, they will all end up with the same temperature. However, the amount of heat energy in each substance will not be the same, as each substance has a different heat capacity or specific heat. According to Einstein the specific heat of a substance will vary directly with its mass.

At first heat was considered a weightless substance. Now, however, Einstein's equations assign mass to it. In other words, a hot iron will possess more mass than a cold iron, and the same is true of other substances. Of course, the reason heat energy was at first considered weightless was because of the exceedingly small ratio existing between the mass of a material body and its unit of heat energy. Heat energy given to a material object results in expansion phenomena, whereas heat energy radiating from a body results in contraction. Heat has the property of seeking equalization of temperature as between all bodies. Pressure has the effect of increasing the temperature; release of pressure has a cooling effect.

The phenomena of heat are currently explained as the result of molecular vibration. But why do not molecules vibrate at absolute zero temperature?

VI. Magnetic Fields Co-existing with the Flow of Electricity

The phenomena of magnetic fields registering with the flow of electrons within a conducting medium, as well as that of the induced current, were first observed by Faraday. Laws involving such fields have been formulated for application in connection with electricity. Clerk Maxwell stated these phenomena in mathematical form. However, no satisfactory explanation for the existence of such fields has been forthcoming.

VII. The Differentiation between Magnetic Waves

Radiant energy waves (such as light, infra-red, Xray, and gamma-ray waves), as well as carrier, radio, and television waves, are all currently classified as electromagnetic waves, transverse in nature rather than longitudinal.

The passage of radiant energy waves is interfered with or blocked entirely by mass-energy, depending on concentration. Even gamma-ray waves can be stopped by a three-foot-thick concrete wall. However, carrier, radio, and television waves can penetrate a three-foot-thick concrete wall as though it were almost non-existent.

Carrier waves are alternating vibratory electrical waves of a fixed high-frequency sent out into space by a radio or television station. The radio waves are converted magnetic sound wave pulsations riding on a carrier magnetic wave. Television waves are converted magnetic light wave pulsations also riding on a carrier magnetic wave.

As all the above-mentioned waves are classified as electromagnetic waves, how account for the differences of penetrability existing between them as indicated?

VIII. Planck's Unit Constant in his Quantum Energy Theory

Max Planck proposed a quantum theory of energy to explain why, say ultra-violet rays with faster oscillations, should generate less heat than infra-red rays with much slower oscillations. Heat will vary with the frequency of the wave. In his theory he used a constant "h" in determining his energy quantum, multiplying the constant with the frequency, with time as the variable, to determine the quantum of energy. This constant unit of action is independent of the frequency and even of everything variable. It has been found to be a true natural unit, comparable to the electron as the natural unit for matter and electricity. Einstein used this constant in his equations, especially in his quantum of energy equation. However, he multiplied the constant by the speed of light, which was then divided by the frequency of the wave. The energy value assigned to this constant is 6.55×10^{-27} erg-seconds.

What is the nature of this constant?

Concepts, with their Definitions, Under the Theory of Latent Energy

"The laws of physics," according to Bertrand Russell in his book 'Human Knowledge', "are laws as to the changes in the distribution of energy." In the same book he defines the scientific method as follows: "Broadly speaking, scientific method consists in inventing hypotheses which fit the data, which are as simple as is compatible with this requirement, and which make it possible to draw inferences subsequently confirmed by observation."

In this same connection Albert Einstein and Leopold Infeld state in their joint work 'The Evolution of Physics': "The purpose of any physical theory is to explain as wide a range of phenomena as possible. It is justified in so far as it does make events understandable." They later went on to say: "We think of a substance as something which can be neither created nor destroyed. Yet primitive man created by friction sufficient heat to ignite wood." Einstein subsequently maintained that heat is a substance.

Furthermore before proceeding with the exposition of our proposed theory, we shall endeavor to give a little perspective of the current atomic hypotheses of matter in relation to space. First to give an idea of the nature of the nucleus of the atom, Fritz Kahn in his book 'Design of the Universe' states that "The nucleus, like a peach, has a hard core which is surrounded by a softer middle section. Both are covered by a skin which is as fluffy as the velvet of a peach." What is the size of this nucleus? "If we were to close the gap between the two pillars of the letter U by a fence composed of a million sticks, the gaps would be very small. Yet if we were to close the space between two of these sticks with another fence of a million laths, the gaps of the second fence would still be wide enough to let an atom-nucleus pass."

As to the distances between atoms? Fritz Kahn has this to say: "The distances between the atoms of a substance, even between those in solid substances, are similar. The atom itself is enormously spacious. We compared it to a cherry (the nucleus) and a few mosquitos (electrons) half a mile or so distant. Where will you find the nearest cherry? On a tree nearby? No. We must start on a journey. The trees are as distant from each other as are the great cities on the continent of North America.

The atoms of gases are ten times farther apart. On the whole continent we would find only three or four 'neighboring' trees, one in Vancouver perhaps, the second in Philadelphia and the third in New Orleans." Fritz Kahn goes on to state: "Despite the vastness of the atom, it is extremely difficult to press one atom against another or to compress the orbits of the electrons."

In the attempt to throw light on the eight problems enumerated, with the background of the immediately foregoing statements, the following concepts within the proposed deductively formulated theory of latent energy are postulated, along with their definitions and assigned properties. It will be noted that certain concepts enumerated appear within other theories. However, in accordance with the law of parsimony their specific meanings have simply been amplified for use under this theory rather than creating new concepts.

Latent Energy

So-called space above the earth is not as empty as it appears, for we already know that it contains such invisible elements as carbon, oxygen, hydrogen, nitrogen, and photons, all vital for the existence of organic life. Inorganic material also has "life" qualities, for present physical theory maintains that it is composed of unitary vortices in a constant state of vibratory action. Thus it also must require an energy source for its maintenance, for movement requires energy. As organic life obtains a part of its energy from invisible space, so it would suggest that the inorganic likewise gets its "living" sustenance also from so-called space.

The concept Latent Energy is therefore postulated as an extremely fine crystalloidal-like suspension, possessing the characteristics of both separateness and prehensiveness (Whitehead terminology), as it is composed of extremely fine elements within a gaseous-like environment or medium in a latent or neutral state. These two aspects of Latent Energy are defined individually as follows:

1. *Latent Quantum Energy*—It is composed of exceedingly fine basic neutral elements, possessing the characteristic of separateness. These elements are relatively free of external resistance within its suspension medium, even though such medium is in an activated state. However, as two particles cannot occupy the same space simultaneously, particles of so-called mass-energy

will interfere to that extent with the freedom of movement of latent quantum energy. However, as has been observed heretofore in the introductory section to these concepts, there are comparatively vast spaces within the atom itself for its free movement.

(It is tentatively suggested under this theory that the particles which have already been postulated by physicists as a result of the loss of mass in beta-decay processes, namely so-called "neutrinos" of Fermi, may constitute the latent quantum energy particles under our theory. The neutrinos, so far as is known, have never been observed but are the product of the process of elimination, "reductio ad absurdum." They possess no charge and have no *observable* mass. Attempts are being made to detect this particle by means of an apparatus set up in an Ohio salt mine. So-called anti-neutrinos also have been heretofore inferred from certain experiments. It is estimated that five billion of these neutrinos from the sun pass through one's hand every second.)

Be that as it may, it is postulated under the Latent Energy Theory that the exceedingly fine basic particles are the very unitary elements which, together with latent binding energy, constitute the latent energy sea (space), and thus are the basic raw material elements of mass-energy.

2. *Latent Binding Energy*—This is the postulated latent neutral medium which possesses the characteristic of prehensiveness, and in which the latent quantum particles are distributed and move. It is also the medium out of which is activated magnetic waves and fields, and so-called magnetic lines of force. In its relatively latent stationary state it offers no resistance to the passage of mass-energy. Latent binding energy is also the source of magnetic wave phenomena coincident with all radiant energy, as well as all magnetic fields coincident with electrical energy in motion.

Magnetic Lines of Force

Magnetic lines of force have been defined as follows: "In electric and magnetic fields the electric and magnetic forces of repulsion or attraction are taken to follow certain imaginary lines radiating from the electric charge or magnetic pole. It is assumed that any unit electric charge or unit magnetic pole placed in the appropriate field will be acted upon so as to move in the direction of these imaginary lines."

Magnetic lines of force, as Faraday stated, behave like elastic fibers, and by the use of certain techniques they are directly observable. They carry no energy units or particles such as do radiant energy waves, and are emitted from a source where heat energy is being generated with no radiation outlet, or where there is an inadequate outlet. Bipolar molecules align themselves along such lines of force.

It is postulated under this theory that the alternating to and fro movement of electrons between the positive and negative poles of molecules in alignment progressively activates or creates within the latent binding energy sea small magnetic waves which travel along the aligned molecules in the direction of the positive pole of the total linear alignment. This phenomenon takes place only under conditions where heat generation occurs with insufficient heat radiational outlet as within the center of the earth, within the nucleus of the atom, or in a so-called magnet where heat generation is in a state of equilibrium because of the reciprocal alternate movements of the electrons between the aligned molecules.

When these progressively intensified magnetic waves reach their north pole terminus, they take a semi-circular course through the latent binding energy sea directed to their south magnetic pole. The activated latent binding energy between these two poles thus carries extremely small transverse electromagnetic waves to the south magnetic pole of the magnet.

Magnetic Waves or Fields

It is postulated that magnetic waves or fields originate from latent binding energy as needed for radiation purposes, energy production, form building, or as storehouses for mass-energy complexes as atom nuclei. They appear when mass-energy (configurated energy) is being maintained or created, or are coincident with the alternating or direct flow of an electric current (movement of electrons through a conducting medium), or when radiation or heat-generating phenomena occur.

For instance, magnetic waves appear when an electron of an atom retreats to its normal or next inner orbit or shell within such orbit. At this point the theory postulates that spent energy

401

particles slip into the latent energy sea. Coincident therewith magnetic waves appear of equivalent energy which immediately retrieve latent quantum elements from the latent energy sea, restoring their charge or spin so to speak. The magnetic waves thus created will move outward from their source, in the course of which they will periodically, according to their initial energy or wave length, transmute from within the latent energy sea spent latent energy elements into restored energy elements. Such magnetic waves are transverse waves within the latent energy sea.

In terms of the theory of pycnosis the magnetic wave restores the spin of a latent energy element and thus re-establishes its energy or charge. The magnetic wave reproduces a simple harmonic motion, and each time it crosses the axis of the moving element, it produces an opposite spin to an element; and thus the forward-moving element possesses an alternating spin.

The greater the number of spent energy units which return to the latent energy sea at any initial point of radiation within a fixed time interval, the greater will be the element-carrying capacity of the magnetic wave, inasmuch as the frequency of the wave is greater. For instance an Xray will give the magnetic wave power to transmute latent quantum energy elements a greater number of times per second than the light ray, and likewise a light ray more times per second than an infra-red ray. Thus the frequency of the wave determines its energy-carrying capacity. It is also postulated that where energy is being generated with inadequate radiational outlet, magnetic fields will appear to be activated from latent binding energy to transmute latent quantum elements to spinning or charged elements.

Enerjons

This is a postulated concept under this theory to designate a latent quantum energy element after it has had its spin or charge restored by a magnetic wave or within a magnetic field. It possesses a determinable mass as it has been transmuted one step out of the latent energy sea. Each radiant energy wave passing through the latent energy sea transmutes latent quantum energy elements into enerjons as many times per second as its frequency. It is a continual process of energy transmutation, a process which appears consistent with the law of conservation of mass-energy, at least as regards radiation phenomena.

In areas, such as in the central core of the earth where terrific heat generation is constantly going on because of extreme pressure and with inadequate radiation outlets, a tremendous number of latent energy elements are continually being converted into enerjons, and coincidentally creating magnetic fields from latent binding energy. These enerjons, under extreme pressure, become the building blocks of more complex atoms or molecules along the periphery of the hot molten mass (plasma) in the earth's interior, a nuclear furnace in a very real sense of the term.

Enerjons are the smallest mass-energy elements or particles. If their number carried by a magnetic wave is within the frequency of gamma rays, or Xrays, or light rays, or infra-red rays, they produce the phenomena of those respective waves as they strike a material (mass-energy) object at its transmutation point. The greater the frequency of the wave, the greater is its inertial mass or penetrating capacity into the earth's surface before it deposits its enerjons. Hence the penetrating capacity is in direct ratio to its unit frequency and in inverse ratio to the amplitude of the wave. However, the penetrating ability of radiant energy elements into the earth's surface or in fact any material object is extremely limited at best, for even gamma rays are unable to penetrate a three-foot-thick concrete wall.

The creation of enerjons at heat generating points in the earth's interior, in order to maintain normal atomic configuration and space relationships under steadily increasing pressure, will cause a flow of latent energy elements to restore the concentration of latent energy elements within latent binding energy at such energy-producing areas. Thus every material object has a latent quantum element "flow-force" (gravitational force) equal to its energy demand or specific heat to maintain its magnetic form. The absorption of such enerjons beyond its specific heat requirement, especially from solar rays, by a material object causes it to expand, where expansion is possible, and coincidentally register the phenomena of heat. At the same time it will proportionately increase the mass of the object insofar as such energy units are not subsequently radiated. Subsequent radiation results in contraction of the material object, with a proportionate loss of mass.

When incoming enerjon carrying waves (radiant energy) are reflected from an object, they will cause no flow of latent quantum energy at that point. However, all radiant energy waves are mass-creating when such enerjons are absorbed by a material object. Enerjons are thus the basic building blocks of all matter, including electrons and even nucleons within an environment of extreme pressure and no radiation outlet.

Configurated Energy

This postulated concept possesses the characteristic of modality mentioned by Whitehead. It is identical to Einstein's concept of mass-energy. However, while Einstein's concept mass-energy postulates the inclusion of all energy, nevertheless it would not include the latent energy herein postulated. Therefore, the concept Configurated Energy was necessary to avoid confusion of meanings. Thus all energy would include not only Configurated Energy (mass-energy) but Latent Energy as well.

Application of the Foregoing Concepts in the Solution of the Inter-related Problems

I. The Phenomena of Light

The phenomena of light under this theory becomes a composite of a transverse magnetic wave and a corpuscle or particle. In other words, using a term suggested by a certain physicist, light or in fact any wave of radiant energy is a "wavicle."

We can generally see or feel a wave of radiant energy without artificial conversion, but we cannot see or feel so-called electro-magnetic waves (except of course the passage of electrons along a conductor) unless they are artificially converted. Why? Because radiant energy waves alone carry particles without a so-called material conductor.

At this point we may very logically raise the question that if transverse waves in so-called ether, which Einstein maintained would require a substance finer than any gas and more elastic than the hardest steel, why postulate such a substance as Latent Energy? We are not postulating such a substance from Einstein's mass-energy. Under the Latent Energy Theory we have postulated not only Einstein's mass-energy as Configurated Energy but also Latent Binding Energy and Latent Quantum Energy. Out of this latent energy is activated Einstein's mass-energy, and it is within this latent energy that the transverse waves occur. If no other energy existed but Einstein's mass-energy (Configurated

Energy), then transverse waves could not logically be postulated for reasons indicated by Einstein.

The Latent Energy Theory would thus explain the Young and Fresnel experimental results as to the effect of a light beam passing simultaneously through the two adjacent pin holes. It would likewise explain the effects of a beam of homogeneous light directed at certain metals such as selenium, producing the phenomenon known as photo-electric effect. It would also make intelligible the so-called "bullet" effect of a light beam on a screen.

The bending of light rays as they pass the sun would therefore appear to be the resultant of both the inward flow of the latent energy sea toward the sun (the sun's gravitational field) as it affects the inertial mass of the photons of the light rays, along with the proportionate counteractions of both the radiational pressure and the magnetic lines of force of the sun.

II. (1) *The Loss of Mass in Beta-decay Processes*, (2) *Packing Loss in Helium Nuclei Formation*

(1) The loss of mass which occurs for instance in the disintegration of a neutron into a proton and an electron has been accounted for by Enrico Fermi by a process of "reductio ad absurdum," which caused him to create the hypothetical particle called the "neutrino." Under the Latent Energy Theory, the binding energy supplied by the enerjon becomes dissipated and the enerjon loses its spin and becomes a neutrino, which particle slips unnoticed within the latent energy sea. Simultaneously, however, it releases a magnetic wave which restores that energy, which energy travels to some other body of configurated energy.

(2) Packing Loss in Helium Nuclei Formation—It is postulated that a smaller quantity of activated Latent Binding Energy (appearing as magnetic fields) is required to bind four particles into one organic unit than four particles in separate units. For example it would take four bags to pack four oranges separately and only one bag to pack four oranges together. The difference in the weight of the paper of the two methods of packing would be the "packing loss" so-called.

That activated Latent Binding Energy possess weight is postulated and based upon the observed phenomena of "ectoplasm" (activated Latent Binding Energy), as cited under the remarks made at the close of this thesis.

III. The Force of Gravitation

In view of the relative absence of radiating possibilities for the heat energy constantly being generated within the interior of the earth, or any configured energy body for that matter, (endothermic greater than exothermic reactions) it causes a low concentration of latent energy elements in the latent energy sea at such points. The continual attempts to equalize this concentration causes latent energy to flow in from the exterior of the earth in vectors pointing toward the center of the earth from all directions. As is true of water as it runs out of the bottom of a conical container, it progressively accelerates in speed as it nears the outlet at the bottom. Or one might say it is roughly comparable to a body of water equally distributed external to a hypothetical sphere with fish swimming in such water, the surface of the sphere being sieve-like to permit the passage of the water to replace the steam being created within the sphere, with an assumed outlet for steam pressure. The swimming fish must, of course, continually compensate for the inflowing water to maintain their inertial position within the medium.

It becomes obvious that the nearer the latent energy flow approaches the earth's surface, the more acceleration it will have picked up. Thus the phenomenon of progressively increasing gravitational force is explained. Any body of matter, large or small, above the earth's surface will thus be carried in toward the earth at equally accelerated speeds with the movement of the latent quantum energy sea, except as modified of course by any inertial movement of a body within that sea.

Therefore the so-called "pulling" force of the earth and the "answering" force of the body are identical and the object will progressively accelerate in speed with the latent energy flow. Thus the gravitational acceleration of all objects regardless of mass will be the same. This phenomena would also be comparable to a V-shaped lake with water flowing toward a dam at its narrow outlet. If a log and a twig were placed in the water at the far end of the lake, both the log and the twig would be carried by the flow of the water at the same progressively accelerated speed toward the over-flowing dam. The inertial mass of both the log and the twig would register proportionately more mass (scale weight) at each point where they are stopped, until they reach the dam. If they were stopped half-way to the dam, their inertial mass would be less than at the dam, and so on, just as scale weight increases as altitude decreases.

This theory would also appear to shed light on the negative results of the Michelson-Morley experiment. The ether sea they were endeavoring to detect does not flow horizontal to the earth but toward the center of the earth. Thus its effects were equalized in any horizontal direction on the earth's surface.

The same Newton laws will likewise apply, except of course as modified by Einstein's theory. However, under Einstein's theory the gravitons are postulated entities, generated by the gravitational field. Under the Latent Energy Theory, however, the latent energy elements are relatively basic nonpolar entities, thus uncreated, and possess no determinable mass, as they cannot be raised out of its medium without becoming enerjons.

Whereas Fitzgerald suggested that gravitation was caused by the change of structure of the ether, under the Latent Energy Theory it would be more accurate to say that gravitation is caused by the movement of the ether (latent quantum energy) caused by heat-generation.

The relationships of the paths (curved space) of celestial bodies are thus the resultants of fields of force (magnetic lines of force and radiational pressures) emitted by all bodies, combined with the effects of flow of the latent quantum energy from areas of high concentration to areas of lesser concentration. In other words, the relative flow of the latent quantum energy is determined by the relative amount of latent energy elements required at the heat or enerjon producing areas.

IV. *The Earth's Magnetic Field*

All Configurated Energy units (mass-energy) are heat generating and thus have a magnetic field. In fact, it is this individual magnetic field that gives them individuality. Furthermore, all configurated elements, molecules or larger bodies, are more or less bi-polar.

Iron is particularly bi-polar and therefore has a relatively strong magnetic field. When iron molecules line up in a strong magnetic field, we have what is known as a magnet, with magnetic lines of force connecting the north-seeking with the south-seeking poles of the magnet. The earth is such a magnet, the north-seeking pole being located in Antarctica near South Victoria Land, and the south-seeking pole in the Arctic near Hudson Bay.

Walter M. Eleasser suggests a logical theory to explain or partially explain this phenomenon. He proposes that the rotation of the earth sets up slow eddies in the molten core of iron. These eddies produce an electric current circling from west to east with the earth's rotation, thereby producing magnetic lines of force within the earth's center which move toward the north magnetic pole (south geographic pole) and then circle the earth to the south magnetic pole (north geographic pole).

The Latent Energy Theory augments Eleasser's theory by stressing that it is heat generation without adequate radiation outlet that particularly activates the Latent Binding Energy within the latent energy sea at the earth's center. This direction-oriented activated Latent Binding Energy (magnetic lines of force) seeks and establishes connection between the north and south magnetic poles, thus creating the earth's magnetic field. These lines of force can be compared to the flow of the Gulf Stream which travels from the warm Gulf of Mexico up to the cold waters of the Arctic—a sort of river within a sea. Likewise, magnetic lines of force are activated Latent Binding Energy within a sea of latent energy connecting the north to the south magnetic pole.

To amplify more fully these thoughts, the stimulated electrons in the center of the earth are prevented from forming an outward flow of current because of the incoming flow of latent quantum energy. Thus the resulting reciprocal or alternating movement of electrons between the north and south magnetic poles of the iron molecules produce magnetic waves which travel along the magnetically-aligned iron molecules toward the north magnetic pole. These waves are progressively intensified from molecule to molecule (just as the flow of electrons increases from battery to battery in a series circuit). At the north magnetic pole the magnetic waves turn back in an outward curve in the general direction of the south magnetic pole, where they complete the circuit. These so-called magnetic lines of force are thus actually "rivers" of transverse magnetic waves within the latent energy sea, moving from the north to the south magnetic pole. These waves were created by the sum-total of the reciprocal or alternating movement of electrons between the aligned molecules along the axis between the two magnetic poles. These magnetic waves (analogous to water waves) will tend to carry other waves going in the same direction. Thus this tendency creates the phenomena of attraction at points where the south-seeking lines of force connect at the south magnetic pole. Conversely where magnetic waves of opposite direction meet at like magnetic poles, the phenomena of repulsion appear.

Faraday himself believed that these lines of force had a more real meaning than just "lines of force" and that they represented a "real state of strain in the ether in which all material bodies are immersed."

The original VanAllen belts were drawn with little deviation between the solar-ray side and its opposite. Recent satellite data, however, have shown considerable deviation of the earth's magnetic lines of force as between the solar-ray side and its opposite. On the solar-ray side the magnetic lines of force are apparently pushed in, so to speak, by the magnetic fields of the incoming solar rays. On the opposite side, however, the lines have been found to extend far out into space. This phenomenon would suggest that the magnetic fields of radiant energy from the sun curving in toward the opposite side and aggravated by radiation from the earth's surface at night, extend outward the magnetic lines of that side.

It should be noted that the flow of latent quantum energy moving toward the core of the earth is not affected by the magnetic lines of force. Evidence for this fact is that the gravitational force or barometric pressures at the poles are pretty much the same as at the rest of the earth's surface, except as modified by varying heat-producing points exterior to the surface of the earth caused by solar rays and the movement of invisible mass-energy particles in the so-called atmosphere.

V. *The Phenomena of Heat*

Heat phenomena are made more understandable under this theory. The enerjons carried by magnetic waves will enter a material body, specifically within the orbits of atoms making up such a body. This causes its electrons to move out into the next orbit or shell within an orbit; thus expansion phenomena are explained. If the magnetic waves of enerjons are immediately reflected, however, relatively no effect is registered on either the reflecting object or the movement of the latent energy sea. This is illustrated in the apparent neutral effect of solar rays on

409

the shiny fin of a radiometer. The black fin, however, is not only a good absorber but also a good radiator of heat waves.

The alternating spin of the enerjons entering a physical body at the frequency of heat waves will produce the sensation of heat in that body. Likewise it is postulated that the alternating spin of enerjons within the nuclei of atoms causes the continual transmutation of protons and neutrons, with its meson-like intermediate particles. It will be recalled that this fast hypothetical alternating process is currently suggested to explain why the repulsive forces of the positive charges of the protons within the nucleus do not cause them to fly apart.

Count Rumford was correct in his surmise that heat was produced by movement. That movement, of course, is relative to the movement of configurated energy within the latent energy sea, under varying conditions of pressure, in an attempt to maintain its atomic configuration. Furthermore, it is postulated that it is the alternating spin of the enerjons which causes the molecules to vibrate.

VI. *Magnetic Fields Co-existing with the Flow of an Electric Current*

The energy consumed in perpetuating the flow of electrons from areas of high to low potential along a conducting medium results in the periodic slipping of spent enerjons into the latent energy sea. As such spent enerjons slip into the latent energy sea, they at the same time activate a magnetic wave transverse to the flow of current from within latent binding energy. This reciprocal action transmutes a like number of spent energy units into enerjons and thus continually restores the spent energy.

In a so-called electro-static area, there is no magnetic field observable. However, any initiation, perpetuation, acceleration, stopping, or reversal of direction of the electron flow will register with magnetic fields.

It is interesting to observe in this connection that metals such as copper and iron are both good heat conductors as well as good conductors of electricity. Moreover, as the conducting medium is narrowed with a fixed electric potential, electrons are broken down into enerjons as in electric heating.

VII. *The Differentiation between Magnetic Waves*

That radiant energy waves are stopped by mass-energy (configurated energy) is explained under the Latent Energy Theory by the fact that radiant energy is composed of both a physical element (latent quantum unit) as well as a magnetic wave.

Carrier, radio, and television waves are strictly electro-magnetic waves within the latent energy sea. Incidentally, these waves are artificially converted to radiant energy waves within the TV set.

When one considers, as heretofore brought out, the large relative space between nuclei and their respective electrons within atoms, together with the vast relative space between individual atoms, one can appreciate why carrier-radio-television waves have no difficulty in passing through a concrete wall that even a gamma-ray wave cannot penetrate because of the physical particle it incorporates.

In view of the foregoing determinations, it would appear that it is confusing to consider both radiant-energy and carrier-radio-television waves as so-called electro-magnetic waves. It would appear less confusing to limit the term electro-magnetic waves only to carrier-radio-T.V. waves, and to magnetic waves coincident with the flow of electrons within a material conductor.

VIII. *Planck's Unit Constant in his Quantum Energy Theory*

The Latent Energy Theory postulates that Planck's constant energy unit "h" and the center point of each enerjon (radiant energy) wave are identical units. Some waves, of course, are short and others long, but the average energy of each wave unit is constant. It is the number of enerjons passing a point per second at the speed of light that determines the quantum of energy.

Suggested Observations and Experiments to Check the Theory's Validity

It has been previously observed by scientific experiment that a suspended iron ball placed near a mountain-side will be attracted toward the mountain-side and slightly away from the earth's gravitational center. This phenomenon is said to be caused by the gravitational attraction of the mountainous mass, but no explanation is suggested for the phenomenon itself.

Furthermore, in this connection, when the twelve-and-a-quarter mile Simplon tunnel was bored through the Alpine mountain in Switzerland, great heat was found to be constantly generated, especially in the deepest section of the tunnel. This condition even necessitated air-conditioning for the workmen.

Now we have the two simultaneous phenomena of so-called gravitational attraction and of abnormal heat generation without an adequate radiational outlet. Therefore the problem is to prove or disprove a relationship between them. An experiment to shed light on this problem would be to use two equal masses, one solid and the other slightly broken up to allow for a greater radiational surface. The mass with greater radiational surface should possess a lesser "gravitational" attraction than its solid counterpart. Possibly an apparatus adapted from that used by Henry Cavendish could be used for the purpose of the suggested experiment.

Incidentally, the latent energy theory would appear to throw light on an observable phenomenon of smoke rising from an outside circular charcoal brazier. With no breeze stirring, the heat from the brazier will cause the particles of smoke to expand and rise perpendicularly to it. However, if there are two or three persons standing motionless near one side of the brazier, the smoke will tend to go toward them rather than continue in its perpendicular rise. If the persons all shift their positions to the opposite side of the brazier, the smoke will still tend to go in their direction.

Under this theory, the latent energy will tend to flow toward the heat-generating points with inadequate or disproportionate radiation outlet, and in this case toward the persons' bodies; their bodies are generating far more heat than they are radiating because of metabolic activity within them. The brazier, on the other hand, is immediately radiating its generated heat in all directions.

Adaptation of the ideas suggested by the aforesaid phenomenon could also be used to validify or disprove the theory.

In addition the theory would appear to explain the phenomenon of a low-pressure area in front of as well as at the eye of a cyclonic storm, such as a hurricane, followed by a condition of normal barometric pressure in its rear area. This phenomenon is rather difficult to explain if only atmospheric air is considered. Under the Latent Energy Theory, however, it is postulated that the terrific heat-generating cyclonic disturbance gets its basic sustenance from the latent energy sea directly in its path, and coincidentally causing the low barometric pressures in front of as well as at its eye.

Inasmuch as one unit of radiant energy, such as that of light (photon), involves the progressive transmutation of only one unit of latent quantum energy in its path, it becomes understandable why the speed of light is the limit of velocity as postulated by Einstein. This becomes clearer when one makes the common sense assumption that only one physical particle can occupy the same space at any one instant. It would thus account for the relatively slow forward speed of a hurricane as it involves the movement of an almost infinite number of transmutations of latent quantum energy elements to maintain its form and movement. Incidentally, the speed of the latent energy flow is not so limited.

Once the inertial mass (the resistance created by the incoming latent energy from all directions to maintain the normal structure of a body) has been overcome by an external force within a relatively static latent energy sea, its persisting forward movement is facilitated by the low-pressure area progressively created by its requirements of heat energy (enerjons). It is this phenomenon, too, that would appear to explain the persistence of motion in a straight line as asserted in Newton's first law of motion.

We can now better appreciate the prohibitive increase in mass as a body approaches the speed of light as postulated by Einstein. It appears to be nature's brake in its attempt to maintain its basic structure within its established laws under impossible environmental conditions.

Incidentally, the Latent Energy Theory would suggest a possible physical explanation of gyroscopic phenomena, in addition to their present mathematical explanation. Furthermore, it would suggest an explanation of the so-called strange or "unnatural" behavior of molecules as they approach absolute zero temperature ($-273.18°$). It is reported that as molecules approach absolute zero, there is practically no further vibratory activity (dead so to speak) as all free heat energy has been withdrawn. Consequently, under this theory there would be no transmutations of energy required and no need for latent energy elements. With no incoming flow of latent energy to the molecules, their consequent lack of "inertial mass" would account for their so-called strange or "unnatural" behavior.

The theory also appears to suggest an explanation for the collapse in a 100-mile per hour wind of three out of six adjacent high-electric-power cooling towers which the National Physical Laboratory in England had by wind tunnel tests determined would withstand a wind up to 275 miles per hour. As the incoming latent energy sea herein postulated, determining thereby the degree of inertial mass and hence stability, would be changed both by proximity of the towers as well as by the use to which they are to be operated (in this case as so-called cooling towers), these two factors, it would appear, should not be ignored in any wind tunnel tests.

General Concluding Observations

This theory appears to throw light on the eight problems initially cited. It would also seem to support G. P. Thompson's and de Broglie's conception of the electron as a particle accompanied by a composite series of waves. However, under the Latent Energy Theory it would be a "packed" particle, that is, consisting of a composite or compresent unit of enerjons, as suggested by electric heating.

Interestingly, too, the latent energy elements seem to correspond with Leibniz' windowless monads, his theoretical building blocks of all matter. However, it is only after they receive energy, charge or spin during heat generation that they respond to the natural laws found applicable to mass-energy which Leibniz called pre-established harmony.

It is desired to make clear that when radiating enerjons enter an atom, its outer orbit is affected first, and then as the intensity of the enerjon bombardment increases, the effect is carried back progressively from one orbit to another and ultimately to the inner orbit of the atom. However, it requires a compresence of enerjons in the form of neutrons to pierce or break down the magnetic lines of force protecting the nucleus of the atom. As the radiant energy is dissipated, i.e., loses its spin so to speak and drops into the latent energy sea as spent enerjon elements, the magnetic waves produced thereby radiate from the atom to restore or conserve such energy. The longer waves or red waves are emitted from the outer orbit as an electron slips back into its normal orbit, and so on. Naturally there are more long waves radiated in this process than short under normal conditions, causing the contrary phenomena which led Max Planck to develop his quantum of energy theory.

Under the Latent Energy Theory the gravitational and magnetic phenomena are not comparable. However, it is the movement of latent quantum elements toward local equilibrium of configurated energy, with resultant pressure and heat generation, which gives rise to both phenomena.

Likewise, the actual inertial mass of a body and its weight are not necessarily identical. For instance, the weight of an object will vary according to its location in a particular gravitational field not its own. It has no determinable weight within its own gravitational field. However, the ratio of the weights of various objects in the same general location within a gravitational field not its own would be identical as regards the ratio of the actual inertial mass of the objects. The actual inertial mass of an object is really the amount of outside force necessary for that object to be freed from its own gravitational field, that is, from the incoming flow of latent quantum energy while in a relatively non-flowing latent energy sea. This explanation of inertial mass would appear to be consistent with its definition by physicists, namely, that it is the resistance to motion by the body.

To cite an illustration, when the Gemini 5 was sent up, great initial thrust was necessary to free it from the earth's gravitational field and against the resistance of the lower atmosphere. However, once it attained a height where it was relatively free of the earth's gravitational flow and atmosphere, only a slight thrust was necessary to accelerate or decelerate its speed or change its direction. The explanation suggested by the Latent Energy Theory is that in its initial take-off from the earth, the Gemini 5 had to "buck" both atmospheric resistance and the incoming latent quantum energy flow caused by the earth's heat-generating requirements. Once the Gemini 5 attained so-called relative "weightlessness" in space, it required no further thrust to overcome the resistance of the incoming latent quantum energy for its own heat-generating requirements. It was the latent energy sea which made possible the original thrust, as witness Newton's third law of motion—"With every action (or force) there is an equal and opposite reaction." It serves as a counteracting medium as does water for the steamship's propellers.

The difficulty the astronauts have with their "umbilical" cord clinging to their space suits appear understandable under the Latent Energy Theory. Furthermore, the excessive heating generated within the space suit while the astronaut is endeavoring to perform some task outside the space-ship may also have an explanation within this theory; incoming latent energy elements are not stopped by the insulation of the space suit, whereas the heat generated within the space suit can find no radiation outlet because of the insulation. It has the same effect as a semi-permeable membrane has in osmotic pressure phenomena in the field of biology.

The question might be raised as to why the atomic elements in the atmosphere are not all carried to the earth's surface with the latent quantum energy flow. Incidentally the atoms in the earth's atmosphere result from chemical reactions of the elements on the earth's surface. The spatial relations between such freed atoms are the resultant of their individual magnetic fields, as well as the gravitational force and radiational pressures to which they are subjected by both incoming and outgoing radiant energy waves. As to radiational pressure, it will be recalled that Svante Arrhenius, a Swedish astronomer, maintained that the radiation pressure of sunlight is sufficient to propel living germs throughout the solar system. Lebedew, a Russian, subsequently substantiated by experiment the existence of such light pressure.

As evidence tending to support the contention that electro-magnetic phenomena are form builders, the electro-metric experiments on the amblystoma by Northrup-Burr-Lane-Nims in 1936-37 are cited. These experiments revealed that magnetic lines of force were observable prior to the appearance of matter. From the results of their experiments they concluded "that living creatures are electro-magnetic systems and that field physics applies to them."

As evidence that mind can influence magnetic waves, the observation of Dr. Edmund M. Dewan, an experimenter of brain waves at the Air Force Cambridge Reserve Laboratories at Bedford, Mass., is cited. Dr. Dewan recently discovered that he could change the form of his alpha waves by thought alone and without muscular movement. This observation would suggest that mind (psychic energy) can initiate or affect magnetic waves. Thus it would appear to give a physical support for the phenomena of auto-suggestion, popularized by Emile Coué.

As further suggesting this same thought, we also wish to cite the observations of Drs. Thomas Duane and Thomas Behrendt, ophthalmologists at Jefferson Medical School in Philadelphia. These two doctors observed under scientifically controlled experiments that the alpha wave pattern in one twin brother would register in the alpha wave pattern of the other, separated by eighteen feet and two partitions. For instance when one twin was instructed to close his eyes, his alpha wave pattern registered the action. At the same time it registered in the alpha wave pattern of the other twin with his eyes open and who was unaware of his twin brother's action or reaction. Apparently the alpha waves of each of the twins were consonant with one another within the latent binding energy sea.

Furthermore, Dr. W. J. Crawford, a mechanical engineer, for several years made what was perhaps the most exhaustive study ever made of psychical mediumship under the most rigid scientific controls, and recorded his results in such books as "The Psychic Structures of the Goligher Circle" (1921), published by E. P. Dutton & Co., New York. In this book he brings out that the medium generated ectoplasm (defined as "a sort of externalized protoplasm" in the Columbia Encyclopedia) in his presence along with the presence of other witnesses. This phenomenon was accomplished under subdued lighting. Opportunity was given to examine physically the so-called ectoplasm. When Dr. Crawford passed his hand through the structures, he experienced a cold, disagreeable, sporelike sensation. He took photographs of the phenomena and observed that a magnesium flash tended to break down the ectoplasmic structures, but with a severe effect on the medium. When the ectoplasm solidified it possessed weight. This phenomena appears to suggest that a magnetic field also possesses mass, as it is suggested under the Latent Energy Theory that the so-called ectoplasm did not come out of the person's body but on the other hand was the "materialization" of the latent binding energy in space, which materialization was brought about by the waves of psychic energy emanating from the medium. The concentration of enerjons involved in bright lighting appears to break up these structures which involve only latent binding energy.

Based upon the foregoing inferential evidence (admittedly sparse), and furthermore, in view of Einstein's conclusion that the universe reflects a supreme intelligence, it would imply that the universe represents the creation of a supreme mind. This thought would thus suggest the following causal line progressive equations, especially in view of the immediately foregoing observations:

417

Mind (supreme intelligence + a directing entity) =
thought (psychic energy waves);

Psychic energy waves + latent binding energy = magnetic waves;

Magnetic waves + latent quantum energy = configurated energy (mass-energy)

Current physical theory considers the universe as a sort of self-created chance phenomenon. The possibility of this occurring would appear even more improbable than Eddington's suggested logical possibility, as mentioned by Lord Russell in his book 'Human Knowledge' "that perhaps all the books in the British Museum had been produced accidentally by monkeys playing with typewriters." Yet inconsistently in such a chance universe scientists are persistently seeking out natural laws based on the assumption and expectation that nature's functioning is universally logical and consistent.

It must be conceded, however, that the analytical approach of science appears to be not only the most logical method but also the most productive of both constructive, and even destructive, results. Moreover, scientists have yet to discover reasons for losing faith in the logicality of natural phenomena. Their current analytic procedure suggests the following schematic representation:

Chance Universe (Mass-Energy — Electromagnetic Waves)
plus Finite Mind (Intelligence + a Directing Entity)
equals Mathematical Equations and Natural Laws.

Scientists appear to shy away from the cited causal line series of equations which ironically are suggested by their own findings, but persist in entertaining the two basic contrary assumptions of a chance universe with universal laws. The foregoing dynamic analytical approach functioning in the foreground of the suggested causal line equations of a created universe would appear more logically consistent. As Einstein would phrase it: "It is certainly more satisfying to have the (mystery) story follow a rational pattern."

Furthermore, the mathematical physicists appear to ignore the unexplained phenomena mentioned at the beginning of our present exposition, and confidently persist in working with their present basic equations which, if inaccurate, would result in a progressively increasing probability of error. But after all, weren't they successful in igniting the atomic bomb? This situation could be naively compared to the amateur auto mechanic who surveyed his smoking and ruined motor just assembled, ignoring the parts scattered around on the garage floor which he had failed to fit into his assembly, and proudly commenting, "I'm on the right track all right, for she sure popped off!"

However, in spite of this possibly unfair comparison, it could conceivably be that if the unexplained physical phenomena are fitted into a more coherent theory, it might lead to some revision in the present basic equations. However, only a naive layman with no professional standing to lose would venture the suggestion of the possibility of the highly improbable rather than the very high degree of improbability of the possible. It does seem, however, that because of the extreme importance of the basic equations, they should be periodically scrutinized in the light of most recent general data.

Man believed in the existence of air which he could not see because he soon became aware that he required it in order to breathe. If a molecule possessed awareness and could speak, would it perhaps inform us that it also believes in the existence of the unseen in space as it requires it to "breathe"? Because a quivering and spinning molecule cannot speak for itself, man appears to ignore its need for sustenance against the voice of his own sense of logic.

Before closing our present thesis on Latent Energy, let us momentarily turn toward the more philosophical, and venture the observation that the general tendency of nature to seek equilibrium or a status quo as to form apparently produces movement, with coincident heat energy. For instance Latent Quantum Energy seeks to maintain its concentration within its medium of Latent Binding Energy. Thus it moves toward areas of lower concentration produced at heat-generating points with inadequate or no radiation outlet. This compensatory movement to attain equilibrium causes the phenomena of gravitation and inertial mass.

The resulting gravitational phenomenon coincidentally creates pressures within and between bodies of mass-energy (configured energy), with consequent heat phenomena. The attempt of atoms and molecules to retain their normal spatial relationships necessitates increased counteracting energy production to maintain these normal relationships under the increasing pressure. However, if the pressures become too great to be compensated for, the atoms themselves in the ultimately resulting nuclear furnace environment, transmute from relatively spatially large but lighter in atomic weight to relatively smaller spatially but heavier atoms. Hence, we suggest that atom building results within an environment of extreme pressure with consequent high enerjon production.

It is also observed, on the other hand, that enerjons in a freely radiating environment in turn seek an equalization of temperature between individual atoms and their molecules, as well as their complexes, according to their specific heat. Here again we detect a relationship between specific heat, mass, and so-called gravitational force.

Likewise in the area of electrical phenomena we observe the tendency of nature to attain equilibrium, as electrons tend to move from an area of high concentration (potential) toward one of lower concentration in the absence of a barrier to such movement. Again the movement ceases when a state of equilibrium is attained.

Under the Latent Energy Theory electricity may be defined as the phenomena resulting from electrons passing successively from one molecule to another within the latent energy sea, the direction of flow being determined by the magnetic lines of force or by the unequal concentration of electrons in separated areas connected by a conducting medium.

Magnetism, on the other hand, may be defined as the phenomenon resulting from the vibration of electrons occurring between aligned molecules spinning in successively opposite directions, which vibration activates latent binding energy and results in magnetic waves within latent binding energy, termed magnetic lines of force. These magnetic lines of force can cause on contact temporary magnetic phenomena in metals whose molecules are not so aligned.

There is no passage of electrons between the molecules of a magnet but simply a passage of magnetic waves induced by the vibration of electrons between the molecules making up the magnet. Whenever conditions exist permitting the successive passage of electrons from one molecule to another, the phenomenon of an electric current is observable. The direction of the current alternates with the direction of the magnetic lines of force.

Thus it appears that so-called natural forces are the result of nature's attempt or tendency to maintain its forms in a state of equilibrium so far as the particular local environment permits. A mind entity alone appears to be the only medium that can direct, expedite, change, or relatively reverse nature's tendencies to maintain a status quo or equilibrium. This effect a mind accomplishes either purposively by acquired knowledge of nature's laws, or accidentally through ignorance of those laws.

Consistency and coherence of all natural phenomena, together with agreement with observations of nature, are the expressed goals of scientific theory. Therefore, if the foregoing thoughts (both admittedly brazen and naive) contain a fertile idea to break the present impasse involving the phenomena of light and gravitation, we shall consider ourselves richly rewarded. This would be especially true if it serves to strengthen the apparently faltering faith of the theoretical physicists in the existence of a "physical" universe by suggesting new possible epistemic correlations between theory and observed phenomena. In other words, the Theory of Latent Energy endeavors to reestablish spatio-temporal continuity within the science of physics by supplying a physical basis for the unification of gravitational and magnetic fields. And incidentally it reinstates Newton's concept of Force to gravitational phenomena.

Thus we have returned to Newton's statement: "The interchangeability of bodies and light conforms with the essence of nature which seems delighted with transmutations."

XXIX

A BACKWARD GLANCE AT PHILOSOPHY AND CERTAIN INDEPENDENT THOUGHTS AND SPECULATIONS

A Backward Glance at Philosophy

As we glance back at the various contributions of the philosophers of the past we find that each philosopher contributed some new idea or unifying aspect of natural phenomena. We also observe that the particular contribution of each philosopher is more or less determined by three principal factors: (1) by his personality type; (2) by the culture wherein he developed his ideas; and (3) by the period of history in which he lived. No one man, culture, or even period can think of everything. Philosophy after all is a dynamic, living study, progressively modified and amplified as truths are revealed and perceived.

All philosophy is dependent on the miscellaneous scattered facts unearthed by science and by other cultural studies. All science in turn is dependent on philosophy for the gathering together and the unification of those data, and possibly suggesting new hypotheses for science to investigate. Science, because of its very nature, tends toward logical analysis, whereas philosophy concentrates its labors principally in the field of logical syntheses. Whenever the investigations of science run into a fruitful field, it more or less ignores philosophy. However, when it runs into a stubborn impasse, it again looks to philosophy for hints and directional guidance. Ralph Linton, the late renowned anthropologist at Yale University, once likened scholars to chickens; when feed is thrown into one corner of the chicken yard, the chickens all rush over to it; if before they finish eating that feed another batch of feed is thrown in the opposite corner of the yard, the chickens will all rush over there. Scholars do appear to rush into something new because it happens to be "fashionable."

The initial problem to which philosophers turned their attention was the problem of becoming, which problem occupied the minds of such early Greek philosophers as Thales, Anaximander, and Anaximenes. They were followed by the Eleatic philosophy of such men as Xenophanes and Parmenides involving the negation of becoming. They, in turn, were followed by Heraclitus who deified becoming—in other words, everything was in constant motion and change. Incidentally, the philosophy of Heraclitus is quite at home in modern times.

The attempts to explain becoming then occupied the time of such thinkers as Pythagoras, Empedocles, Anaxagoras, and Democritus. Democritus, by the way, originated the idea of atoms as building blocks of nature.

The age of criticism of this early period was begun with its philosophy of mind. This period was represented by the thoughts of such thinkers as Protagoras and Socrates. They were followed by Plato and Aristotle, with their apotheosis of thought.

Epicurus then appeared on the scene with his negation of thought-substance and the apotheosis of matter. The Stoics then appeared with their contributions involving the deification of will.

At this point the Greek philosophers had touched on practically all basic philosophical problems, and it was now time for the sceptics to take over, which they promptly did. This put an end to further philosophical speculations until the conversion to Christianity of the rhetorician Aurelius Augustinus in North Africa, who subsequently became St. Augustine and fathered a system of philosophy known as Christian Platonism. Between the period of the Greek sceptics and Christian-Platonists, the philosophers served principally as instructors to politicians in the art of "double-talk," first to win office and later to hold office.

Philosophy from St. Augustine to the peripatetic scholastics was mostly Christian theology. However, with the resurrection of the works of Aristotle during the thirteenth century, churchmen such as Duns Scotus and particularly St. Thomas Aquinas proceeded to incorporate Aristotle's philosophy into the theology of the Church. Incidentally we must not overlook that St. Thomas Aquinas contributed an orderly method of thinking which was of considerable assistance to science at a subsequent period.

The modern period then opened by the contributions of such independent thinkers as Bruno and Campanella, Bacon and Hobbes, Descartes (the revealer of the coordinate system), Spinoza with his extended and thinking substance, and finally Leibniz with his theory of monads and concrete spiritualism. The last three philosophers mentioned incidentally were mathematicians.

The age of criticism of the modern period then opened, with such men as Locke, Berkeley, and Condillac. These men were subsequently followed by Hume; and then by Kant and German idealism, including Hegel's whole philosophy of nature based upon logic alone. We recall that Hegel contributed a philosophy of art that has not been surpassed in the opinion of some authorities.

We then have Schopenhauer's philosophy, emphasizing the concept of will, and Nietzsche with his superman philosophy which influenced Hitler.

Darwin's theory led to philosophy taking a "back-seat" to science under the name of positivism and logical analysis. James' Pragmatism, Bergson's Vitalism, and Kierkegaard's Existentialism were the subsequent reactions to this dominance by science.

Certain Thoughts and Speculations on Philosophy

There exists inductive inferential evidence in nature to support three planes of being, namely, the physical, the mental, and the spiritual. All three planes have the Whitehead characters of separateness, prehensiveness, and modality. The physical plane possesses these as latent quantum energy, latent binding energy, and mass-energy, all as postulated under the latent energy theory herein. Once the latent energy is activated, we have radiant-energy, the electron and magnetic phenomena.

The mental plane possesses the three characters as ideas (thoughts and notions), instincts with its sentiments, and personality with its non-living cultural creations.

The spiritual plane, the highest, possesses the three characters as Divine Wisdom (Father), Divine Love (Holy Spirit), and the personality of the Father, as personified in His Only Begotten Son and objectified in His living culture.

The physical plane represents both the objectification of the creative thoughts of the spiritual plane, with its living culture, and of the mental plane with its non-living culture.

The existence of the three foregoing planes of being are supported by objective and subjective phenomena which are enumerated in the works of physics, biology, psychology, philosophy, and theology with its spiritual phenomena. Which came first, the conception or its objectification? It is now quite apparent that the conception preceded its objectification.

With this picture of the three planes of being before us, the ever-recurring controversy between idealism and realism becomes less confusing. At this point it is desirable to stop and briefly clarify a few terms. We recall that in the Middle Ages what we now consider as realism or materialism was then considered as idealism in its modern conception. Furthermore, what we now consider as realism or materialism they then considered as so-called nominalism. The Church of the Middle Ages found it necessary to espouse Plato's view of considering ideas as real, for the Church to maintain its dominant position must be considered as the one real collective entity rather than the individual physical church structures or members. Strange as it may seem, the terms subjective and objective during the Middle Ages also carried meanings just the reverse of what they carry today.

Therefore, we desire now to make clear that the meanings given hereafter to the terms idealism and realism, as well as objective and subjective, are in accordance with the modern connotation or usage of the terms, namely, that idealism and the subjective represents ideas, notions, laws, names and species prior to their objectification, and that realism and the objective connote the actual objectification thereof.

With this clarification having been made, we shall proceed to state that the physical plane is the objectification of the mental and spiritual plane, which objectification is denoted as realism and the objective. All cultures, both living and non-living, are the products of both the mental and spiritual planes of being. Non-living culture represents the objectification of man's mental plane, and the living culture, which incorporates the Universe as a whole, including man himself, represents the handiwork and objectification of the supreme mind on the spiritual plane.

Thus the spiritual plane is the highest plane of being, with the mental plane intermediate or between the spiritual and physical planes. It is the mental plane which serves as the communicating medium between His (God's) creation and Himself from the spiritual plane. Communication as between men's minds is via the physical plane; hence the privacy of thought and the commonality of the physical environment of man. In a larger sense it would appear that the spiritual contributes through Divine Love the binding force, the mental the creative element, and the physical the objectification of the creations of both the Infinite Mind and the finite minds.

Man, the highest representative of the living culture of the Supreme Mind, operates within two planes, the mental and the physical, mind and body. He also may choose moving upward into the spiritual plane as well. In this respect he may be considered a potentially "triphibious" organism so to speak.

The best way man can "subdue" nature and learn to know the laws under which it functions is to study nature using scientific methods. Thus man may change quantities to qualities, that unique capacity of the mind of man.

Such study also enables man to know something of the mind of the Creator of the Universe, for by His works ye shall know Him. Man with this acquired knowledge is thus enabled to create a culture of his own, even though non-living. In other words, man becomes an active co-worker with his Maker in the future development of the living cultural creation in which he functions. Thus the very essence of man is directly related to that of his Maker as well as to that of his fellow-man.

In addition to the knowledge of the Creator which can be acquired by studying nature (His handiwork), more or less direct communication may take place between man and his Maker via prayer, meditation, and by the study of His Word. Those individuals, however, who eschew such direct communication, will hear the occasional warnings of their Maker's prophets, thereby aggravating the inner unrest of their spirit. God, Himself, does not approach man objectively except via His creation, for He Himself is a spirit and mind.

Because of the apparent failure of the foregoing means of communication with His children, He finally resorted to his present and final means, by objectifying His Son, the chief corner-stone of His entire creative endeavor. If this last means does not suffice for man, there is no other source of hope for him.

From the foregoing thoughts, we conclude that pure mind or spirit existed originally, and this Eternal Entity after fully creating the Universe, including mankind, in and through His Son, finally objectified His creative thoughts, first in inorganic creation, and subsequently in progressive steps completed his organic creation up to and including man—man who was created in His image and becomes his son, the very zenith of His creative effort. Thus, the creative activity within the mind of the Creator was completed before its objectification, just as man creates within his mind an invention prior to its physical production or objectification. Then to say that a creative form does not exist until it is objectively produced would not be factually true.

Individualism is definitely encouraged by the Creator and free choice is positively existent in man as an individual. True he is limited in that he must function within the fixed laws of nature or take the consequences, but at the same time free choice has significance only in such a rationally-consistent Universe. Just consider how man can ignominiously unseat determinism by his choice to forgive.

Man as a physical being operates within the receptacles of space and time. The physical phenomena are limited to the speed of light but the mental aspect of man is not so limited. Thus while mental activity is not handicapped by the receptacle of space, it does require, as we have many times observed to our embarrassment, the receptacle of time. Time thus furnishes a technique of ordering the sequence of movement in space, and activity within mind, of all energy, namely, mass-energy, latent energy (when mass-energy is present), and psychic energy (the energy of the mind.) Of course, if nothing but latent energy existed in the receptacle of space, the technique of time for sequential ordering in the physical world would be unnecessary and meaningless.

A culture cannot be perpetuated by man from one generation to the next unless it is communicated from the minds of one generation to the minds of the next. Thus man is the one responsible organism with the capabilities of becoming a co-worker in the creative activity of his Maker.

The significance of the mind could not have been more

forcibly demonstrated than by the action of heads of all governments, including the most outstanding materialistic one, in rushing in at the close of World War II to capture the scientific minds who created the missiles rather than to possess the missiles themselves.

Now let us briefly consider the meaning of the word "truth," the meaning of which Pilate questioned Jesus. Concisely, truth is generally interpreted as the agreement of thought and its object. The significance of this definition is dynamically illustrated in the following little episode:

> A gentleman coming out of a metropolitan department store caught a glimpse of a man suddenly reaching out and then falling to the sidewalk. Rushing over to the fallen man he solicitously inquired: "My dear man, what happened?" The man on the sidewalk looked up and sheepishly explained, "I grabbed for a pole that wasn't there; brother am I drunk!"

Here we have an example of the thought and the object not being in agreement. Thus it would appear that if man would remain upright, he should seek and embrace truth; for it is not always a "haughty spirit" that goeth "before a fall."

Jesus used the word truth on many occasions, for instance in John 14:6 he is quoted as saying:

> I am the way, the truth, and the life: no man cometh unto the Father, but by me.

Also in his prayer of consecration of his disciples, Jesus uttered the following words as recorded in John 17:17:

> Sanctify them through thy truth: thy word is truth.

What did Christ mean by the word "truth" as used on these two occasions? Christ is truth for his life was in agreement with his Father's (the Creator's) thoughts. His Father the Creator's "word is truth" for His word (thought) as revealed through His prophets and as objectified in His Creation (the Universe in which Christ represents the finished product), are in total agreement.

Man's efforts to "subdue" the world are successful to the same extent that the products of his efforts to determine its laws agree with the thought of his Maker (as reflected via sense-data from natural phenomena, His creative work), and furthermore that man abides by those laws.

Thomas Paine in his "Age of Reason" states in part: "The word of God is The Creation we behold and it is in this word, which no human invention can counterfeit or alter, that God speaketh universally to man." "The Creation," of course, includes man, naturally; and whereas man alone cannot "alter" his instinctual nature, his Creator can as we shall subsequently discover.

Of the many interesting analogies among natural phenomena, we should like to cite the following two or three. Heat and love are analogous forces in their respective planes of action. Heat has a two-fold action on the physical plane—it melts solids, and it has a recombining action which leads to new forms. Love likewise has a two-fold action but on the psychical (mental) plane—it melts hatred and it has a recombining action leading to a new individual and a new society of individuals.

Mankind of the present civilization is persistently engaged in the search for new sources of heat energy and in the most efficient application thereof. It is no exaggeration to state that it is most imperative that mankind not by-pass the binding energy of "love of God" if it wishes that civilization to endure and not blow up in its face.

When seeds are sown by the Sower, each seed appears not to bemoan its individual lack of particular qualities or the environmental conditions into which it falls. Rather it appears to accept the responsibility of making the best possible adjustment to its particular environment.

Observe the lichen, that dual plant and fungus organism whose seed falls on the cold bare rocks of the bleak far north. Does it appear to bemoan its fate, shrivel up and die? No, with the heat generated within the chlorophyll of its single-celled algae body from the meager absorbed sunlight that appears over the horizon during the brief summer, it melts the water caught and frozen on the branches of its partner, the fungus, thus enabling both entities to live and co-exist. With the joint activities of these two simple organisms, the cold hard rock on which they exist is gradually and irresistibly broken down—a first step to prepare the soil for a more specialized seed of scrub pine later to sprout and grow.

Wise the man who can learn from the lichen—to accept the fate of his individually inherited qualities and the particular predicament in which he finds himself, and to proceed from there to make the best possible contribution to the work of his Maker, to his own welfare, and to the welfare of his fellow-man. This attitude is neither one of pollyannaism nor Stoicism—it is simply operating from cold realistic facts. Spaulding stated in his interesting book "A World of Chance" that "Nature itself, and all that it contains, is only 'one deal of the cards'." Thus it appears the better part of wisdom for each man to "play the cards" dealt to him in a manner that he can later look back upon with reasonable pride. Certainly he shouldn't try to consign himself to non-being based upon an impulsive judgment, for even the pessimist Schopenhauer concluded that such an attempt would prove futile. However, as each and every man is a unique creation, he owes it to his Maker to objectify his given "talents" in his own particular courageous way, and thus honor his Maker. His Maker, in turn, will inevitably reciprocate by both honoring and compensating His unique creature.

Another philosophic observation in this phase of our discourse: Let us freely acknowledge that it was a marvelous act of wisdom on the part of our Maker to provide for the privacy of man's thoughts, as well as to furnish him with an external world in which he may observe, if he so desires, their objectification in the presence of the mutual criticism of his fellow-man via the unifying prism of logic. If man's thoughts were to lack privacy, his existence on this planet would have long since come to a violent end. Democracies make much of its "freedom of speech," but of even more importance is its "freedom of silence."

The dignity of man rests essentially on the factors of privacy of individual thought and the freedom of individual choice. Responsibility for the objectification of such thought is his alone, although he should keep ever in mind that "as a man thinketh, so is he;" embarrassingly he so judges himself.

It is well also that the Creator placed a limit on man's capabilities of sensation, for were we able to see the invisible activity going on continually within so-called space, man would be living in a far greater "fog" than at present. For even the "gestalts" within his present perception are still a challenge to his finite mind.

For the Creator to provide the whole wide external world, a world in which natural laws consistently function, as an objective workshop for all men—the philosopher, the scientist, theologian, and the layman alike—together with the weather as an introductory confirmatory check before entering into more abstruse discussions, are indeed acts of extraordinary practical wisdom. Yet it is faith and faith alone which enables man to free himself from the prison of his own intellect.

We realize, of course, that we are currently being challenged in our foregoing conceptions by certain so-called "God-is-dead" theologians, an apparently periodic "deciduous" phenomenon. In the words of one such theologian—"We must recognize that the death of God is an historical event; God has died in our time, in our history, in our existence."

There was once a little brook that had its source at a spring which continued flowing even during severe droughts. Everybody spoke glowingly of this ever-flowing spring. The little brook felt it was being ignored, and started "babbling" that the spring had ceased flowing. How the brook could keep "babbling along" without the ever-flowing spring is not a question to be answered within the realm of logic but rather within the realm of desire.

Likewise, how a finite existential being can pronounce the death of Being itself, (—i.e., "God is dead") unless of course he does it "with his tongue in his cheek," cannot be answered within the realm of logic.

Pinpointing Man's Most Urgent Need

Let us now try to pinpoint man's most urgent need today. We shall begin with the reasoned conclusion of Ralph Linton, the late world-renowned anthropologist, i.e. "Man is an ape with an overactive brain." This is an obvious case of asymmetry; and with that conclusion as our reference source, let us set up an imaginary situation:

We shall start with two dice, one throw of which has 36 different possibilities. Now let us take 12 men, representing twelve different nations, each of whom may have one throw of the dice. Then assume that the 36 possibilities of one throw are 36 laws of nature. Only one man in the group has accumulated sufficient knowledge and skill to know and control the operation of the 36 laws. That man can produce in one throw a double-six at will.

Now let us assume a double-six is not "box-cars" but an atomic bomb. Therefore that man who can throw at will a double-six is a potentially dangerous man, along with the nation he represents, not only to himself but to the remaining eleven men with their respective nations.

Now let us say, all twelve men are possessed with an "overactive brain" yet have the instincts of an ape. Will additional knowledge, such as making the remaining eleven men equally educated and skillful so that they also can produce the atomic bomb at will, result in a greater or less danger? It is quite apparent that the danger would become infinitely greater.

The knowledge involved in producing the atomic bomb can also tap a great potential power source, and thus produce untold benefits in which all twelve men and their nations may participate. Whether "to be or not to be" is now up to a group of twelve men with great knowledge and skill but with the instincts of an ape. The probable choice of any one of the twelve is frightening, especially so if his sentiment of self-regard is aroused.

It brings man face to face with the necessity of doing something to recreate his own instincts. That would appear to be man's basic need today.

In closing these remarks, it would appear that when philosophy, science, and religion eventually make contact, when the triadic linear equation is solved, the impact thereof will produce both startling and revolutionary results for all mankind. One fact appears certain and that is that man as presently constituted will eventually become one of the "missing links" between the ape and man as he was ultimately conceived in the mind of his Creator. Certainly man as presently constituted can entertain no hope of permanently surviving even as a cladogenic branch of creative activity.

Amplification, analysis, and synthesis of the foregoing thoughts follow in the remainder of our thesis as a suggested solution of our triadic linear equation.

XXX.

THE BIOLOGICAL PROBLEM OF ORGANIZATION

A Review of the Problem

Biological science has about completed its so-called natural history stage, with its various concepts of inspection. It is now faced with the task of constructing an adequate deductively formulated theory to account for the organization found in nature, and whose concepts of postulation can be successfully related to the biological concepts of inspection determined in the natural history stage.

H. S. Burr and F. S. C. Northrup propose a theory called "The Electro-Dynamic Theory of Life," which appears in the 1935 issue of The Quarterly Review of Biology. In the presentation of this theory they briefly review the prior theories of biological organization. Among these they mention the theory first formulated by Aristotle, the first major natural history theory of biological organization. This theory in modern biology is known as Vitalism. The vitalist ascribes the activities of living organisms to a "vital force" as Driesch's "entelechy" or Bergson's "elan vital." They assert that the phenomena of life possess a character which causes biological phenomena to differ radically from physico-chemical phenomena. Thus, the concepts of biology under this theory are irreducible to those of any other science. This appears to be supported by the concepts of inspection of biology in the natural history stage. Living creatures as observed do differ from observed, inorganic objects. Thus, the apparent irreducibility of biology under this theory offers no connection with the other sciences.

As living creatures display a persistence of form or organization throughout the influx or outgo of material, it is natural to conceive of the living organism as a composite of two basic factors: its observed material and observed form. The development of the embryo observed by biologists makes this conception (vitalism) a natural one to them.

As attractive as this theory is to biologists, it does not explain the breakdown of the organism's organization at death. Thus, the organization is not an ultimate, irreducible factor but comes and goes. Secondly, species modification and the origin of new species emphasized by Darwin are not explained by the theory. These phenomena emphasize the non-irreducibility of form for the species, as death emphasizes in the case of the individual.

Finally, biologists have found that a more consistent and adequate conception of biological form could be attained only by recourse to the postulated entities of physics and chemistry rather than by attempting to understand biological phenomena in terms of concepts derived from directly inspectable items. The physicists, it will be recalled, also learned from experience the truth of St. Paul's statement that "what is seen was made out of things which do not appear."

F. S. C. Northrup, the logician in the Burr and Northrup team of biological theorists, warns against "muddling" the concepts of inspection of the natural history stage with the concepts of postulation under the physical and chemical theories, as these two types of concepts belong to two different worlds of discourse. Biologists, in other words, must choose whether to develop a strictly natural history biology or a deductively formulated theory based on the entities of physics and chemistry. Of course in order to verify such a theory, the postulates would have to be joined to what we immediately inspect in the natural history stage by so-called epistemic correlations. This procedure would also require concepts by postulation to effect the organization of these entities. The task then is to find a postulated relational factor determined by physical and chemical theory which can be epistemically correlated with the immediately observed organization taken from the natural history data.

Burr and Northrup mention three theories of this organic factor: 1) the chemical theory; 2) the thermo-dynamical theory; and 3) the electro-dynamic theory of life respectively. They stress that all three theories are involved in the chemical factors already experimentally demonstrated to be present in living organisms. However, the concepts and theory of chemistry have not yet been formulated deductively as precisely as in the case of physical science.

As the interacting chemical elements also obey the laws of energy, the structures of chemical systems are also subject to the laws and postulates of thermo-dynamics. Chemical entities are also known to constitute electrical components. As living organisms in addition depend on radiant energy from the sun, electro-magnetics consequently becomes a significant factor for the continuing existence of living organisms.

Burr and Northrup begin the development of their theory by briefly reviewing the contributions of the French scientist Lavoisier to the chemical theory during the latter part of the eighteenth century. Lavoisier demonstrated that a living system when viewed chemically cannot be interpreted as the mere collection of chemical compounds within its visible bodily surface. He determined in his investigations of metabolism and respiration that the existence and persistence of a living organism depends upon the continuous decomposition, reorganization and reassembling of chemical constituents, a perpetual dynamic process. For instance, the breaking down of carbohydrates in an animal body requires a continuous supply of oxygen. The source of this oxygen has its basis outside the body in the tension (effect of gravitational force) of the atmosphere adjacent to the earth's surface. In addition, if the carbon dioxide resulting from the oxidation of the carbohydrates within the organism was not removed by respiration, the organism would die.

In view of the foregoing, it is concluded that the biological organism is not made up of a set of local protein molecules of a chain or pattern type of atoms, but composed of a great number of chemical factors in continuous flux and interaction. The investigations of bio-chemistry are continually emphasizing the complexity of this process.

Upon the basis of the postulates of chemical theory, and specifically of the theory of atoms, persistence should be in the atomic entities, and not in the structure. Actually, the reverse has been found true, as the chemical constituents have been found in a continual motion and flux. On the other hand, it has been found that it is relatedness that persists. The work of Rudolph Schoenheimer using the technique of "tagged atoms" confirms this view. Individual protein molecules do not persist because of chemical bonds but have been found to be continually built up as constituents are passing out and being replaced continually by others. Schoenheimer's investigations further emphasized that even so simple a structure as the protein molecule would disintegrate if not continuously maintained by energy supplied by food or radiation from without. This is precisely what one would expect from the standpoint of the thermo-dynamical theory of life.

Thus, the chemical theory held up so far as it went; however, it was found to account for a part of but not all the problem of organization. The thermo-dynamic theory, therefore, was considered next.

Unless energy is brought into a thermo-dynamical system, it will automatically break down because of the operation of the second law of thermo-dynamics. If a living organism passes to a state of "maximum entropy," which is the same as a thermo-dynamical equilibrium, the organism dies. As a consequence, energy must continually be renewed from the outside in order for the organization of living organisms to be perpetuated.

The basic concept of thermo-dynamics is energy, which is roughly the capacity to do work. This energy can be classified into two general forms: a form available to do work in an organized living system; and a form which is unavailable for work in an organized living system. This latter form is termed dissipated energy or entropy so far as organized living systems are concerned. Under the second law of thermo-dynamics as stated by Clausius, the entropy of the universe tends toward the maximum.

A complicated and highly organized biological system naturally requires more energy for the maintenance of its organization than a simpler system. Furthermore, biological evolution proceeds from a relatively homogeneous type of organism to a progressively more heterogeneous type. In consideration of these two factors, it appears then that biological systems go counter to the second law of thermo-dynamics by proceeding from a state requiring a lesser amount of energy to one requiring a greater amount. Sir James Jeans is among those arriving at this conclusion. F. G. Donnan, however, pointed out that the second law does not say that the entropy of a system can never decrease with time. It merely states that this can never occur in an isolated system. Hence, in the evolution of a system, energy in a form available for work must be brought into the system from outside. This fact emphasizes that the basis of biological growth and organization cannot be accounted for only by chemical constituents within a system but also involves chemical factors both on the earth's surface and in the atmosphere. These, in turn, depend upon energy relations with our solar system. Thus, without the temperature difference between the sun and the earth, biological growth, organization, and evolution would not be possible on thermo-dynamical grounds. This consideration makes it very doubtful whether the answer to growth and biological organization can be found in some local chemical factor. Sir James Jeans' view may be said to be true as regards the astronomical universe as a whole, namely, that the sum total of entropy tends toward a maximum, that is assuming that the astronomical universe is finite. Be that as it may. the relation between these many moving chemical entities is continuously dependent upon energy coming into the system from without, and ultimately from the solar source. Thus, biological organization is the form of the relation between the motion of its chemical parts. Furthermore, the thermo-dynamical dependence of biological growth and evolution upon energy from the sun, establishes that biological organization has its origin jointly in electro-magnetics, in chemistry and in thermo-dynamics. It is by electro-magnetic propagations from the sun that energy is brought to the surface of the earth and to plants. Furthermore, it is by the mediation of chlorophyll contained in plants that makes possible a process to chemically synthesize this energy into carbohydrates, and the resultant storage of the sun's energy. This process is electro- or photo-chemical in nature, and it brings us to the third theory in the attempt to account for biological organization.

Before discussing the third theory, let us briefly recapitulate our progressive search for a theory of biological organization up to this point. First, the chemical theory was found to account for the constituents of biological organization. However, it failed to account for the flux and movement of those constituents. The thermo-dynamic theory was then brought in to account for the energy required to organize the chemical constituents. Yet, it was found there was nothing in the theory to prescribe the particular relatedness into which the energy organizes the flux of the chemical materials. Technically speaking, there is nothing in thermo-dynamics itself which prescribes precisely at what point in the tendency toward a state of maximum entropy the energy from outside the system compensates that tendency, to produce the persisting state, or the state of mean compensated entropy, which is a living organism. Therefore, what is needed in addition to the concepts by postulation of the chemical and thermo-dynamical theories, is a postulational theory of physics prescribing an irreducible relatedness between moving physico-chemical entities. Field physics now supplies this need.

The conception of living organisms from the standpoint of field physics, the electro-dynamic theory of life as proposed by Burr and Northrup, will now be briefly considered.

Clerk Maxwell was the first scientist, as we recall, to formulate the theory of field physics mathematically and deductively. Maxwell recalled that Ampère's theory of electric currents asserted "attracting forces considered as due to the mutual action of particles." Maxwell stated that "we are proceeding upon a different principle, and searching for the explanation of the phenomena not in the currents alone but also in the surrounding medium." He, of course, had in mind Faraday's field concept. In other words, instead of beginning with the particles, Maxwell was forced to begin with the field in order to account for the existence of light and other electro-magnetic propagations in the universe. Maxwell stated: "The distribution of the currents due to these field forces depends upon the form and arrangement of the conducting medium." He added, "this medium must be so connected that the motion of one part depends upon the motion of the rest." The foregoing statement appears in his final paper on electro-magnetics which contained his famous equations.

Here we have a most significant contribution towards an adequate theory of biological organization. Maxwell goes on to state that we begin with "the form of the relation between the action of the parts," given in the laws of induction, and "the second result which is deduced from this, is the mechanical action between conductors carrying currents."

If this physical theory applies to a living creature, such a creature is not merely a collection of chemical entities needing energy but also an individual which is organized.

Strangely, the postulates of field physics were necessary even to account for phenomena in the inorganic world. Particle physics broke down completely with Huygens' undulatory theory of light. Upon the development of Faraday's field concept, Maxwell was able to show that the undulatory theory of light followed from it. Thus field physics succeeded not only in optics, but also in electricity and magnetism.

The later contributions of Lorentz and Larmor made possible the prediction of the negatively charged electron before Sir J. J. Thomson discovered it experimentally. Northrup calls attention to the fact that the electron is not a concept of particle physics but is defined in terms of the postulates of field physics. Einstein in his theory of relativity further confirmed the assumption of field physics. He stated, "For several decades most physicists clung to the conviction that a mechanical substructure could be found for Maxwell's theory. But the unsatisfactory results of their efforts led to gradual acceptance of the new field concepts as irreducible fundamentals." (1940) Hence, "the form of the relation between the motion of the parts" as asserted by Maxwell has been accepted as irreducible by physicists.

Field Physics Applied to the Problem

As physicists found it necessary to apply the field concept to account for inorganic phenomena, how much more do biologists need this postulate of electro-magnetic theory to account for the persisting relatedness in the organization of living organisms. Therefore, Burr and Northrup seized upon the postulates of this theory in understanding biological organization. Thus, from these postulates they put forward their electro-dynamic theory of life.

Their hypothesis, of course, required that electro-metric experimental methods be used to detect any such systematic, organic, electrical properties of living organisms. On that basis, Burr, with C. T. Lane and L. S. Nims, developed appropriate experimental apparatus to test the theory empirically. Many different species of living organisms were subjected to experimental test with this apparatus. In every case it was found that systematic, distributed, potential differences show up over any living organisms considered as a whole. Their findings in detail were published in 1937. Subsequently later experiment demonstrated that in this theory a type of epistemic correlation existed between the postulated structure of physical theory and the directly inspected natural history data of organization. This experiment by Burr involved the amblystoma, a primitive form of the amphibians. Burr found a fertilized egg of the ambly-stoma in one of its early stages of development of its embryo when no directly inspectable differentiation was observable—no definite organized pattern of potential electro-magnetic differences. With the use of dyes, Burr designated an inspectable pattern on the surface of the organism which corresponded to the postulated potential differences designated by the apparatus. Subsequently, after the organisms was permitted to grow, inspectable natural history differentiations showed up at precisely the locations which his dyes as applied, based upon his prior electro-magnetic readings, had indicated.

In view of these experimental results, the electro-magnetic theory of field physics offers a scientific theory by which a solution of the problem of biological organization is to be found.

Thus, chemical theory provides the postulated entities as the basis of the material constituents of living organisms, the thermo-dynamical theory provides an understanding of the needs of energy from without, and the electro-dynamic theory provides the irreducible relatedness required to understand the organization of the constituents as motivated by the energy.

In this connection G. E. Coghill in his "Anatomy and the Problem of Behavior" published in 1929, had already determined by his study also of the Amblystoma, that: "Nerve cells, like seeds planted by a gardener, spring up and grow according to a definite pattern." He states in a subsequent section of his book: "In the early development of Amblystoma, as already described, there is a great deal more central nervous organization than can express itself through the effectors, and certain elements in this overgrowth can be recognized as elements in the structural counterparts of future behaviour forms.". . . "This predetermination may be regarded, in mechanistic terms, as an act of will. It may arise within the constantly expanding conditioning mechanism by a process of individuation in the same manner as the limb reflex emerges within an expanding total behaviour pattern. In the latter case the mechanism is in process of creating a definite end-result for a long period before the end-result is attained."

Problem of Determining Source of Electro-Magnetic Form

Burr and Northrup have proposed a most exciting theory. But now that we have a clue as to the basis of biological organization, we are faced with the sixty-four dollar question—From whence came the initial electro-magnetic form itself? Can chance account for it? Such a possibility appears incredible, especially in the light of the Lecomte du Noüy's thesis as put forth in his "Human Destiny." Some scientists will simply assert that nature mysteriously operates on mathematical principles, and refuse to go beyond their mathematical equations. Others will state that nature operates according to natural laws but will venture no explanation as to the source of the laws.

We shall venture a possible theory suggested by our theoretical analysis of man's personality. The form of the electromagnetic phenomena in biological organization is the product of the joint functioning of mind and instinct of the living biological entity. The mind-factor is assumed to be mobile and more or less conscious, whereas the instinctual factor is assumed to be a built-in (preprogrammed within the genetic constitution if you will) behavior sequential pattern responsive to certain releasers, all leading toward a goal.

As the primitive living organism appears on the evolutionary scene, its blind instinctive organization plays a predominant role, with its mind-factor beginning to assert a primitive guiding function. As the living organism becomes progressively more specialized and complex structurally, the mind-factor becomes likewise more dominant, while coincidentally the instinctive patterns become less specific and more loosely organized. It should be kept in mind that the mind-factor is limited and must function within the instinctual and structural pattern.

In man we observed the instincts to be more loosely organized than in the lower biological organisms, with the mind-entity abruptly becoming the predominant factor. As heretofore indicated, the mind-factor has been found to register electromagnetic effects in nature. In this connection we shall mention the experiments of Dr. Edmund M. Dewan of the Air Force Cambridge Research Laboratory, Hanscom Air Force Base, Bedford, Mass. While engaged in studying the alpha waves of his brain, he was impressed with the fact that he could control their activity by thought alone. These waves are believed produced by a generalized flow of electricity through the gray matter of the brain.

If the mind of man by the act of thought can control or change the form of electro-magnetic activity in the brain, then it may be inferred that the mind-factor in living organisms below that of man may function similarly. We have also observed that man by his creative thinking, an apparently psycho-magnetic activity, has created successive and progressive forms or contrivances, such as the present-day automobile and the electronic computer. These successive forms then are first a psycho-magnetic reality, shall we say, within the mind of man before they are subsequently transformed into a material (electro-magnetic) reality. It should be emphasized here that the progressive developments of an automobile, or for that matter any invention, are successive in nature rather than continuous. For instance, we may observe a group of automobiles of apparently the same general design, chassis, wheels, motor, and the like, but some will differ in body types, such as the sedan, convertible, station-wagon, etc., to adapt to a particular use or need; these too are inventive creations, though minor in relation to the automobile as a whole. However, there are in this group of car models two significant branch groups, one group possessing the self-starter and the remainder without this newer inventive feature. The group having the self-starter may be considered as being on the lead branch of the main trunk (anagenic) so far as car evolution or improvement is concerned. The remainder, however, are on a sideways (cladogenic) deployment, and will eventually disappear from use. The main inventions have thus first appeared on the lead branch.

The electronic computer can be cited as an excellent illustration of the preprogramming by the mind of man of certain functions within a created machine, which machine will respond subsequently at a specific pre-set point after it has been set in operation with its so-called "input" cards. In view of this capability of man, is it so unreasonable to suggest that the natural laws found operative in the cosmological sector and the instincts functioning in the biological sector are also preprogrammed?

Let us briefly consider the biological sector. In the most primitive organisms, we observe instincts to be very tightly patterned, in fact resembling almost the natural laws in the cosmological sector. The so-called mind-factor dimly appears as a unifying organizational entity. In the plant kingdom this organizational entity or mind-factor remains in its most primitive form, apparently never reaching self-awareness, the organism of the plant kingdom remaining non-motile.

In the animal kingdom, however, both the instincts and mind-factors progressively reach their highest form. The factor of instinct perhaps reaches its highest relatively undeviating form among the insects in the sub-phylum arthropoda. There are species of ants which have not changed in fifty million years, based upon living fossil evidence. The bees particularly have a highly developed instinctual organization, and represent the highest development on the insect branch. They possess no culture, however. Their extraordinary performance in building hives of such accurate and equal hexagonal sections is a natural marvel. Is it a conscious performance? Incredible, for if conscious the construction of the hives would show individual deviations. In the light of present knowledge we can only speculate that the mind factor in the bees are guided in their hive-building by built-in inherited magnetic patterns within their genetic constitution—termed as instincts by biologists and psychologists.

As we go up the trunk of the biological tree and reach the deployment of the sub-phylum chordata, we observe the mind-factor growing more significant for the organism's immediate environmental adjustment. However, the factor of instinct is still very much in evidence so far as determining general adjustment patterns and limits are concerned, even among the great apes of the primate group.

Homo-sapiens (man), however, makes the significant breakthrough in that the mental entity comes into dominance. This does not mean that the instincts are not still present, not only as limitations but as general guides and tendential motivators of action to assure perpetuation of species and self-perpetuation of individuals, self-preservation, and the like. However, the conscious mind of man has been observed to even over-rule these general instincts, witness the phenomena of suicide among homo-sapiens in spite of strong self-preservative instincts. The fact that the individual conscious mind can now control its instinctive organization creates a responsibility which should make man stop and seriously meditate.

McDougall, an outstanding dynamic psychologist, came to the firm conviction that "mind must be considered a potent cause of evolution." What is the major objective evidence of the control of the organism by the mind factor?—the existence of a culture—a mental creation pure and simple. It is definitely not an epi-phenomenon of the physical brain.

From whence came instinct and mind? The factor of chance has been thrown out as too incredible for serious consideration. Natural selection then as suggested by Darwin? In part yes, for it checks with observation and appears credible as far as it goes. Incidentally, Darwin's conclusions drawn from observing the various species of ground finches on the Galapagos Archipelago are most interesting. The finches, by the way, represent the highest development in the bird deployment. As regards Darwin's study of these birds, it seems odd that he was not particularly intrigued to study a little more closely the one species which apparently did not wait for natural selection in the scientific biological sense to give it the long beak of a woodpecker in order to extract insects from the crevices in the bark of trees. Rather, the great grandfather of this finch family apparently had a "brain storm" and picked up a little twig to extract the choice insect morsels otherwise out of reach. (Can we say the finch acted instinctively? Hardly, for it would appear more logical to assume that it was an intelligent action by the mind-entity of the finch. The finch's act was basically no different from that of a boy placing a wad of chewing gum on a weight tied to a string, and dropping it through a grating to retrieve a dime otherwise out of reach.) We can then go on and speculate that the finch built up a guild, with the cooperation of his proud mate. This guild apparently became a closed society, or family in biological terms. Could not that original great grandfather finch be considered the original user of tools? But possibly it would be maintained that he did not periodically sharpen the twig. However, be that as it may, he is no longer around to press his claim.

Dr. Einstein readily admitted that the harmony of laws found in nature reflected the work of a supreme intelligence; in fact, he was not even allergic to the term "god," though his associates gingerly double-talk the term. The objective evidence found in the phenomena of nature points definitely to the existence of a living, ever-functioning, and intelligent directing entity. The evidence fairly screams out this conclusion. If to ascribe a directing entity to the supreme intelligence is to create a personal god, then we can see no logical way of avoiding the conclusion. After all, what is so unscientific about it? Man concedes he did not create himself. Yet, many intellectuals feel as soon as they as scientists become aware of a few universal laws in nature, they become as little gods unto themselves just for having detected them, and jointly proceed to ward off intruders from their domain. When man reaches that state of mind, we are witnessing the ultimate in idol-worship—a state of mind most dangerous for the future development of homo-sapiens as a psycho-social being.

Many biological authorities will cling tenaciously to the term evolution and eschew any mention of a creative process. Perhaps this is so because the use of the term "create" suggests a creator, which to them of course brings in the "supernatural." However, one biologist of good professional standing, namely N. J. Berrill, considers even the reproductive process itself is a creative process. As substantiation we quote the following paragraph from his book "You and the Universe":

> The remarkable thing about an egg, whether fertilized or not, is the absence of all that is to come. Potentially everything is there, certainly, or else nothing would emerge, but actually very little is present to begin with that is not in most cells that are not over-specialized. Development is not an unfolding,—it is creation in the most real sense of that word.

Julian Huxley, that world-renowned evolutionary biologist and a grandson of Thomas Henry Huxley the able spokesman and defender of Charles Darwin's views, clearly outlines the operation of natural selection and states that it is the only effective agency to explain the so-called evolutionary process. In addition to the factor of natural selection, the term originated by Darwin, Huxley cites the factor of biological improvement as unifying the great variety of forms manifested by life during its evolution. These two principles he restates in two general evolutionary one-way equations. One is that reproduction plus mutation produces natural selection, and the second is that natural selection plus time produces the various degrees of biological improvement found in nature.

The so-called mutations or inaccuracies occurring in the reproducing process are said to furnish the materials for natural selection. Yet strangely, the great majority, if not all, of these mutations are deleterious rather than advantageous to the species. The tendency appears to be toward the mean of the probability curve of each species. For example in experiments on the drosophila or fruit fly, an occasional blind mutant will appear, but over a period of time by intercrossing, the blindness will gradually disappear in future generations, in other words return to the normal for the species.

Huxley, very considerately, defines in his book "Evolution in Action" the terms "struggle for existence" and "natural selection," which definitions we quote from his "Evolution in Action":

> The "struggle for existence" merely signifies that a portion of each generation is bound to die before it can reproduce itself: while "Natural selection" is a shorthand phrase for the differential survival and reproduction of variants, and its effects in each generation.

A good illustration of these two factors in operation is in the case of insects sprayed with DDT. Initially the spraying appears effective in killing. However, there are some mutant genes (individual variability) in insects which produce insect types immune to the spraying operation. The insect types possessing this gene will survive and reproduce, whereas the others will die out. The evolutionary biologists maintain that this process, given sufficient time, accounts for new species.

Another case, involving the fruit fly, is sometimes cited to support Lamarckianism, the inheritance of so-called acquired characters. Thorpe raised drosophila grubs on media flavored with peppermint. As a result the adults were attracted by the same odor to lay their eggs—a case of olfactory conditioning.

In the case of a species of migrating birds, the so-called whooping cranes, man has practically wiped them out, there being only some fifty at present known to exist. The National Wildlife Service is desperately endeavoring to save the species from total extinction. In this case natural mutations cannot save the species, and the expansive driving force of reproduction of the species is not sufficiently great to compensate for its disastrous environment (man). Only a conscious purposeful choice by man can save it from extinction, but that is a possibility.

Yet it is generally true that each species appears to carry within itself the potentiality of adaptation to its ever-changing environmental conditions and thus survive. And this process is known as natural selection, conscious or unconscious.

Huxley acknowledges the incredibility of any explanations heretofore attempted to account for the larger gaps existing between species, especially on the so-called upward evolution along the main trunk. This aspect of the evolutionary process is termed *anagenesis* by Bernhard Rensch, as against branching

446

or sideways evolution, which he terms *cladogenesis*. Huxley in partial answer to this problem of explaining the larger gaps in the evolutionary tree cites the phrase used by Professor R. A. Fisher: "Natural selection is a mechanism for generating an exceedingly high degree of improbability." Huxley goes on to explain: "The clue to the paradox is time . . . All living things are equally old—they can all trace their ancestry back some two thousand million years."

In explaining the development of mental activity, Huxley makes a rather startling confession with regard to the brain and mind:

> The impulses which travel up to the brain along the nerves are of an electrical nature, and differ only in their time relations, such as their frequency, and in their intensity. But in the brain, these purely quantitative differences in electrical pattern are translated into wholly different qualities of sensation. The miracle of mind is that it can transmute quantity into quality. This property of mind is something given: it just is so. It cannot be explained: it can only be accepted. But we can study the way in which the mind-matter relation changes during the process of evolution.

Summary, with Conjectures, on the Mystery of the Evolutionary Process

Let us now briefly summarize some of the main points and interpose some of our own conjectures as we go along.

The term evolution appears to involve two general processes. One is the upward, advance, or progressive process along the main trunk—*anagenesis* as Rensch terms it. The other process is a periodic sideways or branching adaptive activity from the main trunk—*cladogenesis* as it is called by Rensch. This branching adaptive process appears to be a deployment of a general species to make maximum exploitation of the available food supply, and at the same time an adaptation to the varying environmental conditions. For this adaptation its innate instinctive patterns set the general limits and direction, which the mind-factor within these limits modifies to meet immediate specific adjustments. Such deployment appears to continue so long as

447

the environmental adjustment is within the limits set by the organism's instinctive patterns and mind. As heretofore suggested each species appears to have a built-in adjustment limit (pre-programmed in data-processing terminology), beyond which it cannot go. Within this limit set by its genetic constitution, the phenomenon of natural selection functions.

So in brief we may classify the sideways or branching process as *reproductive and adaptive creationism,* the limits for which are determined by the organism's inherited genetic pattern related to the particular environmental conditions. The reciprocal action of instinct and mind responds significantly to innate releasing mechanisms set off by particular environmental conditions. Natural selection, if you will.

The forward, advance, or progressive process, i.e., anagenesis, appears to involve both a progressive, as well as a reproductive creative process. Huxley states in his Evolution in Action: "Progress is inevitable as a general fact, but it is unpredictable in its particulars." The advance process appears on the main trunk abruptly, even without any apparent environmental stimulus. It is immediately below these abrupt appearances of distinctively new species that so-called "missing links" are sought. It appears that on the advance up the main trunk, the instinctual limits become less tightly patterned and more loosely organized. The mental aspects, however, become progressively and successively expanded. Hence the lead branch would seem to be the one to observe closely for a clue as to any new anagenetic activity. If even reproduction is a creative process as suggested by Berrill, how much more must this be true of the anagenetic activity on the lead branch.

In view of these observations, the question is raised whether evolution is the correct term to apply to this abrupt appearance of progressive complexity of the living organism. It does seem that the term *progressive anagenetic creationism* is more truly descriptive of the phenomena, followed by adaptive and reproductive cladogenetic creationism. The conclusion to be drawn then appears to be that nature, which, of course, includes man, is the product of a creative activity, and that so-called nature constitutes the living culture of a creating entity revealing a supreme intelligence.

As regards the subject of culture, it will be recalled that man is quite unique among all creatures in that he alone possesses the three capacities necessary to create a culture, namely, of communication, of inventiveness, and of social habituation. Now we suddenly become aware that man is not the original creator of a culture; furthermore, that he himself is only a part, although a most significant part, of the living culture of the original creator.

We must concede to the original creator the capacity of inventiveness, as any scientist will evidence. But what about social habituation? Man has the problem of social habituation only as to one species, homo sapiens. The original creator, however, has the problem of social habituation for all species, and these we know are innumerable. And how have we discovered he solved it? By reproduction according to kind and the use of instincts and their inheritance of course. With man, however, the instincts are significantly very loosely organized.

Then what about communication? Does the original creator communicate with his creation? Yes, we have found he solved this problem via the mind of the individual living creature. This is quite indirect if true at all, some will vehemently protest, and follow up their protestation by asserting that there is no direct communication. But what about the prophets, who are men who talk with God and talk for God among their fellow-man? This phenomenon we will subsequently discover is very difficult to ignore in the face of quite positive evidence.

But let us return to the hard-headed scientist. Huxley makes this very significant statement regarding man:

> Whether he knows it or not, whether he wishes it or not, he is now the main agency for the future evolution of the earth and its inhabitants.

He also states that man has learned to understand, control and use the forces of external nature, but must now learn to understand, control and use the forces of his own nature. We must conclude that here he must have reference to man's emotional and value-determining nature, for the control of the forces of external nature is also very much the product of his own nature.

Professor John Read, an outstanding English organic and stereochemist, also voices a similar conclusion: "Man *must* learn to master and control himself as he has learned to master and control nature."

As man has had approximately a million years, according to evolutionary biologists, to accomplish the control of his emotional nature, he should by this time realize that he needs help, by mutation or otherwise.

XXXI.

SEARCH FOR A SOLUTION TO THE PROBLEM OF MAN'S VULNERABILITY

Introduction

G. K. Chesterton once said that whatever else is true about man, it is certainly true that he is not what he was meant to be. Why? Because of sin, and sin according to St. Paul is a universal human predicament. The fact that it kills goodness, beauty, human love and fellowship, conscience and character is proof enough of its killing power. Truly "the wages of sin is death."

If knowledge is relative and requires contrast for its intelligent determination, then man surely cannot now maintain the innocence of Adam and Eve for lack of knowledge of good and evil to enable him today to make a knowing choice as between the two.

Particular Contributions of the Various Religions of the East

In view of the conclusions of both Huxley and Chesterton as to man's vulnerability, let us see what light is cast on this problem by briefly reviewing the respective contributions of the various religions, the value-determining institutions of mankind.

First, let us consider *Hinduism.* A significant contribution by this religion is known as Karma or the *Law of the Deed.* This is also called the law of life, which provides that good is rewarded with good while evil is rewarded with evil. Also, subsequently reformers of Hinduism expressed their objections to idol-worship.

Next, we shall consider *Shintoism*. The significant contribution of this religion is its *"love of the beauties of nature."* The Japanese reflect this love in the interior decorations of their homes; and thereby and in that manner they honor their "mother earth." Japanese people feel themselves a part of nature, a feeling not shared by the average European or American, even though they will proudly acknowledge they are its "flower."

Buddha, an outstanding reformer of Hinduism, called attention to the fact of suffering among people, and encouraged *sympathy for the sufferers.* He also came out *against the caste system, as well as the worship of idols.* He, too, espoused the Hindu *Law of Life:* "From Good must come Good, and from Evil must come Evil." He amplified this law with a *constructive psychological analysis* as contained in his *Eight-fold Path:* Right Belief, Right Resolve, Right Occupation, Right Speech, Right Effort, Right Contemplation, Right Concentration, and Right Behavior. Right Behavior was further amplified by the *Five Commandments of Uprightness:* Do not kill, steal, lie, commit adultery, or become intoxicated at any time. He also taught that *hatred ceases with love.*

Nataputta Vardhamana, or Prince Mahavira, the founder of *Jainism,* and another reformer of Hinduism, espoused *reverence for life,* and a doctrine of salvation by good works. "Not in prayer, nor in idol-worship, will you find forgiveness and the way to the good life. *Only by doing good can you reach Nirvana. Within yourselves lies salvation."*

Lao-tze, The Old Philosopher, is the founder of the Chinese religion known as *Taoism.* Tao is the central concept of Lao-tze's philosophy, and the philosopher himself is quoted as having said: "The Tao that can be understood cannot be the real Tao." Authorities in this religion, however, state that *Tao "is the way of ultimate reality,"* . . . *"Something eternally existing."* It is life's "basic mystery, the mystery of mysteries, *the entrance into the mystery of all life." Man is a part of nature and should adjust himself to it,* as water passing over the rocks. Lao-tze taught that the basic character of man is inherited, and hence he clashed with Confucius. However, Lao-tze apparently detected a secret basic releaser of the good in the inherited nature of man as reflected by his statement: *"To those who are good to me I am good; and to those who are not good to me I am good. And thus all get to be good."*

Chiu K'ung, popularly known as *Confucius,* appears to be

the original founder of modern-day humanism. While he, himself, embraced no religion, he rather encouraged the religions embraced by others to serve as necessary motivating forces to encourage people to follow his particular precepts. One of his outstanding contributions was his *practice of analyzing a problem before attempting its solution.* His success in cutting down the incidence of crime in one locality was explained by him as: *"I rewarded those who were good and punished those who were bad."* This teaching, of course, was contrary to that of Lao-tze. A Chinese Duke requested Confucius to survey the basic cause of crime in his province, and Confucius came up with this report: "If we could do away with poverty and ignorance, then we would have no more crime in the land." How? By educating people in useful trades, which procedure would do away with both poverty and crime.

It does seem that they should not have permitted Lao-tze to go over the border, for a composite teaching of both of these philosophers would have produced a more well-rounded religious philosophy.

Mo-Ti, the founder of *Mohism,* furnishes us with certain original and most constructive suggestions. First he emphasizes the *importance of establishing standards,* and secondly, after progressively reviewing and eliminating certain possible standards, *he decides very definitely in favor of standards set by "Heaven."*

From China we go to Persia. *Zoroaster,* the founder of *Zoroastrianism,* was a man of most unusual social consciousness. He used his education to ease the suffering of his fellowman rather than to build up wealth and social position for himself. And this behavior was rewarded apparently by several theophanies, progressively revealing certain truths to him. The basic revelation he received involved the correspondence between the physical phenomena of light and darkness, and the spiritual phenomena of good and evil. "The Good must always be good, and the Evil must always be Evil," just as light and darkness can never change their characteristic nature. *Although nature is divided by the two conflicting principles, good and evil, man is a free agent and will bring about the final triumph of the right. How? By choosing the right. Then, too, the power of evil is limited in time, as continuance in evil leads to death. Zoroaster, incidentally, was informed in one of his theophanies of and predicted the future appearance of a great prophet.*

452

The religion of *Islam,* founded by Muhammad, was based on "The Book" and was further augmented by the revelations of its prophet. We recall that this prophet, when challenged by his critical audience to give proof of the existence of Allah, pointed to the sky with its myriad stars. (This awesome starry display of the heavens subsequently also made a profound impression on Immanuel Kant, and later on Thomas Paine.) This religion definitely re-emphasized the evils of idol-worship, and submission to the will of the one God, whose name is Allah. Among several specific prohibitions, such as idol-worship, this religion emphasizes the evil of intoxication. As a positive commandment it advocates the giving of alms to the poor in addition to submission to the will of God.

While many constructive ideas of *what man should do* but has not, are contributed by the foregoing religious leaders, none of them furnish a solution to the current basic problem facing mankind—namely, man's inherited self-centered instinctual constitution which must now be modified to insure his future survival as a species on this planet.

XXXII.

CURRENT DYNAMIC EVOLUTIONARY ACTIVITY

Significance of Judaism and Christianity

We now come to the two inextricably intermeshed religions of Judaism as revealed by the Old Testament, and Christianity as revealed by the New Testament. These two religions are most unique in that they are progressively revealed in an historical account beginning at the close of the ice age.

Let us assume tentatively that God is the creator of man to whom He gave the power of reasoning. Does it not seem reasonable that He would subsequently try to communicate with him? As it does seem reasonable, then let us consider the Bible as such means of communication, as we have heretofore considered the foregoing religions.

What other book deals with the relationship between the personality of man and the personality of his creator as does the Bible?

What other book reveals the progressive purpose and goal of the creator as does the Bible?

If the Bible were only the uninspired writings of the Israelites, why do they write of themselves in such an uncomplimentary manner?

In the Old Testament Biblical scholars have determined that the expressions "The Lord said," "The Lord saith," "The Lord spake," and the like, occur over two thousand times. What other book possesses such uniqueness?

What other book possesses such a wide distribution and

454

inspires all men to better living regardless of race as does the Bible?

But the most compelling support for the inspiration of the Bible is its prophecies and their progressive fulfillment within the history of mankind.

At one time scholars would consider themselves most gracious and condescending to concede that the Bible was great literature, but that was all to which they would commit themselves, at least professionally. As a typical illustration in this connection from an unbeliever, further biased with a hatred of Jews in his heart, we quote from H. L. Mencken's "Treatise on the Gods," published in 1930:

> Allow everything you please . . . no other literature, old or new, can offer a match for it.
>
> Nearly all of it comes from the Jews, and their making of it constitutes one of the most astounding phenomena in human history. For there is little in their character, as the modern world knows them, to suggest a talent for noble thinking . . . The Jews could be put down very plausibly as the most unpleasant race ever heard of. As commonly encountered, they lack many of the qualities that mark the civilized man: courage, dignity, incorruptibility, ease, confidence. They have vanity without pride . . . and learning without wisdom . . .
>
> Yet these same Jews, from time immemorial, have been the chief dreamers of the race, and beyond all comparison, the greatest poets. It was Jews who wrote the magnificent poems called the Psalms, the Song of Solomon, the books of Job and Ruth; it was Jews who set platitudes to deathless music in Proverbs; and it was Jews who gave us the beatitudes, the sermon on the mount, the incomparable ballad of the Christ Child, and the twelfth chapter of Romans.
>
> All these transcendent riches Christianity inherits from a tribe of sedentary Bedouins, so obscure and unimportant that secular history scarcely knows them. No heritage of modern man is richer and none has made a more brilliant mark upon human thought, not even the legacy of the Greeks . . .
>
> The story of Jesus . . . is touching beyond compare.

455

It is indeed the most lovely story . . . ever devised . .
Beside it the best that you will find in sacred literature
of Moslem and Brahman, Parsee and Buddhist, seems
flat, stale, and unprofitable.

Another unbeliever in the supernatural, Thomas H. Huxley
(1825-95), an English naturalist and the very able defender of
Charles Darwin's theory of evolution, arrived at the following
conclusion after careful research with respect to The Bible:

The Bible has been the Magna Charta of the poor
and of the oppressed; down to modern times, no state
has had a constitution in which the interests of the people
are so largely taken into account, in which the duties, so
much more than the privileges, of rulers are insisted
upon, as that drawn up for Israel; . . . nowhere is the
fundamental truth that the welfare of the state, in the
long run, depends on the uprightness of the citizen, so
strongly laid down . . . I do believe that the human race
is not yet, possibly may never be, in a position to dis-
pense with it (the Bible).

More recently, however, archaeologists have discovered that
if carefully interpreted the Old Testament will lead to rare
archaeological discoveries. In other words, the historical sections
of the Bible have been found surprisingly to be reliable. Cases
supporting this claim have been the unearthing of the tunnel
built by King Hezekiah in Old Jerusalem, Herod's villa-palace
at Masada, the discovery of the lost cities of Shechem, Ashdad,
and Arad (which are over 5000 years old), just to mention a few
discoveries made possible by clues obtained from the Bible.

The first chapter of Genesis was shrugged off at first as
having no biological significance. In an earlier Babylonian epic
of Mesopotamia, from which locality the Hebrews originally
came, a creation story is related in which creation took place
in a haphazard way after a cosmic struggle involving many
gods. The Genesis account, on the contrary, reveals creation as
an orderly process by one God. Many scientists now marvel how
the sequence and content of the creation account coincide so
well with the general findings of both physicists and biologists.
Biologists will generally agree to the sequence of the creation
account, but they do not agree with the representations of it

as a "creative" activity by a specific directing entity. They prefer rather to interpret the phenomena as a natural evolutionary sequence in which reproduction, with persistence of form, together with occasional mutations and natural selection, as the keys to the mystery of the progressive appearance of new living organisms. They will concede to the general phrase "reproduction according to kind," as a "Stop mechanism" to regressive evolution (devolution), which is an observable fact. But on all advance stages it is mutations and natural selection, given great time periods, that account for the origin of new species and represents the true scientific explanation of creation.

The very first verse and part of the second verse of the Bible have been subjected to considerable ridicule. This part reads:

> In the beginning God created the heaven and the earth. And the earth was without form, and void.

In the famous Scopes "Evolution Trial" in Tennessee the defense attorney delighted in challenging the late William Jennings Bryan to describe how to create something "without form and void." However, it would appear after a little thought that God, like his creature man, creates first within his mind before objectifying that creation.

Man Created in God's Image

To the twenty-seventh verse of the first chapter of Genesis, evolutionary biologists cannot give the least consideration. This verse reads:

> So God created man in his own image, in the image of God created he him; male and female created he them.

Scientists of good professional standing not only maintain that there is no god, but that man created a so-called god in his (man's) own image, in other words an anthropomorphic god.

Let us apply a little logical analysis to this phase of the problem. With apologies to Euclid we shall construct a triangle and establish the following keys for its interpretation on a point-instant basis:

Let base arm represent "Supreme Intelligence" expressed
via magnetic waves;
Let adjacent arm represent "Latent Energy;"
Let interior triangle represent "Living Culture" (Mass-
Energy);
Let origin represent directing entity or mind.

We then have the following construction:

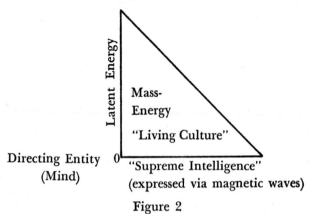

Figure 2

Dr. Einstein himself inductively arrived at the fact of
"Supreme Intelligence." Induction also suggests that intelligence
finds its basic expression via magnetic waves. The directing
entity, possessing supreme intelligence, transmutes latent energy,
by means of magnetic waves, into configurated energy, or mass-
energy if you will, which obeys fixed laws. The directing entity
then goes on to progressively create a living culture, with man
as its "flower." In another aspect, nature is the directing entity's
garment. Man certainly cannot deny the objective existence of
such a living culture, without eliminating himself.

So now we have the three aspects of our right triangle inductively accounted for. But what about the "origin"? The average
scientist would undoubtedly concede that Washington Irving's
character "The Headless Horseman" is obviously both simulated
and fictional. Yet he resorts to all kinds of circumlocution and
resists all sense of logic in maintaining that the "Supreme
Intelligence" is for all practical purposes "headless," that is, it
possesses no directing entity. In other words, we are encouraged
to believe that nature was evolved by the natural selection of a

"headless horseman." Anyone who maintains otherwise he insists is just lacking in scientific know-how and biological knowledge.

We shall go on and construct another right triangle, with the following key for its interpretation, also on a point-instant basis:

Let the base arm represent Intelligence expressed via magnetic waves;
Let the adjacent arm represent "mass-radiant energy";
Let the interior triangle represent a "non-living culture;"
Let the origin represent directing entity or mind.

We then come up with the following construction:

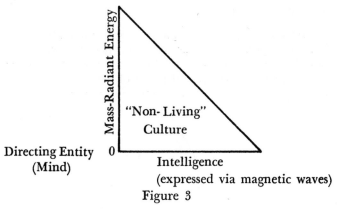

Figure 3

As it was necessary to resort to the field concept to account for physical phenomena, so it is necessary to do likewise to account for mental phenomena. In our prior logical analysis of man as a personality, we determined the existence of a directing entity, which we termed the "RI." By postulating a directing entity within the mind as the "origin" in our first geometrical construction (which postulate does not seem illogical), what do we find now? We are suddenly confronted with two similar triangles, the second being an image of the first. We shall call these two polygons similar triangles of nature; we find the second one a part of and enclosed within the first. In other words, we discover a non-living culture being created within the living culture.

Does not this similarity suggest that God created man in His image? It would certainly appear from inductive reasoning that such an interference is quite logical and reasonable. Why were not equilateral triangles chosen for the construction? Because the creation of cultures, both living and non-living, is an active and going process. The terminal side in both cases revolves around its origin as it progressively moves upward to greater syntheses.

We shall proceed with a comparable geometrical construction reflecting a logical analysis of the two respective directing entities, i.e., the origins of our two "right triangles of culture." Again going back to our analysis of man detailed in Part I hereof, we abstract the following data for constructing a triangle representing the salient aspects of the mind of man. This time we shall use the equilateral form, with the following key for its interpretation:

Let one side represent "instincts" (self-centered);
Let the opposite side represent the "personality;"
Let the base represent the "RI," with its intelligence, imaginative faculty, and prism of logic;
Let the interior triangle represent "finite mind."

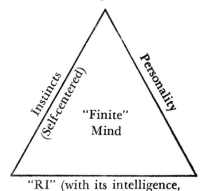

"RI" (with its intelligence, imaginative faculty and prism of logic)

Figure 4

Now from Biblical (Matthew 28:19) and theological sources we shall construct another equilateral triangle, this one representing the directing entity or infinite mind of the Creator. The key to this triangle follows:

Let the base line represent Divine Wisdom (Father);
Let one side represent Divine Love (Holy Spirit);

Let the opposite side represent the Personality of God, (His only begotten Son);

Let the interior triangle represent the Infinite Mind (Holy Trinity).

Figure 5

We have chosen to make the sides of the foregoing triangle open because the aspects have infinite and unlimited possibilities. Divine Wisdom (Father) determines their length, which is infinite.

Incidentally, in the first equilateral triangle it is quite obvious we are not creating three individuals, but merely revealing the qualitative, and not quantitative, aspects of the one individual. Likewise, in the second equilateral triangle, we are not creating three gods (three infinite minds) but merely revealing the three qualitative aspects of one God, one Infinite Mind.

Does not the foregoing pair of equilateral triangles further confirm that man was created in the image of God? Ironically where the social scientist is inclined to believe that man projects or creates a god in his own image, in other words an anthropomorphic god, we now find very good inductive evidence that the reverse is true—that God created man in His own image as stated in the biblical creation account. Robert Boyle, the renowned English physicist and chemist, considered that man's rational soul bears the image of its creator, that it is "a nobler and more valuable being than the whole corporeal world."

We shall proceed with certain conclusions we may draw from these two pairs of triangles. In the first pair (triangles of culture), it is quite apparent that the second right triangle, with its non-living culture, is within and dependent upon the first with its prior living culture—in fact, the creator of the non-living culture is the zenith of the current creative activity of the Creator of the living culture.

The second pair of triangles, triangles of the logical analysis of mind, suggests an answer to the mystery of the mind of man. It appears that the RI with its consciousness and prism of logic, is an outright gift to man from his Creator (The Father). In this connection it will be recalled that we have heretofore concluded that the prism of logic is the so-called "supreme court" of the RI's reasoning process. Hence, it would appear that man as a social entity fit for the psycho-social stage of evolution is not limited by his mind but rather is determined quite largely by the limits set by his instincts, which up to now have been strictly self-oriented.

At this point it should be emphasized that the foregoing construction is a conception of the Creator by man's mind as passed through his prism of logic (the gift of the Creator), for how else does He mean by His invitation to man—"Come let us reason together."

For man to stop here with the foregoing "idea" of God the Creator as an object of worship would be the most subtle form of idolatry. For a living active relationship with the Creator involves the impact of the individual living personality of man with the living personality of the Creator. It is only in such a relationship that true worship, free of idolatry, is possible. As the chemical analysis of hydrogen and oxygen affords no clue of the product *water* resulting from their mutual impact, so man's analysis of his own personality and that of his Creator has no living consequence until the two make impact, a very personal, satisfying, and overwhelming experience. It is the reconciliatory meeting of finite being with absolute being, its original source—in fact the revelation of the absolute itself to finite being.

We shall proceed with an analysis of Genesis 1:28, which reads as follows:

> And God blessed them, and God said unto them, be fruitful, and multiply, and replenish the earth, and *subdue it;* and have dominion over the fish of the sea, and over the fowl of the air, and over every living thing that moveth upon the earth.

"Every living thing that moveth upon the earth" would include all mass-energy, according to present-day physicists.

It will be agreed generally that man has made outstanding progress in fulfilling that part of his Creator's injunction relative to multiplying which is contained in this verse. Witness the concern over the population problem, first as expressed by Malthus, and now by Julian Huxley as voiced in his "Evolution in Action." In that book he said: "Population increase is together with war, the greatest threat to civilization and progress." To be or not to be is no longer a question but a dilemma, a dilemma requiring a choice of some overt action.

There is the other injunction cited in this same verse, namely, to "subdue" the earth. To the fulfillment of this injunction we are greatly indebted to the labors of scientists and other scholars, both of the past and of the present. By their patient and brilliant efforts these men have made it possible, by the discovery of natural laws, for man to make significant progress in subduing nature, that is, outside of himself, rather than being subdued by nature. However, the man of perception is now becoming uncomfortably aware of the limitations of his own inherited instinctual constitution.

Certain intellectuals have had great sport in ridiculing the account of the creation of woman from the rib of man, as cited in Genesis 2:21-2 as follows:

> And the Lord God caused a deep sleep to fall upon Adam and he slept: and he took one of his ribs and closed up the flesh instead thereof;
> And the rib, which the Lord God had taken from man, made he a woman and brought her unto the man.

When one considers the ribbon-like paired chromosomal genetic structure of man and the fact of a double X chromosome in woman and only one X in man, the creation account of man doesn't seem quite so ridiculous.

The Fall of Man

The question of the so-called "fall of man," "original sin," and "born in sin" will now be considered. The occasion is related in the third chapter of Genesis.

A father well appreciates the concern he has for a newly-born son, especially for the first-born. He, along with the mother, feeds and protects their son, guides him by advice, and in every way tries to impart knowledge and wisdom to him. Eventually, however, the son begins to assert his own will; he eventually matures, breaks parental ties and leaves the protective influences of home. This, however, doesn't free the father of concern for his future welfare, because he loves his son and is consciously aware of his son's limitations.

With the foregoing picture in mind, does it seem too unreasonable to believe that the Creator was concerned about the "flower" of his creativity, namely, mankind represented by Adam? Does it seem so incredible that He should at first have kept in very close communication with man? Apparently man as originally created was limited by self-oriented instincts. These instincts, of course, were at first necessary so that he could develop individuality, as is also true of the lower living organisms. However, there is no indication that man was limited as to his cognitive faculties, as he apparently possessed his prism of logic and imaginative faculty. It appears that the Creator wanted to guide man by intimating the present and temporary limitations set by his individualizing and self-centered instincts. His Creator did not interfere, however, with man's power of free choice but let him go. However His great concern for the welfare of man did not decrease therewith, for He apparently followed his experiences in the world with great interest and concern.

Thus man cuts off communication with his Creator, and sets out confidently to "subdue the earth," with apparently unlimited mental capacities but vulnerable on the instinctual side of his nature which made unbiased judgments practically impossible, a weakness not at first perceivable to him. As the elapsed time of man's communicative relationship with his Creator increased, each generation of man became more and more dimly aware of the Creator's very existence.

Noah and the Flood

As a resultant of the melting and evaporation of snow and ice at the close of the ice age, heavy rains fell, causing a great flood, myths concerning which have been found in many ancient cultures. It is here that Noah and his ark enters the biblical account. Noah apparently was attuned to the Creator's warning of the coming danger and built an ark for himself, his family, and certain animal life, much to the amusement and ridicule of his neighbors.

After the flood waters subsided, Noah's family deployed in all directions over the earth. Adaptations to the different climates apparently brought about the various races of man, but not new species.

Noah's offspring still carried the limitations of its own instincts and eventually also fell away from close touch with the Creator. This must have greatly disturbed God, and finally the time came when He felt He must do something about it without being too obvious and thereby weakening the most significant aspects of man's dignity, namely, faith and free choice. Man had by now developed his individuality, but remained in great danger because of his instinctual selfish nature. God apparently felt out many contacts with man as potential leaders of the enlightenment, as witness the founders of the many religions.

Abraham

God, it would appear, found in Abraham the qualities required of such leadership. Why? Apparently because Abraham obeyed his sense of logic and rebelled against idolatry, which basically is a projected worship of self (the calf). The biblical account of the Creator's initial and future contacts and guidance of Abraham and his "seed" Isaac, Jacob (Israel) et al, is given in the account of Judaism heretofore outlined.

Moses—the Law Giver and Leader of God's Chosen People

After Jacob (Israel) we come to Moses. Here the Creator saw a man he could enlist on a mission of the utmost significance to mankind. He revealed to Moses on Mount Sinai a sequential outline of His creative activity (his created culture) up to that time. This is suggested by the Creator revealing his "back parts" to Moses as mentioned in Exodus; this the Creator did as a compromise to Moses' request to see God in person. (This would be as impossible as for man to make his "RI" visible, except through his culture.) As God instituted the seventh day of the week as a day of rest, the Sabbath, He called the attention of Moses to the fact that He Himself on the seventh day after the "first week" of His creative activity, *rested and was refreshed.* In other words He let Moses know by inference that He had now returned to His creative activity after a so-called latent period.

And what was the Creator's next step in the process? He revealed to Moses His plan to use the Israelites as a nucleus, in biological terminology, or what might be called "a pilot plant" in modern industrial terminology, for the observation and guidance of all mankind. But take particular note of this important fact—the Creator instructed Moses first to present the plan to the Israelites and obtain their agreement to serve in such a capacity. We know from the biblical account that the voice vote of the Israelites was unanimously affirmative.

The Creator thereupon proceeded to give Moses the initial ten commandments. Many will say that the commandments were "old stuff," for Hammurabi and others had come out with them long before Moses. But upon analysis the difference between the old forms and the Ten Commandments is most striking. The commandments of Hammurabi and others involved only the last five commandments. They were the product of social necessity to assure a relatively stable society of man limited by selfish instincts.

The special significance of the Ten Commandments, however, was that the first four pertained specifically to the relationship of man with his creator. The fifth commandment unites the first group with the second group, which pertains to man's relationship with his fellowman. The tenth commandment, incidentally, has an original connotation in that it uses the word "covet," a subjective term, rather than steal, an objective term.

Let us re-examine the wording of the fifth commandment, which by the way is the only one that carries with it a promise worthy of serious meditation:

> Honor thy father and thy mother: that thy days may be long upon the land which the Lord thy God giveth thee.

Many have wondered why this commandment appeared midway among the commandments. Whereas it would apply to man's physical father and mother as it is generally interpreted, it would seem to have an even broader connotation, one which explains the mystery of its sequential position. It seems quite apparent that the word "father" in the broader sense applies to the "Fatherhood of the Creator," and the word "mother" in the broader sense to "mother earth." Hence, the ten commandments of Moses to the Israelites are most definitely unique and carry a definite message to mankind.

Moses without question was the greatest mortal man who has appeared on this planet. The Creator recognized Moses' greatness or he would not have chosen him to reveal His plan for mankind. His greatness of soul was especially exemplified on the occasion when the Israelites began worshipping a golden calf while Moses was still conferring with the Creator on the Mount. This happened shortly after the Israelites had unanimously agreed to become a "peculiar" nation of priests, the nucleus whereby the Creator would reveal His purposes to all mankind. Abruptly the Creator called to the attention of Moses that the Israelites at that very moment were worshipping a golden calf, expressed His anger and said He would now make His chosen people the seed of Moses rather than the seed of Jacob (Israel). It may be that the Creator wanted to test Moses by this temptation. God apparently was already convinced that Moses possessed the intellectual capabilities of a leader, but did he have control of his instinctual self? And how did Moses respond to this temptation? He surprisingly pleaded for his Israelite brethren, and offered himself up for punishment for their transgression. That response by Moses made him the "most humble of men." The Creator was undoubtedly pleased with Moses' response; and upon the subsequent repentance of the Israelites, the Creator relented, and instructed Moses to proceed with the proposed plan.

The ten commandments, together with their later amplifications, were to impress upon man the vulnerable weakness in his personality, namely his self-centeredness and his need for assistance. As Apostle Paul later put it, the law was the "schoolmaster" to make mankind receptive to the message of Jesus. Incidentally, the future coming of Jesus, the greatest of prophets, was revealed to Moses by God as Moses prophesied his future appearance.

The Torah, the book of the Law, gave not only Judaism and Christianity but the modern law of Western civilization, its vital "basic principles of equal justice and humanity to all."

The subsequent successful conquest of the idol-worshippers of Canaan under the leadership of Joshua was proof of the reliability of God's promise to that leader upon the death of Moses outside the borders of the "promised land."

Judges and Kings

The so-called Judges who served as leaders of the Israelites, following the death of Joshua, represented a motley group; it was a loose form of theocracy. The Israelites eventually wanted a king like the other nations, and approached Samuel (the last of the Judges and a highly respected priest) to anoint a king. Samuel was at first reluctant to agree to their request as he considered that under the original covenant the Lord was the only true king of Israel, and furthermore that a temporal king would ultimately enslave them. He further predicted in the following words: "In that day you will cry out . . . But the Lord will not answer you."

The Israelites persisted in their insistence that Samuel anoint a king. God finally said to Samuel: "Listen to the voice of the people as respects all that they say to you; for it is not you whom they have rejected, but it is I whom they have rejected from being king over them." So Samuel anointed Saul as the first temporal king of Israel. It should be observed that in spite of the covenant made with God, the Israelites were still free agents, for they were permitted to break the covenant. However, they must face the consequences of their action.

David of the tribe of Judah became a protege of Saul and followed him as king. Under David all the tribes of Israel were united and prospered. He made Jerusalem the capital of Israel, and led the Israelites to victory in battle with the surrounding nations. He finally got involved in an adulterous relationship with Bathsheba, the wife of one of his generals. This relationship led David by indirection to kill Uriah, a general and the husband of Bathsheba. Nathan, the prophet, was aware of his treachery and severely reprimanded David in the name of God. Surprisingly, David publicly acknowledged his guilt, repented, and asked God's forgiveness. He thereupon married the widow Bathsheba who later bore him Solomon. David, it will be recalled, contributed many of the psalms in the Book of Psalms.

Solomon succeeded his father David as king of Israel. He

was renowned for his great wisdom, as well as for being the builder of the original temple at Jerusalem. This ambitious project led to forced labor and a heavy tax burden on the people, with later disastrous consequences. That outcome of the Israelites' desire for a king had been predicted by Samuel. Solomon died at 58 years of age, a *spent* man as revealed in Ecclesiastes, that "all is vanity."

Solomon's reign represented the high-water mark of the Israelitic nation. From then on there was a gradual disintegration, beginning with its division into the Kingdom of Judah and the Northern Kingdom. The Northern Kingdom was conquered by the Assyrians in 722 B.C., and the people of that kingdom permanently dispersed as slaves. Judah, after casualties of over 200,000 men, made a settlement with Sennacherib to pay tribute. However, the Kingdom of Judah was later conquered by Nebuchadnezzar in 597 B.C. He destroyed the temple at Jerusalem, and took the Israelites of Judah as slaves to Babylon.

The Age of Prophets, Leading up to Jesus

Coincident with the period of kings was the age of the prophets. The prophets persisted in warning the kings and the people of future troublous times they were creating for themselves in breaking the original covenant made with God, with Moses as their mediator.

The warnings of the prophets were ignored. Isaiah had prophesied a century before the Babylonian captivity in the following manner:

Hear the word of the Lord of hosts: Behold, the days are coming, when all that is in your house, and that which your fathers have stored up till this day, shall be carried to Babylon . . .

The Israelites in Babylonian captivity frankly conceded, as voiced by the Prophet Ezekiel, that they were being punished by God for their sins.

The principal prophets and their message will here be briefly reviewed:

Elijah, the forerunner of the age of prophets, came from

469

across the Jordan. His principal message was incorporated in his words:

How long will you go limping with two different opinions? If the Lord is God, follow him; but if Baal, then follow him.

Elijah challenged some four hundred and fifty prophets of Baal to a test involving the consumption of two bulls on an altar by an unlighted fire. The prophets of Baal failed miserably, amid Elijah's taunts. Elijah thereupon in the name of the Lord succeeded in this crucial test, to the utter humiliation of the prophets of Baal.

The first so-called classical prophets appeared by the eighth century B.C., such as Isaiah, Amos and Hosea. Hosea, it will be remembered, was asked by the Lord to marry a prostitute as a symbol to the Israelites of their intermixture with the pagans. The Prophet Hosea emphasized God's love, mercy, and forgiveness.

Amos was a shepherd who received a direct call by God to prophesy, a call which he felt impelled to accept. He carried the warning that if righteousness and social justice did not prevail in Israel, it would perish. He also emphasized that God was the guardian of the other nations as well as that of Israel. In other words the Israelites were not to feel that they were the only people with whom God was concerned. They were chosen only to become good examples to all of mankind.

Isaiah was a citizen of Jerusalem, and prophesied from about 740 to 700 B.C. The holiness of God was his main theme, and he called attention to God's intolerance with human pride. The importance of faith in God was especially emphasized. A most significant prophecy is contained in the fifty-third chapter of the Book of Isaiah. The sixth and seventh verses of this chapter are here quoted:

All we like sheep have gone astray; we have turned every one to his own way; and the Lord hath laid on him the iniquity of us all. He was oppressed, and he was afflicted, yet he opened not his mouth: he is brought as a lamb to the slaughter; and as a sheep before her shearers is dumb, so he openeth not his mouth.

470

Jeremiah received his call to prophesy 627 B.C. He was a prophet of deep feeling, and spent considerable time in prayer. One of his most significant prophecies was the following from Jeremiah 31:31-34:

> Behold, the days are coming, says the Lord, when I will make a new covenant with the house of Israel and the House of Judah, not like the covenant which I made with their fathers. . . . *I will put my law within them, and I will write it upon their hearts:* and I will be their God, and they shall be my people. And no longer shall each man teach his neighbor and each his brother saying 'Know the Lord,' for they shall all know me, from the least of them to the greatest says the Lord; for I will forgive their iniquity, and I will remember their sin no more.

Ezekiel lived during the time of Jeremiah. He was younger than Jeremiah and was among the exiles to Babylon in 597 B.C. His preaching placed emphasis on individual responsibility, that everyone is to be held accountable for his own sins only. He prophesied the physical restoration of Israel, as suggested by the vision of the valley of dry bones restored to life by the breath of the Lord.

The Book of Jonah, written about 200 B.C., reveals God as merciful, especially when he took pity on the people of sinful Nineveh after they all repented. Even though the people of Nineveh repented as a result of his preaching, Jonah revealing a human weakness was disappointed that God had been merciful to them.

The Book of Daniel is apocalyptic, and its contents are popularly quoted by present-day "prophets." This book speaks of the coming judgment and the kingdom of God. This prophet, incidentally, made a great impression on the Jewish historian Flavius Josephus.

Upon the return to Jerusalem of the remnants of the Jews after their Babylonian captivity, a revolutionary group under the Maccabees became active. Both Jeremiah and Ezekiel cautioned them against this dangerous activity and advised them rather to place their trust in God. Their warnings went unheeded and even led to Jeremiah being killed and Ezekiel being exiled to what is now Tel-Aviv. The revolutionary activities of the Maccabees were finally crushed by the Roman legions. In anger the Romans finally around 70 A.D., after continued uprisings by the Jews, completely demolished Jerusalem with its walls, even including the rebuilt temple. The remnants of the Kingdom of Judah were thereupon permanently dispersed as slaves.

XXXIII.

JESUS OF NAZARETH—THE GREATEST PROPHET AND THE VERY FULFILLMENT OF PROPHECY

Prophecies Predicting His Appearance

We shall now consider the greatest of all prophets, in fact the very fulfillment of prophecy, Jesus of Nazareth. His coming had been consistently prophesied from time to time in the Old Testament, in fact certain biblical scholars have determined some 330 prophesies and quotations cited in the New Testament from the Old Testament. He was and remains the very core of God's revelation to man.

Moses, considered to be the greatest prophet of Israel, recorded the following words of the Lord, which we quote from Deuteronomy 18:18-19:

> I will raise them up a prophet from among their brethren, like unto thee, and will put my words in his mouth; and he shall speak unto them all that I shall command him. And it shall come to pass, that whosoever will not hearken unto my words which he shall speak in my name, I will require it of him.

The prophecies relating to this great prophet increased in number as the time for his coming approached. The fifty-third chapter of Isaiah plainly describes this prophet. Furthermore, Jeremiah 25:5-6 contains the following prophecy:

> Behold, the days come, saith the Lord, that I will raise unto David a righteous Branch, and a King shall

reign and prosper, and shall execute judgment and justice in the earth. In his days Judah shall be saved, and Israel shall dwell safely, and this is his name whereby he shall be called, The Lord Our Righteousness.

Conditions prevailing in Israel around 1 A.D. indicated that the time was ripe for the coming of the predicted prophet; it was during a period of universal spiritual need, a universal rule under Rome, a universal peace (though forced peace), and a universal language (Greek). Then there appeared a certain John the Baptist in the Jordan wilderness. Even John the Baptist's appearance was prophesied, as witness Isaiah 40:3:

> The voice of him that crieth in the wilderness, Prepare ye the way of the Lord, make straight in the desert a highway for our Lord.

Furthermore, in the first chapter of Luke it will be recalled that the angel of the Lord stated to Zacharias when he informed him that his wife Elizabeth would bear him a son to be named John:

> For he shall be great in the sight of the Lord, and shall drink neither wine nor strong drink, and he shall be filled with the Holy Ghost (Spirit) even from his mother's womb. And many of the children of Israel shall he turn to the Lord their God. And he shall go before him in the spirit and power of Elias (Elijah), to turn the hearts of the fathers to the children, and the disobedient to the wisdom of the just; to make ready a people prepared for the Lord.

John did just that. He preached in the Jordan wilderness "the baptism of the repentance for the remission of sins." He declared to his hearers:

> There cometh one mightier than I after me, the latchet of whose shoes I am not worthy to stoop down and unloose. I indeed have baptized you with water; but he shall baptize you with the Holy Ghost.

John subsequently baptized Jesus in the Jordan, and singled

him out to the people as the very person whose coming he had foretold. Furthermore, John's followers and converts later became Jesus' disciples, the very nucleus of his subsequent ministry. Incidentally, Jesus baptized no one with water.

Jesus had this to say of John, as appears in Luke 7:27-28:

> This is he, of whom it is written, Behold I send my messenger before thy face, which shall prepare thy way before thee. For I say unto you, Among those born of women there is not a greater prophet than John the Baptist: but he that is least in the kingdom of God is greater than he.

Did Jesus here have reference to the new creation of mankind which he came to form?

Some will impatiently question, why all these prophesies? they seem to be so superfluous. However, it should be borne in mind that just as scientific laws cannot be ignored if they have proven to have predictive value, so Biblical prophecies cannot be ignored for the very same reason. Both are given by the same law-maker for such predictive value and guide to both individual choice and individual action. Whereas so-called natural laws involve a contingent "if—then," prophecies generally do not involve an "if" clause. The prophecy of Jonah, for instance, is an exception to the general rule. Joseph ben Matthias (Flavius Josephus), (37 A.D.-?), the famous Jewish historian, makes the following significant statement with regard to prophecy at the close of his work "The Jewish Antiquities," the statement having particular reference to the Prophet Daniel:

> All these things, as God revealed them to him, he left behind in his writing, so that those who read them and observe how they have come to pass must wonder at Daniel's having been so honored by God and learn from these facts how mistaken are the Epicureans—who exclude Providence from human life and refuse to believe that God governs its affairs or that the universe is directed by a blessed and immortal Being to the end that the whole of it may endure, but say that the world runs by its own movement without knowing a guide or another's care. If it were leaderless in this fashion, it would be shattered through taking a blind course and so end in

destruction, just as we see ships go down when they lose their helmsmen or chariots overturn when they have no drivers. It therefore seems to me, in view of the things foretold by Daniel, that they are very far from holding a true opinion who declare that God takes no thought for human affairs. For if it were the case that the world goes on by some automatism, we should not have seen all these things happen in accordance with his (Daniel's) prophecy.

Now I have written about these matters as I have found them in my reading. If, however, anyone wishes to judge otherwise of them, I shall not object to his holding a different opinion.

The Book of Daniel, as mentioned, is one of the prophetic books most often quoted by present-day interpreters of prophecies applicable for today.

It does strike one as incredible, first that there is a Creator of the Universe and of a living creature called man, and secondly, that He can and does communicate with man through so-called prophets (speaks for). It likewise strikes one as incredible, yes even more so, that this finite living creature called man can and does create space-ships (non-living creations) and can and does communicate with them thousands of miles out in space and have them obey his directions. These two phenomena do seem most incredible to the mind of man, and yet facts can be cited in support of each of their occurrences.

The many intermediate and progressively increasing number of prophecies prior to Jesus' appearance on earth were intended to point out to mankind in every way imaginable that Jesus was no ordinary man but represented the very zenith of the Creator's activity, in fact, His Only Begotten Son—the very sentimental core of His (the Creator's) personality. (The fact of the Creator's personality most definitely does not limit His field of action, but on the contrary infinitely augments His influence over man whom He has used and plans to use cooperatively in His future creative plans.)

It will be recalled that in our chronological account of Christianity as a religion Jesus from time to time specifically and progressively called attention to His fulfilment of prophecy. One Biblical scholar has determined that there were some twenty-five predictions, specifically, made by different prophets over a period of approximately five hundred years between 1000 B.C. and 500 B.C. which were fulfilled in the person of Jesus of Nazareth within the twenty-four hour interval of His betrayal, trial, death and burial. This is truly a "laser-like beam" pinpointing and emphasizing His uniqueness and significance.

Parthenogenesis (Virgin-birth)

Some hold up to ridicule the possibility that Mary conceived without the impregnation of spermatozoa. Yet all biologists will concede that the phenomena of parthenogenesis (virgin-birth) does occasionally occur in nature and they do not ridicule such observations. True, this phenomenon has not yet been observed to occur in mammals, but this does not necessarily mean it cannot occur or has not occurred.

Julian Huxley maintains that the evolutionary process came to a stop with man, and asserts that from now on man is responsible for the choices to make possible the psycho-social stage in evolutionary activity. Judging on the basis of man's past performance, he has proven himself incapable of making the choices required of that stage, at least as he is presently constituted. In view of this observation we should seek a way out of the impasse, and our attention should thus be alerted to any natural phenomena that promise a possible solution.

If, as we have heretofore concluded in our thesis, the so-called evolutionary activity was really a periodic creative activity on the "main trunk" of the evolutionary tree, man's attention should be directed to any phenomena suggesting such renewed creative activity.

In this connection it should be recalled that the Creator stated to Moses that He rested on the seventh day and *was refreshed*. From this statement we may reasonably infer that He has returned to His creative work after a latent period. In this further connection it will also be recalled that Mary was specifically informed by the angel that she was the chosen earthly agent, to which she consented after initial skepticism. Thus Mary was actually the physical being chosen by the Creator to give birth to a new creation conceived by the Holy Spirit. Hence, Jesus her first-born son is most specifically the son of the Creator.

Ironically here we find the Creator actively engaged in accomplishing a creative step on the main trunk of the evolutionary tree with biological science being completely oblivious to the phenomenal mutation having occurred.

The Biblical record indicates that Joseph, Mary's espoused, was quite disturbed at Mary's pregnancy as he definitely was aware that he was not responsible for her state. We can appreciate, therefore, why he was about to leave her, when he was informed in a dream concerning the significance of Mary's pregnancy and was thereby reconciled to it.

His Message—The Phenomenon of being Born-Again, the Holy Spirit, and the Kingdom of God

Jesus as a man became aware after his baptism by John at the Jordan River that he had become the recipient of extraordinary powers, as witness the temptations within his own mind to which he was subjected in the wilderness by the tempter himself eagerly soliciting his worship. He won over the temptations and determined that his powers were to be used for the welfare of all people and not for his own selfish aggrandizement. In other words he won over the promptings of his selfish instincts inherited from Mary, as it is stated that he was tempted just as we. Jesus after his temptations in the wilderness made a definite and specific intellectual choice in favor of the use of his great powers for the welfare of others, for subsequently, as Peter later testified, Jesus "went about doing good."

Jesus placed every emphasis in his teachings on the importance of being "born again" in order to become a subject fit for the kingdom of God, which kingdom he was establishing. You will recall that Jesus expressed surprise to Nicodemus that such a learned man as he was not aware of the necessity of man having to be born-again in order to have eternal life. Today Julian Huxley suggests having such awareness.

Jesus prior to his crucifixion specifically informed his disciples that it was necessary for him to leave them to return to his Father in Heaven so that the Comforter might come. And who was the Comforter? The Comforter was the Holy Spirit, which spirit was to replace man's selfish instinctual spirit (the breeder of fears) with the spirit of love and truth of God the Creator (the breeder of confidence). Thus man is given the choice of either becoming a "new creature" fit for the kingdom of God—the psycho-social stage of man which was in the very process of formation—or becoming a part of a so-called "dry

478

branch." According to Jesus the kingdom of God was to be a creation within man, and was to come into being gradually within the individual hearts of men. This characteristic of gradualism it will be recalled was also true of the insignificant early mammals slowly but surely replacing the giant dinosaurs, which animals eventually became extinct.

As was brought out repeatedly in our review of the significant developments in Old Testament history, the Creator never forced his will on man but left it up to man to make the choice. True the Creator could frighten man into temporarily agreeing to anything, but His wisdom told Him that man's nature could not be effectively and enduringly changed by fear but only through love.

At this point let us consider the significant question of why God required His Son to suffer the agonies of hell and the ignominy of death on the cross. Couldn't He have accomplished the same end in some other way? Let us apply our reasoning to this tantalizing problem, for God entreats: "Let us reason together." To facilitate such reasoning, we shall set up the following idealized situation:

Let us assume that there is only one man in existence and that this man were able to create at will. What would be his initial impulse? Possessing self-awareness and knowing that he was ALONE, his first impulse would probably be to create a suitable objective environment and then to create "friendly companions and co-workers." Their existence would indeed make his existence a most pleasant and happy one. True he could create puppets but that would take the meaning right out of "friendly companions and co-workers." Therefore, to have companions and co-workers, the man-creator must create self-centered free-choosing responsible creatures, with both the capacity and ability to choose. But how can our man-creator bring into existence such creatures who will be motivated to work cooperatively not only with him but with his fellow-creatures as well?

Before attempting to answer this question, let us further assume that the man-creator finally decided on and did create such free-choosing creatures, and furthermore that these creatures eventually not only ignored him but became threats to their fellow-creatures and to all his present and future planned creative work as well because of their creative ingenuity and self-centeredness.

What would we then suggest to the man-creator as his next step to accomplish his creative ideal? Some would impulsively suggest that he make his recalcitrant creatures do his will by inciting fear in them. But once such a course were followed, fear would have to be applied intermittently to become even partly effective. And furthermore, what would then become of his desired ideal of "friendly companions and co-workers"?

With this situation facing the man-creator, we finally conclude that the only way for him to bring about the desired ideal state would be for him to appeal to his creatures on the basis of both love and free choice. As they were already free-choosing creatures, our man-creator to win their love must himself become a love-object to his creatures. (Incidentally Mao Tse-tung in order to get the cooperation of his subjects at first followed the example of Stalin, who was Mao Tse-tung's ideal, and proceeded to instill fear in his subjects by exterminating over a million of his recalcitrant and uncooperative subjects. Industrial and farm production still fell far below his goal. At present it is understood that he is in the process of creating a myth around a certain soldier named Lei Feng who is supposed to have died in an accident at 22 years of age. Around this soldier is now highly propagandized the motto—"*Love* and emulate **Lei Feng**," making Lei Feng the personification of Marxian-Lenin virtues. It is interesting that even Mao Tse-tung has finally arrived at the conclusion that only love sufficeth to gain the loyalty and cooperation of his subjects.)

Thus man's selfish nature is such that only the physical sacrifice of the Creator's son was adequate to conciliate man and to serve as the necessary love object within the heart of man. In respect to this point the following excerpt from the prophecy of Jeremiah bears repeating:

> I (the Lord) will put my law within them, and I will write it upon their hearts.

Thus the glad tidings of Jesus hailed the coming of the Holy Spirit to set man free from the limitations and slavery of his selfish instincts—to set him truly free.

Can anything be more plainly stated that God anticipated the very need which Julian Huxley via scientific analysis has come to realize as necessary for the next stage of man's evolution—namely, the psycho-social stage?

The cited idealized situation is of course based upon self-centered man. However, inasmuch as God is love itself, we can assume His motivation for creation of relatively free-choosing entities, with man as its zenith, was His desire to share with His creatures His mind, His freedom, His creativity, and lastly His love. Man alone is given the opportunity of working toward God's likeness, first because of his God-given reasoning power, and now by the acceptance of His all-encompassing love, induced by the conciliatory act of love and justification of His incarnate Son, Jesus of Nazareth.

Jesus' Historical Existence Questioned and Rebutted

It is true that certain of the higher critics, after minute examination of all so-called historical records, have arrived at the conclusion that the very existence of an historical Jesus cannot be supported or proved, and a book was written by such a higher critic supporting this contention. In other words, Jesus is a myth pure and simple. That book, incidentally, inspired a certain French scholar to write another book, using a similar technique of historical criticism, proving that Napoleon never existed.

We can only conclude from this determination of certain history scholars that if Jesus did not physically and bodily exist in Israel around the period indicated in the New Testament, then the historians should proceed immediately to account for the phenomena which up to the present are accounted for only on the presumption of Jesus' historical existence. In this connection H. G. Wells, the historian, who incidentally did not presume to be a Christian, considered both sides of the problem, and finally chose the assumption of the actual historical existence of Jesus as being by far the easier one to accept as true. In the July 1922 issue of American Magazine, H. G. Wells states:

Jesus of Nazareth . . . is easily the dominant figure in history, I am speaking of Him, of course, as a man, for I conceive that the historian must treat Him as a man, just as the painter must paint Him as a man . . . To assume that He never lived, that the accounts of His life are inventions, is more difficult and raises more problems in the path of the historian than to accept the essential elements of the Gospel stories as fact.

Of course you and I live in countries where, to millions of men and women, Jesus is more than a man. But the historian must disregard that fact; he must adhere to the evidence which would pass unchallenged if his book were to be read in every nation under the sun.

John Stuart Mill, another unbeliever and an English economist and philosopher who lived in the middle of the nineteenth century, had this to say about Jesus in one of his essays on "Nature, The Utility of Religion, and Theism";

Christ is still left; a unique figure, not more unlike all his precursors than all His folowers, even those who had the direct benefit of His personal teaching. It is of no use to say that Christ as exhibited in the Gospels is not historical, and that we know not how much of what is admirable has been superadded by the tradition of his followers . . . Who among His disciples, or among their proselytes, was capable of inventing the sayings ascribed to Jesus, or of imagining the life and character in the Gospels? Certainly not the fishermen of Galilee; as certainly not St. Paul, whose character and idiosyncrasies were of a totally different sort; still less the early Christian writers . . .

When this pre-eminent genius is combined with the qualities of probably the greatest moral reformer, and martyr to that mission, who ever existed upon earth, religion cannot be said to have made a bad choice in pitching on this Man as the ideal representative and guide of humanity; nor, even now, would it be easy, even for an unbeliever, to find a better translation of the rule of virtue from the abstract into the concrete, than to endeavor so to live that Christ would approve our life.

Actually, by the process of logical analysis we cannot prove even the physical existence of the very chair we are sitting on. For Berkeley would bring out that the existence of the chair is simply the product of our sensations which are after all only within our own minds, and this is no proof of the chair's objective existence, the claims of the materialists to the contrary. Bertrand Russell, in turn, would bring out that we cannot observe the whole chair at any one glance, that is from all angles; that would require an infinite number of observations from all angles. Meanwhile not only the chair but the observer himself would not be the same chair and observer from moment to moment during the required observational analysis. In other words it is *physically* impossible for the same observer to observe the same chair (a sensed-object) from instant to instant to prove its existence. But, may the poor tired individual currently sitting on a chair and reading the foregoing have at least sufficient faith in the chair's existence, organizationally at least, until it has adequately served his purpose.

Reliability of the Bible Questioned and Rebutted

Thomas Paine in his book "Age of Reason" written during the time of the French Revolution, has this to say about Jesus Christ:

> That such a person as Jesus Christ existed and that he was crucified, which was the mode of execution at that day, are historical relations strictly within the limits of probability. He preached most excellent morality and the equality of man; but he preached also against the corruptions and avarice of the Jewish priests, and this brought upon him the hatred and vengeance of the whole order of priesthood. The accusation which those priests brought against him was that of sedition and conspiracy against the Roman government, to which the Jews were then subject and tributary; and it is not improbable that the Roman government might have had some secret apprehensions of the effects of his doctrine, as well as the Jewish priests; neither is it improbable that Jesus Christ had in contemplation the delivery of the Jewish nation from the bondage of the Romans. Between the two, however, this virtuous reformer and revolutionist lost his life.

From the foregoing quotation we can infer that whereas Thomas Paine did not believe in Jesus' divinity, he did admire him as a person, especially as concerns his attitude toward priests. Priests and priesthood apparently were Paine's "pet peeves." This attitude apparently had its beginning from his father, who was a Quaker. It was this antipathy toward priests that apparently motivated him to "pull the rug" from under the priests' major source of arguments, namely, by discrediting the Bible. Without the antipathy for priests, we possibly never would have had the benefit of the concise critical analytic review of the Bible by this acute mind as appears in Paine's Age of Reason. Of course Part I of the Age of Reason was speeded up by Paine's fear of the action of the leaders of the French Revolution who temporarily "took the bit in their teeth" and started running amuck toward the so-called primitive society. They guillotined many scholars, including Lavoisier, the brilliant French chemist. Paine, too, was about to be imprisoned, possibly as a preliminary to execution.

Paine asserted that the Creation was the "word of God" and was by far more reliable than the Bible; that man could study Creation without the inherent dangers of misreading God as through the Bible. The priests' immediate rebuttal to the publication of Part I of his Age of Reason led Paine to write Part II, where he really went to work to pick out definite inconsistencies in the Bible and to raise questions of authorships, to throw in the face of his critics, the priests.

Thomas Paine had a little background in astronomy, Dr. Bevis of the Royal Society having been an acquaintance. This gave Paine an opportunity to study and observe with awe through a telescope the vastness of the Universe. This incredible phenomena Paine's reason could not explain except by acknowledging the existence of God, the supreme mind.

While Paine saw the hand of God in Creation, he appeared to worship as God the Creation itself and his own mind, as he states: "My own mind is my own church." (a temple to solipsism?) The Bible, as Paine looked upon it however, was an object worshipped by the priests of the Jewish and Christian religions. Paine, while studying Creation as the "word of God" under an astronomer, failed to mention that two of the outstanding scientists who lived in the prior century, Newton and Huygens, had read differently the "word of God," as to the nature of light, the very phenomenon which made astronomy possible. Huygens had read from his observation of the "word" that light was a wave phenomenon within the ether. Newton, on the other hand, had read the same "word" as an emission of particles from a glowing source. Hence man appears to be a fallible reader of even the book of Creation. True God has objectified his mental creative activity as the Universe, but man, being finite, must labor tirelessly and patiently to "read" correctly the thoughts of God's infinite mind, i.e., to "reason with God."

The Bible also bears the definite "fingerprints" of God, but here God in order to translate his thoughts into the printed word for the benefit of his creature man must use fallible men as his "prophets" to perform this task, that is, to speak for him. Creation, the Universe, is God's thought which has already been objectified; and in the judgment of Paine, "the word of God." The Bible, on the other hand, is a progressive revelation to man within history, a dynamic current sequel so to speak, to God's already accomplished objective creation.

Paine was entirely right in applying his reason, (which is God given), to "rightly divide the word of truth," and we are indebted to him for his findings. However, he should also have applied his reason for the even more important purpose, namely, to ascertain just what message God is actually endeavoring to convey to man through his prophets, holy and inspired though fallible men.

What can we reasonably conclude that this message is? It does appear from the Bible that man did fall away from an initial close relationship with his Maker, having originally been definitely conscious of His presence. Subsequently man interposed such distance between his Maker and himself as to fear evil spirits and to make and worship physical idols to combat this fear. (We have heretofore determined that as man centers his thoughts about himself, fears arise.) Abraham, the son of an idol manufacturer, apparently reasoned that idolatry was so much non-sense and that there could reasonably be only one God. This reasoning on the part of Abraham was apparently well pleasing to his Maker, for He subsequently communicated with Abraham, advising him that through his seed all mankind would be blessed.

Then God spoke through Moses, revealing the commandments and warning against the continuance of idolatry, and emphasizing that He alone was God. He also through Moses revealed His plan to enlist the Israelites, the seed of Abraham, as a nation to serve as examples to all other nations. The Bible subsequently revealed the Israelites' breaking of this covenant with God to serve as such examples; and this rejection of God resulted in their subsequent dispersion. The physical phenomenon of the Israelites dispersed among all the nations of the world takes the Biblical account out of the realm of mythology.

God also used the prophets to inform man of the future appearance of the most outstanding personality, which proved to be none other than Jesus of Nazareth. The objective existence of the phenomena of "true" Christians takes the account in the New Testament also out of the realm of mythology.

Thomas Paine calls to our attention that the accounts of the four writers of the gospels do not agree, such as who came to Jesus' tomb first after his resurrection. Thus he concludes that the gospels were written independently and without prior contact between the writers. However, Paine fails to mention the very significant events in which their accounts agree. For instance all seem to be in general agreement that John, the Baptist, existed and that he foretold the coming of Christ; that he baptized Jesus with water in the Jordan River, and that after he did so, he called the attention of his hearers and observers that Jesus was the one whose coming he, John, had foretold. John also mentioned that whereas he baptized with water, Jesus would baptize with the Holy Spirit.

Also, most significantly, all the gospels mention Jesus' transfiguration on the Mount. The Gospel of John mentions the event only in a general manner, but Matthew, Mark and Luke mention that the phenomena occurred in the presence of the same three witnesses, namely, Peter, James and John. Furthermore, the account of these three gospels agree as to what occurred, namely, that Jesus shone with great brightness, that He talked with Moses and Elias (Elijah), and that subsequently out of a cloud was heard a voice saying: "This is my beloved son— hear him." Peter personally was anxious to impress this event upon the people before he died as in his subsequent epistle II Peter 1:16-17, he stated definitely that the event of the transfiguration was not a "cunningly devised fable" for he was there.

We were admonished by the voice to "Hear him." So what did Jesus teach? He taught, "as one having authority," the necessity of being born again to gain eternal life. How? By being baptized with the Holy Spirit whose subsequent coming He prophesied. Furthermore, that the resulting new creatures would initiate the Kingdom of God. Jesus' Sermon on the Mount remains unparalleled as a guide to virtuous living in the future Kingdom.

All the gospels agree that Jesus was crucified and buried, later to appear in the flesh before his apostles and others. The Holy Spirit as prophesied by Jesus did come at Pentecost, at which time thousands were "born again," baptized with this spirit of God. The appearance of the resurrected Jesus, along with the pentecostal phenomena, changed his disciples from a frightened bewildered group of men to a confident proselyting group made of martyr stuff; the fears bred of the spirit of self-consciousness were displaced by confidence bred of the Holy Spirit, the Comforter as termed by Jesus.

Thomas Paine ridicules the accounts of the appearances and disappearances of Jesus after his burial. This reaction in Paine's time was a reasonable one. He undoubtedly would also have ridiculed, and rightly so, if a colleague had suggested to him that less than two centuries hence man from a cabinet in his living room would be able to see and hear an event halfway around the earth simultaneously with its occurrence, and furthermore that he could turn it on or off at will by pushing a button. And, bear in mind, this capability was subsequently accomplished by the finite creatures of an infinite mind.

Incidentally, it is suggested that if light phenomena were to be dependent on either the interpretations of Huygens or Newton, there would be no light. Why? Because a magnetic wave as such is not observable by the eye of man until it is made to carry a particle, as witness the necessity of the electronic vacuum tube and fluorescent screen within a TV set. In other words, it appears that a combination of both a magnetic wave and a particle is necessary for its observation by the eye. Yet even with those inadequate theories, the sun continues to send forth its life-giving rays for the perpetuation of organic life on the earth.

Thomas Paine actually believed that by his Age of Reason he had administered the coup d'etat on the Bible. Yet even with the apparent inconsistencies appearing in the Old and New Testaments called to our attention by Paine, the transmutation of God's message to his finite creatures is effected via the printed word of holy and inspired though fallible men. The light of divine wisdom and love, with the radiant personality of Jesus, continues to pierce through these inconsistencies, in other words "shine through" the imperfect medium, to effect a rebirth, via the Holy Spirit, of man's self-centered personality to one fit for the next psycho-social stage of mankind, the Kingdom of God.

It may be interesting to speculate on a reversal of the problem, and set up an idealized situation. Let us suppose that nothing were known about the background of two unique groups of people, and furthermore that they themselves were afflicted with a persistent case of amnesia as to their origin. The two groups, of course, were both considered a peculiar and mysterious lot. They appeared to have certain similar beliefs, one group, however, living under a sacred code of ethical laws and espousing the belief in one God. The other group, too, espoused the belief in one God, but rather than placing emphasis on a specific code of ethical laws, espoused the need of being born again, thus implanting the love of God and fellow-man in their hearts. Both groups lived fairly consistently in accordance with their beliefs.

As no historical record could be found of these mysterious people, historians, anthropologists and archaeologists alike would be completely baffled to explain the phenomena. Then let us suppose that a certain archaeologist digging up and sorting pottery remains from the buried ruins of a Middle East city came upon a partially buried tunnel containing a group of antique vases. In these vases were discovered the parchments of the Old and New Testaments. What a discovery! The historians would rush in and have the parchments translated. What would they then proudly proclaim to the world? Why the great mystery surrounding the two strange groups of people was at last solved. The parchments revealed that there existed some 3300 years ago a man named Moses, from whom came the belief in one God and the ethical laws practiced by the one group. Furthermore, the later parchments would reveal the existence almost two thousand years ago, in fact during the time of the Roman Empire, of a man named Jesus of Nazareth who traveled around in Palestine healing the sick, preaching the love of God and fellow-man, prophesying the coming of the Holy Spirit to give man a rebirth, and proclaiming the coming of the Kingdom of God. Would they doubt the historical authenticity of the parchments? Of course not, for they would not then be in the critical mood to do so.

Yes, to doubt the historicity of Moses, the revealer of the Ten Commandments, and of Jesus, who gave his life to espouse the love of God and fellow-man, would be like doubting the existence of the tuning fork that gives us the pure "C"; moreover, a music lover who has actually heard the beautiful music of a master composer never doubts the prior existence of the one who wrote the "score."

"You protest overmuch," some men will superiorly tell us.

But when the most significant event ever to occur involving the future welfare of all mankind is smugly passed over and dismissed as of no other significance than mythology, then it is definitely impossible to "protest overmuch."

"It is still just a lot of balderdash," some critics will yet insist. To them we challenge—"Come down from the rail of the critics' fence, and try your hand at an independent logical synthesis of all universal phenomena." If they retort that there is no sense or meaning to be found in the universe anyway, then it necessarily follows that their railings are so much nonsense. The challenge is to reason.

The Reasoned Judgment of Certain Unbelievers as to Jesus' Significance

What conclusions have been drawn by certain unbelievers on the significance of Jesus' life outside of the realm of the so-called supernatural. Wm. E. H. Lecky (1838-1903), an outstanding historian and philosopher, and a leading unbeliever of his day, had the following to say of Jesus as quoted from his "History of European Morals from Augustus to Charlemagne":

> It was reserved for Christianity to present to the world an ideal character, which through all the changes of eighteen centuries has inspired the hearts of men with an impassioned love; has shown itself capable of acting on all ages, nations, temperaments, and conditions; has been not only the highest pattern of virtue, but the strongest incentive to its practice; and has exercised so deep an influence that it may be truly said that the simple record of three short years of active life has done more to regenerate and to soften mankind than all the disquisitions of philosophers and all the exhortations of moralists.

In Charles Darwin we recognize one who was an avowed unbeliever but at the same time one who must be recognized as a reliable observer. He had the following to say to those who were engaged in making violent attacks against Christian missionaries upon his return on the "Beagle" after its significant voyage of exploration. His statement has particular reference to his observations in New Zealand:

> They forget, or will not remember, that human sacrifices and the power of an idolatrous priesthood—a system of profligacy unparalleled in another part of the world—infanticide, a consequent of that system—bloody wars, where conquerors spared neither women nor children—that all these have been abolished; and that dishonesty, intemperance, and licentiousness have been greatly reduced by Christianity. In a voyager to forget these things is base ingratitude; for should he chance to be at the point of shipwreck on some unknown coast, he will most devoutly pray that the lesson of the missionary may have reached thus far.
>
> The lesson of the missionary is the enchanter's wand. The house has been built, the windows framed, the fields plowed, and even the trees grafted, by the New Zealander.
>
> The march of improvement, consequent on the introduction of Christianity through the South Seas, probably stands by itself in the records of history.

An outstanding twentieth century thinker once stated that Jesus was not very intellectual but that he possessed a profound insight. This thinker completely failed to appreciate that Jesus' purpose was far more significant than to contribute an original mathematical equation, which after all would have been an infringement of man's prior assigned domain.

The so-called Zealots and the Pharisees also failed to appreciate the significance and purpose of Jesus' appearance and message in history. Jesus' willingness to tolerate tyranny went very much against the grain of the zealots. To the pharisees, and also no doubt to the ascetic Essenes of Qumran, Jesus was most likely considered as loose and easy-going because of his association with "publicans and sinners." Jesus opposed the pharisees for burdening the people with ethical laws when what they sorely needed was a rebirth to counter their self-centered inherited nature.

490

The Real Significance of Jesus of Nazareth

To the Samaritan woman at Jacob's well, Jesus stated who he was, and from John 4:25-26 we quote:

> The woman saith unto him, I know that Messias cometh, which is called Christ: when he is come, he will tell us all things.
> Jesus saith unto her, 'I that speak unto thee am he.'

(Incidentally Jesus' prediction that there would be many false messiahs proved true. Many claiming to be the Messiah of prophecy have appeared but all have disappointed their hopeful adherents.)

Furthermore, Jesus himself is quoted in John 8:56-58 as saying to his audience of Jews:

> Your father Abraham rejoiced to see my day: and he saw it, and was glad.
> Then said the Jews unto him, Thou are not yet fifty years old, and hast thou seen Abraham?
> Jesus said unto them, Verily, verily, I say unto you, Before Abraham was, I am.

Also in the Book of Revelations Jesus is quoted as saying:

> These things saith the Amen, the faithful and true witness the beginning of the creation of God. (God's creative original) (Rev. 3:14)
> I am Alpha and Omega, the beginning and the end, the first and the last. (Rev. 22:13)

And who does Jesus say that God is?

> God is a spirit and they that worship him must worship him in spirit and in truth. (John 4:24)

In answer to certain questions raised by a Jewish audience, Jesus stated in part:

> If God were your Father, you would love me, for I

491

proceeded forth and came from God; neither came I of myself but he sent me. (John 8:42)

Jesus in his prayer of consecration of his disciples shortly before his crucifixion contained these words:

Father, I will that they also whom thou hast given me, be with me where I am, that they may behold my glory, which thou hast given me; for thou lovedst me *before the foundation of the world.* (John 17:24)

Even more enlightening assertions appear in the New Testament, some of which we quote as follows:

God, who at sundry times, and in divers manners spake in time past unto the fathers by the prophets, hath in these last days spoken unto us by his Son, whom he hath appointed heir of all things, by whom also he made the worlds. (Heb. 1:1-2)

O the depth of the riches both of the wisdom and knowledge of God! how unsearchable are his judgments, and his ways past finding out!

For who hath known the mind of the Lord? or who hath been his counsellor?

Or who hath first given to him, and it shall be recompensed unto him again?

For of him and through him, are all things: to whom be glory for ever. (Rom. 11:33-36)

But to us there is but one God, the Father, of whom are all things, and we in him, and one Lord Jesus Christ, by whom are all things, and we by him. (1 Cor. 8:6)

In the following quotations taken from his epistles to the Colossians and to the Galatians, Apostle Paul contributes the most enlightening thoughts as to God, the Father, and Jesus, his Son, which should be of particular interest to evolutionary biologists:

Giving thanks unto the Father, which hath made us meet to be partakers of the inheritance of the saints in light:

Who hath delivered us from the power of darkness, and has *translated us into the kingdom of his dear Son:*

492

In whom we have redemption through his blood, even the forgiveness of sins:

Who is the image of the invisible God, the *firstborn of every creature:*

For by him were all things created, that are in heaven, and that are in earth, visible and invisible, whether they be thrones, or dominions, or principalities, or powers: all things created by him, and for him;

And he is before all things, and by him all things consist (cohere).

And he is the head of the body, the church: who is the beginning, the firstborn from the dead; that in all things he might have the preeminence.

For it pleased the Father that in him shall all fulness dwell. (Col. 1:12-19)

For in Christ Jesus neither circumcision availeth anything, nor uncircumcision, *but a new creature.* (Gal. 6:15)

In Jesus' parable of the husbandmen, the implication is clear that he (Jesus) referred to himself as the son of the owner of the vineyard (the son of the Creator of the Universe). Also Jesus in Luke 23:31, questioned the multitude following him to calvary that if they did what they were about to do with him—the "green tree," what would they do with the "dry" tree? He apparently implied the Israelites. Some biblical scholars consider that here Jesus had reference to the destruction of Jerusalem by the Romans in 70 A.D. However, when one considers the millions of Jews who were killed in Hitler's gas chambers in the light of Jesus' foregoing rhetorical question, one cannot resist associating it with Jesus' statement made at this time.

The metaphor "branch" appears in the prophecies of Isaiah, Jeremiah and Zechariah as regards the coming Messiah. Jesus also referred to himself as the "true vine." (Julian Huxley particularly will appreciate the connotation of the metaphor "green branch.")

All these things spake Jesus unto the multitude in parables; and without a parable spake he not unto them;

That it might be fulfilled which was spoken by the prophet, saying, I will open my mouth in parables (Psa. 78); *I will utter things which have been kept secret from the foundation of the world.* (Matt. 13:34-35)

As we reflect upon the basic thoughts contained in the foregoing scriptural references, we are fascinated by the fact that they correlate consistently with the fundamental ideas portrayed by the graphic representations heretofore constructed from sense-data inductively and inferentially arrived at from the physical world.

XXXIV.

COMPARISON OF THE LIVING AND THE NON-LIVING CULTURAL CREATIONS

As a preliminary introduction to the interpretation of the following additional geometrical representations, we shall quote a part of Sartre's philosophy concerning Existentialism:

Sartre asserts that the belief which all existentialists have in common is that existence comes before essence, that we must begin with the subjective. He attempts to explain the meaning of this by citing as an example the procedure in the manufacture of a paper-knife. The artisan must first have a conception of it and its purpose, and the pre-existent method of producing it. Hence, thinking, a subjective process, precedes the existence of the paper-knife. Production, in other words, precedes its existence.

What Sartre maintains, in other words, is that creation first takes place within the mind of the existent creator, an invisible subjective process, before it is objectified and becomes an objective fact.

An artist will maintain the same principle, namely, that a picture must first be created within the mind of the artist before it can be reproduced on the canvas.

Jesus apparently had this same principle in mind when he stated that he was before the "foundation of the world." It appears also that it is in that sense that Apostle Paul meant by the statement that Jesus was "the first-born of every creature," progressively created within the mind of God; in other words, God's creative original.

In this connection we refer back to our brief discussion of

495

the Law of Biogenesis at the close of Part II of our thesis. There, it will be recalled, it was brought out that man repeats during the development of his embryo his past biological history. In a most startling manner the statements of Jesus and also those of Apostle Paul point to the fact that Jesus was most definitely God's creative original. In other words, Jesus carries within himself the progressive stages of God's creativity. It was "of whom, through whom and for whom all things were made." A new law has been discovered—the Law of Psychogenesis.* As a final step in this phase of his creative work, God sent his son down for the first time to show man the final creative step. He chose Mary of Galilee as his earthly agent to objectify (incarnate) His son. It was, in fact, a case of parthenogenesis (virgin birth), which suggests that all prior stages, on the main trunk at least, of the so-called evolutionary tree, were also of this very nature.

It will be recalled that our original representations were made on a point-instant basis. We shall now attempt comparable representations in a dynamic coordinate form. It will be recalled that Bergson tried to accomplish this in his philosophy by his concept "duration."

The additional representations are shown in figures No. 6 and 7.

This pair of schematic representations again reemphasizes that man is made in the image of his Creator. Furthermore, that the establishment of the psycho-social stage (Kingdom of God) is a joint project between man and his Maker.

The following additional significant conclusions are drawn from all these representations. First, the Creator gave man the sense of logic (the prism of logic as we have termed it) as an initial creative gift. Then after giving man the opportunity to develop his personality with the aid of the selfish instincts, He

---

* The Law of Psychogenesis may be tentatively formulated as:

All current conceptions incorporate within themselves certain pre-conceptions, which become more or less apparent during the process of their objectification. In a "living culture" this is evidenced by the phenomena of biogenesis observed during the development of the embryo of a living organism. In a so-called "non-living culture" this is evidenced by the bibliography appearing at the close of a book of an educational nature, the "history of prior art" appearing in a patent application, and the like.

496

GRAPH OF CREATION OF LIVING CULTURE
(Three General Phases) *

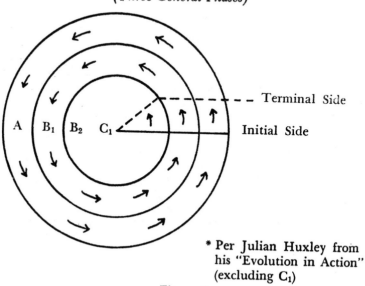

Terminal Side

Initial Side

* Per Julian Huxley from his "Evolution in Action" (excluding C_1)

Figure 6

Key for above graph (later phase superimposed on earlier):
(1) A = Cosmological or Inorganic Phase;
(2) B_1 = Biological or Organic Phase;
(3) B_2 = Human or Psycho-social Phase (Kingdom of God)
 (Joint creation of God and Mankind, currently active);
 C_1 = Supreme Creative Mind.

later endeavored to show man the limitations these instincts have for establishing the coming so-called psycho-social stage (Kingdom of God). These instincts, man has learned, have set him off on a tangent so far as social life and welfare are concerned. After all, man cannot and does not desire to live alone; he wants to be a social creature.

Natural selection and time have already proved ineffective media to change our selfish instincts. Such a change, we conclude, requires: first, a creative act on the part of man's Creator; and second, a conscious selection by man.

The Creator endeavored to teach His Chosen People (the Israelites) their limitations in this respect which would make them receptive to the subsequent step, but without success. In

GRAPH OF CREATION OF NON-LIVING CULTURE
(Three Basic Mutation Phases) **

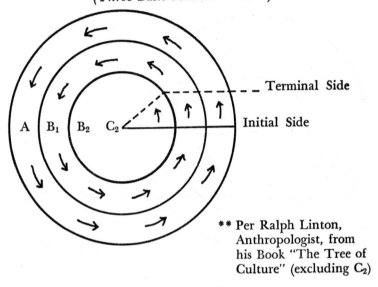

Terminal Side

Initial Side

** Per Ralph Linton,
Anthropologist, from
his Book "The Tree of
Culture" (excluding C₂)

Figure 7 (B₂ of Figure 6)

Key for above graph:
(1) A = Use of tools, fire, and languages;
(2) B₁ = Discovery of how to raise food, immediately followed
by such advances as the smelting of metals, the working
of metals, the development of the wheel, the plow and
loom, the invention of writing, the development on the
social side of city life, of kingship, and drilled armies—
all of which originated in Southwestern Asia, and which
survived very little change to 1800.
(3) B₂ = Discovery of how to get power from *heat*—
first from the steam engine, and later with the internal
combustion engine, jets, and now passing on to present
atomic energy which involves use of its *heat;* Discovery of
scientific method, considered as an invention in itself;
C₂ = Mankind's collective creative minds.

due time, however, He sent His only Begotten Son as a love
object, and to teach man the attitude of mind required and the
necessity of re-birth into a "new creation" to make him a fit
subject for a permanent and happy society.

The Creator not only sent His Son to serve as an example and love-object for this purpose, but followed it up by sending His Holy Spirit, an outright gift as was the prism of logic, the Holy Spirit representing the remaining major aspect of His own infinite personality. And what is the Holy Spirit? It is the spirit of truth and love which will free man from the limitations set by his self-oriented instincts.

Coincident with the acceptance of the Son, man becomes the recipient of the Holy Spirit, thereby transforming him to a fit subject for the Kingdom of God, with Jesus as king and "head corner-stone." The acceptance of the newly created instinct equips man for the psycho-social stage of which Julian Huxley speaks. In short, it involves the choice by man of either accepting the gift of this new all-encompassing creative and life-giving instinct, or continuing as a slave of his present selfish instincts, the very instincts which now threaten to lead him to regression and ultimate extinction.

Incidentally, Ernst Mayr, Director of the Harvard Museum of Comparative Zoology, in a recent interview with a Journal-American reporter, expressed pessimistic views as to man's chances of survival because of his current erratic behavior; in fact, he states we may soon know. Of all life-forms which have existed, he states, 99% of them have become extinct.

"Man is an ape with an overactive brain." That was the sober judgment of Dr. Ralph Linton, the late renowned Yale anthropologist. Dr. Huxley, representing enlightened man, realizes and agrees that man as presently constituted must be changed into a socially-minded man or he will blow up not only himself with his accumulated culture but the rest of life-forms as well. Why? Because his overactive brain and the instincts of an ape cannot survive together.

However, we should not become too pessimistic in the face of the foregoing statements, for we now find that our Creator has anticipated our present need. We have heretofore inductively determined that the Creator has completed his creative work as regards the Mineral Kingdom, the Plant Kingdom, and presently the Animal Kingdom. As the Creator has not regressed "anagenically" in the past, we presume he will not deprive man of his "overactive brain." That leaves man's instinctual nature as the next progressive "anagenic" step, not just into another phylum or class but into the next kingdom of the Lord's creativity—none other than the Kingdom of God.

XXXV.

CERTAIN OBJECTIVE AND SYMBOLIC SUPPORT OF OUR GENERAL THESIS

In support of our general thesis, we shall now proceed to discuss not only the significance of the establishment of the State of Israel, but also the symbolic significance of the Great Pyramid at Gizeh.

Significance of the Establishment of the State of Israel

During the present time a very significant phenomenon is taking place, namely, the gradual return of the Israelites to their so-called promised land after their long dispersion among all the nations of the world. The movement was initiated by Theodor Herzl, who espoused the idea of the Jews re-establishing a nation, and who predicted it should be accomplished in fifty years. The resulting movement, known as Zionism, was proclaimed at the Zionist Congress in 1897. Fifty-one years later the legally recognized homeland for the Jews was established in Palestine, known as the State of Israel. It has become the meeting-ground of Jews of all countries. The cultural differences between this motley group are gradually being eliminated by the establishment of Hebrew as the national language and of a standard system of education for all children.

The significance of the phenomenon currently taking place in the State of Israel can neither be ignored nor overemphasized. From the thirty-first chapter of the Book of Jeremiah, the prophet of God, we quote the following:

For there shall be a day, that the watchman upon the

mount of Ephraim shall cry, Arise ye, and let us go up to Zion unto the Lord our God.

For thus saith the Lord; Sing with gladness for Jacob, and shout among the chief of the nations: publish ye, praise ye, and say, O Lord save thy people, the remnant of Israel.

Behold, I will bring them from the *north country*, and gather them from the coasts of the earth, and with them the blind and the lame, the women with child and her that travaileth with child together: a great company shall return thither.

They shall come with weeping, and with supplications will I lead them: I will cause them to walk by the rivers of waters in a straight way, wherein they shall not stumble: for I am a father to Israel, and Ephraim is my firstborn.

Hear the word of the Lord, O ye nations, and declare it in the isles afar off, and say, He that scattered Israel will gather him, and keep him, as a shepherd doth his flock. (Jer. 31:6-10)

Also from the Prophet Ezekiel and Prophet Amos, we quote the following verses:

When I have brought them again from the people, and gathered them out of their enemies' lands, and am sanctified in them in the sight of many nations;

Then shall they know that I am the Lord their God, which caused them to be led into captivity among the heathen: but I have gathered them unto their own land, and have left none of them any more there.

Neither will I hide my face any more from them: for I have poured out my spirit upon the house of Israel, saith the Lord God. (Ezekiel 39:27-29)

And I will bring again the captivity of my people of Israel, and they shall build the waste cities, and inhabit them; and they shall plant vineyards, and drink the wine thereof; they shall make gardens, and eat the fruit of them.

And I will plant them upon their land, and they shall no more be pulled up out of their land which I have given them, saith the Lord thy God. (Amos 9:14-15)

Roscoe Drummond, a writer for the New York Herald Tribune, sent in an article to his newspaper from Jerusalem during a visit to the State of Israel in June of 1965. In this article are found the following interesting statements:

> The Israelis have performed an economic and social miracle in half a generation—and more is in the making. . . .
>
> They have transformed the most sterile and resource-poor tiny slice of the Middle East into a promising land.
>
> Theodor Herzl, the founder of Zionism, did not live to see his galvanic prophecy come true: 'If you will, it is no dream.'
>
> You have to see this miracle at firsthand to believe it. Wherever I look—at eroded land made useful and productive, at barren hills made green with trees, at new cities, new ports, new factories, and college classrooms crowded with students—I am haunted by the American song, 'Did You Ever See a Dream Walking?'
>
> Israel is today a dream come to fruition at a breathless pace—and there is no evidence that it is slowing down.

In a subsequent article sent in from the same city, the following interesting statements appear:

> One of the most exciting facts about this youthful, maturing 17-year-old nation of 2¼ million is the extent to which it is providing training and skill to help African, Latin American, and Asian nations do what Israel has already proved can be done.
>
> It is Israel which is now assisting 67 other underdeveloped countries to begin to match what it has done so well.
>
> And Israel is acquiring a precious reservoir of friendship and good will.

It would appear from the foregoing that Israel is at last functioning in the capacity, in part at least, God had in mind for them when he discussed the subject with Moses on Mount Sinai some three-thousand years ago.

It will be recalled from our prior review of Judaism that the troubles of the Israelites began when they approached

Samuel to anoint a king for them so that they might be "like unto all the nations," an obvious departure from their covenant with God.

Back in 1934, and prior to the establishment of the State of Israel, the late Martin Buber, the outstanding exponent of Hasidic philosophy, in an address at Frankfort on the Main emphasized that Jewry would never regain their early feeling of security, not even by regaining a political structure, until it returned to its original uniqueness, that of translating "into reality the divine words spoken during the making of the Covenant." He went on to state:

> There is no re-establishing of Israel, there is no security for it save one: it must assume the burden of its own uniqueness; it must assume the yoke of the kingdom of God. Since this can be accomplished only in the rounded life of a community, we must reassemble, we must again root in the soil, we must govern ourselves. But these are mere prerequisites! Only when the community recognizes and realizes them as such in its own life, will they serve as the cornerstones of its salvation.

Martin Buber conceded that not only the original Israelitic nation "had failed the test" but also the Jews subsequent to Saul of Tarsus becoming the apostle to the gentiles, failed as ensamples of righteousness and justice. It is this ensample they must now assume to fulfill the original Covenant.

In a relatively recent lecture entitled "Spirit of Israel and the World of Today," Martin Buber makes the following significant statements:

> The typical individual of our times is no longer capable of believing in God; but he finds it impossible to believe even in his own substance, that substance which has neither pediment nor basis; and so he holds fast to his faith in his expanded ego, his nation, as being the highest authority within his reach . . . he transforms his nation into an idol, he sets up the personality of his people as god; he makes the 'prince' who is a mere ministering angel into a god.

Subsequently he goes on to state that "the purpose of creation is not an everlasting struggle to the death between sects or classes or nations. . . . the world of humanity is meant to become a single body; but it is as yet nothing more than a heap of limbs each of which is of the opinion that it constitutes an entire body." "We men are charged to perfect our own portion of the universe—the human world. There is one nation which once upon a time heard this charge so loudly and clearly that the charge penetrated to the very depths of its soul." As to this charge Martin Buber goes on to state:

> The charge is not addressed to isolated individuals but to a nation. For only an entire nation, which comprehends peoples of all kinds, can demonstrate, a life of unity and peace, of righteousness and justice to the human race, as a sort of example and beginning. A true humanity, that is, a nation composed of many nations, can only commence with a certain definite and true nation. The hearkening nation was charged to become a true nation. . . . The people of Israel was charged to lead the way toward this realization.

Martin Buber brought out that "age after age the Jewish people believed in the messianic tidings. They believed them and proclaimed them, and occasionally even rose to the summons of false Messiahs and hastened to join them. But they did not realize what is incumbent upon the individual and the nation: the commencement. Of course it lies in the power of heaven to introduce the Kingdom of God; the preparation of the world in readiness for that kingdom, the commencement of a fulfillment of the truth calls for men and a nation consisting of men. And now, after a proclamation without fulfilment, there has come some measure of fulfilment without proclamation; but then what is the proclamation of a Kingdom without a King?"

We may rest assured that the King will appear in due time to make the proclamation.

It should not be overlooked that this is the second time that the Israelites have returned to their homeland Palestine. The first time was the occasion of their being freed by Cyrus from their seventy-year captivity in Babylon. Their present and second return was prophesied in the Book of Isaiah, Chapter 11, verses 11 and 12, reading:

And it shall come to pass in that day, that the Lord shall set his hand again the *second time* to recover the remnant of his people, which shall be left, from Assyria, and from Egypt, and from Pathros, and from Cush, and from Elam, and from Shinar, and from Hamath, and from the islands of the sea.

And he shall set up an ensign for the nations, and shall assemble the outcasts of Israel, and gather together the dispersed of Judah from the four corners of the earth.

As no mention of a second failure of Israel to fulfill its destiny is mentioned in prophecy, the progress of Israel should be most closely observed in the light of biblical prophecy.

Jesus predicted the fall of Jerusalem and the dispersion of the Israelites, as indicated in Luke 21:24, as follows:

And they shall fall by the edge of the sword, and shall be led away captive unto all nations, and Jerusalem shall be trodden down of the Gentiles, *until the times of the Gentiles be fulfilled.*

Immediately after His resurrection His disciples point-blank inquired of Jesus: "Lord, wilt thou at this time restore again the kingdom of Israel?" To this question Jesus replied as quoted from Acts 1:7-8, as follows:

It is not for you to know the times or the seasons, which the Father hath put in his own power;

But ye shall receive power, after that the Holy Ghost is come upon you: and ye shall be witnesses unto me both in Jerusalem, and in all Judea, and in Samaria, and unto the uttermost part of the earth.

The Gentiles have subsequently been "weighed in the balance" and they too, like the Israelites, are being found wanting as rulers of a peaceful world, for we now hear the words: "peace, peace, when there is no peace." The initial failure of the Israelites, and now the failure of the Gentiles, to establish a peaceful world government was, and still is, the inevitable result of the inherent weakness of man's self-centered constitution, which fact God apparently wished to impress upon man. However, Jesus will return to establish such a world government, this time as reigning King with Israel as his base of functioning. Support for this conclusion is found in the following prophetic quotations taken from the Book of Jeremiah, the Book of Daniel, and the Book of Revelations, as follows:

For it shall come to pass in that day, saith the Lord of hosts, that I will break the yoke from off thy neck, and will burst thy bonds, and strangers shall no more serve themselves of him: But they shall serve the Lord their God, and David their king, whom I will raise up unto them. (Jer. 30:8-9)

And there was given him dominion, and glory, and a kingdom, that all people, nations, and languages, should serve him: his dominion is an everlasting dominion, which shall not pass away, and his kingdom that which shall not be destroyed. (Dan. 7:14)

And in the days of those kings shall the God of heaven set up a kingdom, which shall never be destroyed; and the kingdom shall not be left to other people, but it shall break in pieces and consume all these kingdoms, and it shall stand for ever. (Dan. 2:44)

And the seventh angel sounded; and there were great voices in heaven, saying, The kingdoms of this world are become the kingdoms of our Lord, and of his Christ; and he shall reign for ever and ever. (Rev. 11:15)

In view of the foregoing, the present and future developments in the State of Israel within the next generations should be carefully observed in the light of prophecy. A period of temporary troublous times is suggested by prophecy for this youthful nation prior to the glorious appearance of the "King of kings."

Symbolic Significance of the Great Pyramid at Gizeh

According to certain ancient history authorities, Egypt was at a very early period invaded by Hyksos, an eastern nation of shepherd kings. They compelled the people of Egypt to close up their idolatrous temples and enlisted them to construct the Great Pyramid at Gizeh. (True Egypt was much later invaded by a nation also known as Shepherd Kings but they had no connection with the pyramids.)

According to a recognized authority on Egyptian archaeology, the late Professor William M. (Flinders) Petrie, born in England in 1853, the stones for the Great Pyramid were all carefully cut to size at the quarries across the Nile and specifically marked for their allotted place in the structure. It involved some 2,300,000 blocks of stone averaging 40 cubic feet in size, with an estimated total weight of 6,848,000 tons. The Pyramid covered approximately thirteen acres of ground. It is square-shaped at its base, with triangular lateral sides leading up to a point directly over the center of the base. Ralph Linton in his "Tree of Culture" states in part: "How extraordinary these structures were can be appreciated if one realizes that the first, largest, and best constructed was erected less than two hundred years after the Egyptians first essayed to use stone in any sort of construction. The pyramids were built with the simplest appliances: ramps, rollers, and levers. Even the pulley was unknown."

As to its approximate dimensions, it had a base length of about 750 feet. It originally measured about 482 ft. from the base to its vertex. It had a slant height of about 568 feet, with an angle of 51° 50'. The foundation stones for the four base corners were removed many centuries ago, but the "sockets" in the rocks are still visible.

According to the Greek historian Herodotus, it took *thirty years* to build the Great Pyramid. As it was the first structure of that type to be built, the place allotted for the head cornerstone was a mystery to the builders, and consequently it became a "stumbling-block."

The earliest excavations at the Great Pyramid were made by Arabs in the hope of finding valuable buried material treasures, but these excavations were doomed to disappointment. They found only a system of bare passages and galleries but no treasures, not even inscriptions or mummies of any sort, which were, incidentally, found in the other later pyramids. The casing stones, however, were later taken as building material for other structures.

Subsequently, however, it has gradually come to be recognized that the Great Pyramid symbolizes many truths of science. Furthermore, biblical scholars have discovered that its internal passages, galleries, and chambers reveal in symbolic form God's plan of salvation of mankind. According to certain interpretations, the descending passage, which begins a short distance up from one of its sides and terminates at a pit, symbolizes man's original fall and present state. The first ascending passage leads upward from the descending passage about a quarter of the distance downward in the descending passage. This passage symbolizes the age covered by the original law covenant mediated between God and Moses involving the Israelites and to which they unanimously agreed. This ascending passage leads up to a horizontal passage which, in turn, leads to the so-called Queen's Chamber. This passage is interpreted as the level of human perfection on the physical plane, the Kingdom of God. At the intersection of the first ascending passage, Jesus Christ whose coming was prophesied by Moses and other prophets, appeared in history—the Only Begotten Son of God. Then there continues upward from the first ascending passage, the so-called Grand Gallery, which symbolizes the so-called "walk of the spirit-begotten," i.e., during the so-called Gospel Age espoused by Apostle Paul. The Grand Gallery leads up to the plane of spirit-born and to the King's Chamber. Thus we have the fatherhood of God on the plane of the spirit and on the plane below it the motherhood of physical nature.

Most significantly there is a narrow well-shaft which leads down from the intersection of the top of the first ascending passage, the horizontal plane, and the beginning of the Grand Gallery. This well-shaft leads down to a grotto, and then continues downward to the bottom section of the descending passage, adjacent to the pit. This well-shaft symbolizes the way of escape from the pit (Hades) made possible by faith in Jesus Christ as a ransom sacrifice.

The so-called plane of human perfection is referred to in Chapter 31 of Jeremiah, which will be quoted later. It is said that this stage of human perfection will not come into being until at the close of the so-called Gospel Age.

Among some of the biblical quotations cited by these Bible scholars having reference to the Great Pyramid are the following: first, from the Book of Isaiah:

> In that day shall there be an altar to the Lord in the midst of the land of Egypt, and a pillar at the border thereof to the Lord.

And it shall be for a sign and for a witness unto the Lord of hosts in the land of Egypt: for they shall cry unto the Lord because of the oppressors and he shall send them a saviour and a great one, and he shall deliver them. (Isa. 19:19-20)

Next, from the Book of Job:

Where wast thou when I laid the foundations of the earth? declare if thou hast understanding.

Who hath laid the measures thereof, if thou knowest? or who hath stretched the line upon it?

Whereupon are the foundations thereof fastened? or who laid the corner stone thereof;

When the morning stars sang together, and all the sons of God shouted for joy. (Job 38:4-7)

The biblical reference to "foundations" in the third paragraph of this quotation is "sockets" and to the word "fastened" the reference is "made to sink."

From the Book of Isaiah, we quote from chapter 28, verse 16, as follows:

Therefore thus saith the Lord God, behold I lay in Zion for a foundation a stone, a tried stone, a precious corner stone, a sure foundation: he that believeth shall not make haste.

From the Book of Psalms we quote:

The stone which the builders refused is become the head of the corner;

This is the Lord's doing: it is marvellous in our eyes. (Psa. 118:22-23)

We shall now go on and quote certain passages from the New Testament of the Bible:

Jesus saith unto them, Did ye never read in the scriptures, 'The stone which the builders rejected, the same is become the head of the corner; this is the Lord's doing, and it is marvelous in our eyes?'

509

Therefore say I unto you, the kingdom of God shall be taken from you, and given to a nation bringing forth the fruits thereof,

And whosoever shall fall on this stone shall be broken but on whomsoever it shall fall, it will grind him to powder. (Matt. 21:42-44)

From the Gospel according to John we quote the following words of Jesus:

Father, I will that they also, whom thou hast given me, be with me where I am; that they may behold my glory, which thou has given me: *for thou lovedst me before the foundation of the world.* (John 17:24)

From the Book of Acts we quote the words of Peter to the rulers and elders of Israel:

Be it known unto you all, and to all the people of Israel, that by the name of Jesus Christ of Nazareth, whom ye crucified, whom God raised from the dead, even by him doth this man stand here before you whole.

This is the stone which was set at naught of you builders, which is become the head of the corner. (Acts 4:10-12)

We shall now return to the Old Testament and quote from the Book of Jeremiah:

Behold, the days come, saith the Lord, that I will make a new covenant with the house of Israel, and with the house of Judah:

Not according to the covenant that I made with their fathers in the day that I took them by the hand to bring them out of the land of Egypt; which my covenant they brake, although I was a husband unto them, said the Lord;

But this shall be the covenant that I will make with the house of Israel; After those days, said the Lord, I will put my law in their inward parts, and write it in their hearts; and will be their God, and they shall be my people.

And they shall teach no more every man his neighbor, and every man his brother, saying, Know the Lord; for they shall know me, from the least of them unto the greatest of them, saith the Lord; for I will forgive their iniquity, and I will remember their sin no more. (Jer. 31:31-34)

From the Book of Psalms we also quote:

Unless the Lord had been my help, my soul had almost dwelt in silence. (Psalm of David 94:17)

As to the "well-shaft" from the "pit" we quote the words of the Lord appearing in Revelations 1:17-18:

Fear not; I am the first and the last:
I am he that liveth, and was dead; and, behold, I am alive for evermore, Amen; and have the keys of hell (grave-pit) and of death.

In this same connection we quote the words of Peter, the Apostle, who not only was personally present at Jesus' transfiguration on the mount but who also conversed with Jesus after his resurrection. These words are taken from I Peter 4:5-6:

Who shall give account to him (Jesus) that is ready to judge the quick and the dead.
For this cause was the gospel preached also to them that are dead, that they might be judged according to men in the flesh, but live according to God in the spirit.

We infer from Peter's statement that the physically dead "live according to God in the spirit." Hence, those in the pit (Hades) exist there in the spirit.

Thus, the Great Pyramid at Gizeh is an altar and sign symbol of the Creator, not only as the creator of the universe with its physical laws, but as revealing His master-plan of creating a man possessing the qualities required of the coming so-called biological psycho-social stage of mankind—a truly master-plan for the salvation of mankind.

As to the static symbolism of the Great Pyramid, a vertical cross-section thereof appears to contain the right-angled triangle, with the remarkable relationship of its sides to its hypotenuse. It will be recalled that it was Pythagoras who proved this significant theorem, as well as revealed the basic importance of number in the constructive interpretation of nature. Plato went one step further by refining Pythagoras' numbers into a theory of ideas.

A horizontal cross-section of the Pyramid appears to contain the symbolism of Descartes' coordinate system. The coordinate system would appear to move discontinuously upward within creative time.

Whereas Einstein called our attention to the intermediate space-time intervals of nature using the constant speed of light in their interpretation, the Great Pyramid appears to represent the infinite spatial-temporal interval in the perpendicular raised from the center of the base to the vertex, the head corner-stone. It appears to represent both the creative and the Master interval, in which the love of God is the motivating principle.

Another rather fascinating application of the pyramidal form (or the more dynamic conical form) is its use in visualizing the phenomena of light and color. This is brought out very effectively by Dr. Robert S. Woodworth in his text-book of "Psychology." On the four corners of the base of the pyramid he places the four elementary colors, red, yellow, green, and blue. The perpendicular raised from the center of the base to the vertex of the color pyramid represents the various shades from gray to white at its vertex.

Colors of all degrees of brightness, intensity, and saturation are thus incorporated and represented in the various pyramidal cross-sections from the base to its vertex, which is white—the combination of all colors and their shades. The reverse pyramidal form (or conical) leads down from the base, with black at its nadir or lowest point. While black is considered by physics as the absence of light, psychologically it is definitely a visual sensation, and is necessary for the verification of physics. Thus we have on the perpendicular all shades of black and white between the lowest point (black) and the highest point (pure white).

The reverse pyramidal form for color also suggests the possibility of other "anti's" in physics—anti-electrons, anti-protons, anti-neutrinos, and the like. In the spiritual realm it suggests "heaven" and "hell," "life" and "death," "good spirit" and "bad spirit" and so on.

Statistically speaking we have represented in the pyramidal form the normal curve of probability, with the true unquestioning and certain fact at the center from the bottom to the top of the normal curve or the apex.

From the viewpoint of metaphysics, the Great Pyramid in its entirety appears to symbolize Whitehead's concept of the "infinite abstractive hierarchy," whose vertex represents the "complex eternal object," and the base with its "infinite simple objects." Progressive analysis from the "complex eternal object" at the vertex toward the realm of actuality leads to more and more components from one grade to another until the finite simple objects at the base are reached. The reversal of direction into the realm of possibility (as in evolution) leads again to gradually decreasing hierarchies, eventually again leading up to the "infinite eternal object" at its vertex.

Aristotle, as Whitehead pointed out in his "Science and the Modern World," was the most outstanding metaphysician who was relatively free of religious and ethical bias. Thus his trend of thought leading him back to the Prime Mover (God) is especially significant. True, as again singled out by Whitehead, Aristotle's physics has undergone change. Yet we feel that even with present-day physics, unallergic to an explanation of the existence of the "simple objects" at the base of creative activity, Aristotle's basic argument supporting the existence of the Prime Mover (God) still stands.

Whitehead states that we now rather require God as the Principle of Concretion. At the same time he states "God is not concrete, but He is the ground for concrete actuality. No reason can be given for the nature of God, because that nature is the ground of rationality." At the same time he issues an implied challenge that if the God of religion is to be conceived as "the foundation of the metaphysical situation with its ultimate actuality" there is no alternative "except to discern in Him the origin of all evil as well as of all good." Incidentally, the origin of evil is in fact assumed by God. God, using Isaiah as his mouthpiece, states:

I form the light, and create darkness; I make peace, and create evil; I the Lord do all these things. (Isaiah 45:7)

The evil, as suggested by Paul of Tarsus, turns out to be the law, which is our "schoolmaster." This law man can break blindly for lack of knowledge or deliberately to attain his selfish purposes. (We "are judged according to the light that is in us," and embarrassingly we so judge ourselves.)

But on the other side of the coin, we discover that it is the existence of the law (evil) that makes significant man's freedom of choice. Thus, the law would appear to incorporate Whitehead's "principle of limitation." Therefore, on the negative side, the discovery of the laws of nature by man appears to increase evil and the responsibility of abiding by those laws; on the positive side, however, it appears to increase his freedom of choice, as well as creative possibilities.

Man was initially instructed by his Maker to "subdue the world" and thereby progressively attain to God's likeness. (Can this be the purpose of God's creation of man in his own image, a thought suggested by Martin Buber? So it appears.)

As was previously mentioned, the builders of the Pyramid found the head corner-stone a stumbling-block until they neared the top of the structure; then they suddenly realized that it was the very model and replica of the completed structure, the original psychogenetic form.

Likewise, we now suddenly become aware of the fact that this so-called stumbling-block, not only to Israel but to all mankind, personifies none other than the Lord Jesus Christ, the Only Begotten Son of God, "the first-born of every creature" within the mind of God before the foundation of the Universe, and who now is in the very process of completing his Father's current great creative task.

Ralph Linton in his chapter on Egypt in "The Tree of Culture," states: "It has been said that the common Egyptians were enthusiastic about the work (The Great Pyramid), since they were building the dwelling of a god on whom the future well-being of the nation would depend." This, in fact, is prophesied in the last half of Chapter 19 of the Book of Isaiah. This chapter, incidentally, closes with the following hopeful prophecy:

> In that day shall there be a highway out of Egypt to Assyria, and the Assyrian shall come into Egypt and the Egyptian into Assyria, and the Egyptians shall serve with the Assyrians.

In that day shall Israel be the third with Egypt and with Assyria, even a blessing in the midst of the land:

Whom the Lord of hosts shall bless, saying, Blessed be Egypt my people, and Assyria the work of my hands, and Israel mine inheritance.

Thus the Great Pyramid of Gizeh represents the labors of many men, the key planners of which, as well as the workmen, were inspired by the same God who inspired the prophets of the Bible.

It is suggested in the 21st Chapter of Revelations that the so-called "New Jerusalem" will have the pyramidal form.

Out of ancient Babylon, around the year one A.D. according to the Gregorian calendar, came three wise men following a star which signified to them the recent birth of a future great king. The star led them to a manger in Bethlehem, Judea, and to the newborn child of Mary of Nazareth, Galilee, whose direct lineage went back to King David; she named the child Jesus according to divine commandment. The wise men believed confidently in the success of their journey, and left gifts for the newborn future king.

Now as we approach the end of the twentieth century, we find that the three wisdoms of science, philosophy, and religion as reflected and refracted through the prism of logic have each independently led to and pinpointed this very same Jesus as being the cornerstone of our Maker's creative activity and the embodiment of His infinite love and wisdom.

Jesus Christ is by no means a "stumbling block" only to the Israelites, who believe the Messiah is yet to come. The scientists and certain other scholars, too, cannot accept Him because they cannot bring themselves to believe in the existence of His Father, the Infinite Mind, as such a belief would involve the supernatural. The critical theologians cannot accept Him as God incarnate, as they cannot conceive how the Infinite Mind could have become incarnate. And the feebleminded stand incredulous because they cannot "shake hands with Him." (That would appear to solve it all, wouldn't it?)

Yet we have discovered good inductive evidence that the Infinite Mind not only created the Universe but that It is still actively functioning as the creator of living forms; that the Infinite Mind did become incarnate in His Son, Jesus Christ, and furthermore at the time of His first appearance on earth around 1 A.D., one could have shaken His hand. Finally, there is very substantial supporting evidence that He was actually the long-awaited Messiah, but that His Chosen People were not prepared for Him at His first appearance. However, Jesus Christ, the long-anticipated Messiah, specifically stated that He would return, at which time He will finally be recognized as the "Promised One." By that time also the "wine in the new bottles" will have had time to age.

XXXVI.

THE ANSWER TO THE PROBLEM OF MAN

What Meaningful Significance, if any, Does Existence Have for Man?

It has been determined by induction, deduction, intuition, and revelation that man is a free-choosing living personality within a law-abiding natural world. He is most definitely not a puppet, but a free-functioning "natural selector." However, as presently constituted, he unawaredly is "fenced" in, so to speak, by his self-oriented instincts.

While he enters this world with the basic fear of loss of support, he need not live or approach physical death with that fear in his soul, for he is not alone, for the eternal God is his refuge, and "underneath are the everlasting arms" (1)

Furthermore, it has been concluded that man is in fact the creation of the Living God in His image; that God is in fact man's Heavenly Father, all men being His children. In addition, they are citizens or potential citizens of His kingdom. (2)

Besides, strong inferential evidence points to the conclusion that the apparent purpose of God's creation of man in His own image is that man may attain or strive toward attaining His Maker's likeness and become co-workers in His kingdom, for it has been revealed that:

He creates that man also may create; (3)
He forgives man his sins as man forgives his fellow
  beings; (4)

He is merciful toward man that man may likewise be
   merciful; (5)
He first loved and served man that man may reciprocate
   by loving and serving both his Maker and his fellow-
   man; (6)
He gave man His Immortal Son that man, if he chooses
   to believe, may also become immortal. (7)

1. Deut. 33:27
2. Luke 11:13, Gen. 1:27, John 3:3
3. Gen. 1:28
4. Luke 11:4, Heb. 4:15-16, Isaiah 1:18
5. Luke 6:36
6. Mat. 5:44-45, John 13:34, John 4:34-38, Mat. 9:37-38
7. John 3:16

XXXVII.

MAN'S SUPREME CHOICE

The late Professor Pintner of Columbia University is quoted as having once stated that "a man wrapped up in himself makes a very small package." This appears to be an apt description, for a man so "wrapped up in himself" continually multiplies his fears and tightens the "strings" of his emotional being by ever-narrowing circular thinking about himself. In fact, such men constitute the majority of the constantly increasing source of income for psychiatrists and consulting psychologists. Pertinent to this conclusion the late Dr. Carl Jung, the renowned "depth" psychologist, concluded after years of consulting experience that his patients never became permanently cured until they had made some sort of reconciliation with the infinite. More recently Dr. Frankl, an internationally known psychiatrist and professor at the University of Vienna, has observed from his experience that the majority of man's mental troubles today arise from the fact that he has "broken with the sense of the reality of God." This is accompanied by a loss of the sense of the meaning of life. Because of this observation Dr. Frankl successfully practices what he calls Logo Therapy (God Therapy).

There are certain serious thinkers who will ask: "Why cannot Humanism fill this need?" The answer is that while Humanism offers a form of godliness, it is either unaware of or ignores the fact that it is man's instinctive nature that must first undergo a definite mutation. Phariseeism was likewise blind to the necessity of being "born-again," but whereas the ethical formalism of Phariseeism was fixed and absolute, that of Humanism is loose and variable because of its so-called democratic approach to its ethical codes.

Dr. Lin Yutang, the distinguished Chinese philosopher and the author of "The Importance of Living," (published in 1937), currently emphasizes this weakness of Humanism. At the time of writing "The Importance of Living," however, he was a "pagan" by his own admission; furthermore, he then advocated to his readers that they seek the meaning of life in man himself and not in religion. At that time he also stated that it was "presumptuous arrogance" for Christians to speak of God's attributes.

Yet after thirty years of "paganism" and at 62 years of age, he became a Christian, joining quietly the Madison Avenue Presbyterian Church in New York City. Sixteen months thereafter he wrote a spiritual autobiography in the Presbyterian Life Magazine. In this autobiography he states, among other things, that during his thirty years of paganism "my only religion was Humanism: the belief in human reason and in man's power, lifting himself by his own boot-straps, to better himself and make a better world." We shall go on to quote further from this autobiography:

> Below the surface of my life, a disquiet began to set in. It was born both of reflection and experience. I saw that the fruit of the humanistic age of enlightenment was an age of materialism. Man's increasing belief in himself as God did not seem to be making him more godlike. He was becoming more clever. But he had less and less of the sober, uplifting humility of one who has stood in the presence of God. Contemporary history seemed to indicate how dangerously near the savage state man may be even while he is more advanced technologically and materially.

He was finally convinced in his own thinking that "humanity is not, and never has been sufficient unto itself," and furthermore that "mankind cannot survive without religion."

The next question he raised: "Is there a satisfying religion for the modern, educated man?" He went about trying to answer this question by examining the great Oriental religions, and concluded that their answers were inadequate. Thereupon he stated that he turned to a study of "the awe-inspiring simplicity and beauty of the teachings of Jesus." . . . "I found that no one ever spoke like Jesus. He spoke of God the Father as one who knew Him and was identified with Him in the fullness of knowledge and love. It was astounding to learn that God, as Jesus revealed Him, is so different from what man had thought Him to be. There is a totally new order of love and compassion in Jesus' prayer from the cross, 'Father forgive them, for they know not what they do.' I saw why men have turned to Jesus, not merely in respect but in adoration. In Him, the message of love and gentleness and compassion becomes incarnate."

To other intellectual seekers "who would reach out to see the incomparable beauty and soul-charging power of the teachings of Christ" he warns that they must be prepared to "struggle against the claptrap that tends to obscure it. But it was Jesus himself who simplified for us the essence of Christianity and its adequacy above any other faith: Upon the two commandments, to love God and to love one's neighbor, 'hang all of the law and the prophets'." . . . "That Person and that gospel I have found sufficient. Nothing less than that Person and gospel can be sufficient for the world."

The giant dinosaurs of the Mesozoic Era did not inherit the earth, but the original timid little mammals eventually did. Likewise, the high and the mighty among homo sapiens of the present era will not inherit the earth, but the meek and the lowly before God the Creator most definitely will. "Fear not, little flock; for it is your Father's good pleasure to give you the kingdom," are Jesus' very words.

The Supreme Reality of Jesus, God's creative original and presently the first-born of a new creation, has been revealed to man by his Maker. Man's supreme choice inherent therein— whether to become a part of the "green branch" of God's creative activity—has come for man's embrace. Its acceptance or rejection involves by far the most intimate and significant decision man will ever be called upon to make. Each man as an individual personality may choose whether to live progressively creative toward the likeness of his Maker, or to regress to the ultimate extinction of his species as presently constituted.

— — — — —

Prove all things; hold fast that which is good. (I Thes. 5:21)

APPENDIX

AN OPEN QUESTION AND ANSWER PERIOD

Let us eavesdrop on an imaginary conversation currently in progress between a university student (whom we shall call Tom) and an old codger, a sandwich-man, both seated on a park bench just behind the General Public Library. The old man's advertising boards lean against the side of the bench beside him.

Tom: So you believe in God. Doesn't one almost have to be a little feebleminded, shall we say, to believe in the existence of an invisible personality—furthermore that such a personality created all of nature, even man himself?

S.M. No, I disagree with you there. A humanist clergyman once visited an institution for the feebleminded, and incidentally observed a hymn-singing service in which the inmates lustily took part. At the close of the service he accosted a boy, a near-idiot, and curiously asked him if he believed in God. The boy stared at him incredulously and finally challenged the clergyman—'Have you ever shaken hands with God?', and therewith ran off cackling. The clergyman thereupon concluded that a belief in God must be the product of mental activity.

Tom: Well then, who created the creator?

S.M. What you are asking in short is whether we should acknowledge the existence of our father whom we know even though we do not know his father. First, incidentally, it is gratifying to know we are, shall we say, legitimate. Furthermore, a God with no apparent limitations of either intelligence, love, or power may be confidently assumed to be 'The Ultimate Father.' It seems, therefore, that until evidence of such limitation appears, we need not be immediately concerned about the creator's father.

Tom: Do you believe the Bible was inspired by God?

S.M. Yes, I do.

Tom: What is the basis for your belief?

S.M. Because it appears to inspire all races of people—because it carries a consistent and coherent message, both from the standpoint of physical science and of psychology. The message checks with both the observation and experience of reality. Like our scientific theories it helps us not only to predict future events but to understand better the world of sense impressions. No other book deals with the reality of personality as does the Bible. It is brutally frank concerning human weaknesses. It records a consistently forward-moving account. Furthermore the fulfillment of the prophecies contained therein is a most convincing proof of its inspiration.

Tom: Do you believe that a whale swallowed Jonah?

S.M. I believe, Tom, that you will find no mention of a "whale" in the Book of Jonah. It does state that "God prepared a fish," to bring Jonah, His servant, back to the coast of Palestine to carry out an assigned task from which Jonah tried to escape. Yes, that I can believe. To Thomas Paine, of course, the Book of Jonah placed just too much strain on his credulity as reflected in his Age of Reason. However, let us consider that man at the present time has himself "prepared a fish" (an atomic submarine) which can carry a crew of a hundred men submerged under water all the way around the world and in the meanwhile in communicable connection with its home port. In view of this fact, then that it should be such a strain on his credulity to believe that God, his very creator, should have been capable of "preparing a fish" to carry one man (His servant Jonah) a few miles back to the coast of Palestine, is a shameful reflection of man's conceit on his God-given innate intelligence. In fairness to Thomas Paine, however, it should be mentioned that he knew nothing of atomic submarines.

Tom: Interesting, but still a lot of hokum. Heretofore you have indicated that the creator is quite concerned about the welfare of mankind, even to the individual man. Isn't that contention rather absurd and incredible?

S.M. Not as is the rationalization of the opposite.

Tom: If the creator is concerned about mankind, how explain the existence of so much suffering and evil in the world?

S.M. In the first place let me make clear that the creator himself states that he created evil.

Tom: On what do you base such a preposterous statement?

S.M. In Isaiah 45:7 we read: 'I form the light, and create darkness; I make peace, and create evil; I the Lord do all these things.'

Tom: Why, then, does he hold man responsible for sinning?

S.M. Because of man's own choosing. Man chose to become a free agent. Without the laws of nature this freedom would be meaningless.

Tom: Why?

S.M. Because he would have no basis for making free choices. For instance, if the law of gravitation were suspended from time to time, the decision to take a step may place a man out in the air rather than down the stairway that he desired and intended to go. On the other hand, if the law is consistently operative and a man slips on a banana peel and breaks an arm, the slip is his responsibility. He simply cannot have it both ways and remain a free agent. If man desires to be free, he must learn the laws of nature and abide by them, or pay the consequences.

Tom: Then it would appear that it is man who is responsible for evil.

S.M. But the Lord created natural and moral laws; and as Apostle Paul puts it, as applicable to moral laws only, 'the law is evil; it is our schoolmaster.' 'God is no respecter of persons.' His so-called natural laws apply to all—'it rains both on the just and unjust.' Incidentally, moral laws would appear to be laws revealed during a higher creative stage than the inorganic physical laws. Actually, they are all natural laws. Furthermore, ignorance is evil because it leads man to violate nature's laws blindly, and selfishness is evil because it leads man to violate nature's laws deliberately.

Tom: What proof can you give for the existence of God?

S.M. Is existence the proper word as regards God? For God is "being itself." The proof of God's being is the existence of Man, and man's confession to his own finitude.

Tom: Let's go on—What proofs have you that design exists in nature?

S.M. [He hesitated, and then said,] I presume you do not believe that man can create a culture.

Tom: Of course, he can; you can see it all around you.

S.M. Created out of chaos? Incidentally I take it that you do not consider yourself a part of nature?

Tom: What gave you that idea? Of course, I consider myself a part of nature!

S.M. Then do you consider yourself competent to judge the proof if it were presented to you?

Tom: Let's skip that one. Now tell me why your creator made such glaring faux pas in his creative work as, for example, his failure to give the poor giraffe a voice.

S.M. [Hesitating briefly and then asking:] How about involving that question in a bit of dream interpretation?

Tom: Okay, but make it a good one.

S.M. Thereupon S.M. recited the following dream: "There was once an agnostic intellectual who was certain he could have made a better job of creation than the creator, that is of course assuming it was a creative act. He continually spouted to his associates the many ways in which he could improve upon nature. One night he had a dream. In the dream a spirit-being approached him and said that the creator was aware of his confidence of being able to improve upon the creator's work, and welcomed his assistance. The spirit-being went on to add: 'The creator is quite willing to give you the opportunity but with one proviso—you must not countermand your decrees once made; in short, you must not regress.' 'I accept—Oh boy what I will do!' he gloated. First he established a retinue of 'yes-men,' for a mangod must first have service, and secondly he must brook no interference from his subjects. He of course condescendingly welcomed suggestions from his subjects on changes and improvements on the present status in the world. One afternoon he was reclining in his easy-chair sipping cocktails with his paramour, a beautiful opera singer, meanwhile being fanned by his loyal personal attendant Friday. He daily enjoyed watching the beautiful sunset. However, he became aware that a certain tree obstructed his view. A mangod should not have to make adjustments for a mere tree, he ruminated, and immediately ordered that the obstructing tree be taken down. As the summer progressed it was found necessary to cut down more and more trees—why should a mangod have to move to watch a sunset?

One day a heavy rainstorm created a flood in which many of his subjects were drowned, at the same time destroying many homes in the valley. The survivors suggested to mangod that he should do something about it. He thereupon decreed an amendment to the law of gravitation by which water would not run downhill during a rainstorm—it was just that simple. His subjects were thereby quite pacified. One night, however, during a persistent, heavy rain a fire went out of control in the city. He was awakened by a telephone call from the excited fire-chief who reported the fire completely out of control and that nothing could be done about it. 'Why can't you do something about it?' Mangod challengingly bellowed into the phone. 'Your recent amendment to the law of gravitation leaves us without any water pressure during a rainstorm,' the poor fire-chief tried to explain. 'Well, you don't expect me to think of everything, do you?' and slammed down the receiver.

One day his chief advisor reminded him that he had not yet done anything for the proverbial giraffe. 'Of course, I shall forthwith decree a voice for the giraffe.' A few days later he asked his advisor what his subjects thought about his accomplishment. They recognized a change all right but they weren't particularly impressed. 'What, do they expect, that I should give the giraffe the voice of an opera singer?' 'Say, that's a splendid idea! That would really impress everybody.' 'Very well, so be it,' and Mangod so decreed.

A few days later his paramour began moping around. 'What's wrong with my little Sweetie-Pie today?' 'Oh you Big Bad Man, you gave the giraffe the voice of an opera singer.' 'Well, aren't you proud of your great big Mangod for being able to do that?' 'No, I want you to take away the giraffe's voice,' she whimpered. 'I can't do that, Sweetie-Pie, except that I extinct the giraffe.' 'Then, extinct him!' she hysterically shouted. 'What's so terrible about my giving the giraffe a good voice!' 'Because now everybody says I sing like a giraffe,' breaking down and sobbing uncontrollably. 'Okay, Sweetie-Pie, the giraffe is forthwith extinct.'

As matters went from bad to worse, Mangod became progressively more irrational in his decrees. Eventually he had exterminated all his subjects, even his paramour who had become quite a nuisance. However, his personal attendant Friday was still with him. 'Tell me frankly, Friday, why have things gone so awry?' 'I don't know nuttin,' for Friday wasn't going to stick his neck out. Finally after being pressed by Mangod for a reply and being assured of his personal safety, Friday blurted out, 'You think you the only pebble on the beach—you is completely teched—you been flappen 'round like a rooster with his head cut off—my but you is bloody, just like Stalin, Hitler, and Mao Tse-tung.' Mangod cut his harangue short, and shouted, 'Friday, you are forthwith exterminated.' 'Thank the Good Lawd,' were Friday's parting words.

All was suddenly very quiet—very quiet indeed. It gradually dawned upon Mangod that he was completely alone, not a living soul but himself left. He started shouting but no response. 'I'm alone! I'm all alone!' he hysterically cried. Finally he fell exhausted face down on the ground and sobbed. Then he heard the soft, calm voice of the spirit-being, 'My dear man, you seem to be in trouble.' 'Trouble you say! I resign forthwith as Mangod. I want to go back to my old job on the fence—there at least I feel superior.' The spirit-being chuckled softly. 'What's so funny about that?' Mangod challenged. 'Why your statement just seemed to confirm Samuel Johnson's definition of a critic.' 'What was that?' Mangod curiously asked. So the spirit-being proceeded to quote:

Criticism is a study by which men grow important and formidable at very small expense. The power of invention has been conferred by nature upon few, and the labor of learning those sciences which may, by mere labor, be obtained is too great to be willingly endured; but every man can exert such judgment as he has upon the works of others; and he whom nature has made weak, and idleness keeps ignorant, may yet support his vanity by the name of a critic.

'However, all quotations aside, the choice is yours. Frankly, though, I believe your Maker would rather you developed your callouses on your hands and feet, and not imitate the regression of the ascidian.'

That is the dream, Tom, now I should like your interpretation of its significance.

Tom: It was very, very funny, excruciatingly funny!

S.M. Believe me it was not so intended. I really wanted to try out Dr. Einstein's idealized experimental technique in the realm of values and wisdom. You will recall how he had us riding up and down an idealized elevator to bring out a point in the law of gravitation which could not otherwise be illustrated or proven.

Tom: All I asked was, why did your creator not give the giraffe a voice! Are you sidestepping an answer?

S.M. Obviously I wouldn't know the answer, for I am, like you, just a product of his creation. Yet I could venture a guess. It would appear from observing nature that the creator very much likes individuality—and he necessarily cannot get individuality without variability—individual differences. Man, incidentally, is bored by similarity.

Tom: Now that's more like it. I can't for the life of me understand why you had to go into that long dream routine. Incidentally, I gather you haven't done much else but read the Bible—it might broaden your views to read some literature on atheism.

S.M. You are quite mistaken, Tom. In my early years in the city I was always intrigued by the street-corner espousers of atheism. At that time, as a naive country boy, I invariably came away from such discourses feeling quite stupid in entertaining a belief in God. And yet certain spiritual phenomena which I had both witnessed and experienced remained unexplained by these apparently reasonable expounders.

So I began reading the literature of the so-called Freethinkers, in fact I got on their mailing list for a period. I recall especially reading among others, Thomas Paine's contributions in the realm of 'freethinking.' I recall being disappointed that the author of the pamphlet 'Common Sense' should suggest that it was unfair to hold that anyone who had not actually witnessed the crucifixion of Jesus should be expected to hold such a belief. He seemed to infer that periodically Jesus should be crucified so that all people could witness it and so believe.

I also recall reading Ingersoll's works in which he discussed the weaknesses of the believer's case; whereupon he would begin very confidently presenting the case of the non-believer, saying in substance as I now recall it: 'Now let's start off on a firm foundation, the atom. There you have something real and tangible and unchangeable.' It amuses me now to think back that even then the atom had never been seen; and now, only its vapor trail in the Wilson cloud-chamber, or the more recent bubble chamber. Its existence then as now is simply within a scientific hypothesis, and furthermore the concept atom instead of being a stable physical unit, has now blown up in Ingersoll's face to reveal untold inner components, which components also are just concepts within a scientific theory.

One book of great value received from the Freethinkers was Kant's Critique of Pure Reason, but I was never successful in obtaining from them Kant's Critique of Practical Reason.

Finally I recall receiving a small book from them entitled 'An Atheist Manifesto.' The thought of that book reminds me of a cute little story I have since heard about a little monkey and an elephant. Have you heard it, Tom?

Tom: No, let's have it.

S.M. There was once a society of monkeys living adjacent to a jungle. Some of the monkeys would relate from time to time having heard that there was a gigantic animal in the jungle called the elephant who had a massive trunk. An eager self-assertive little monkey after hearing these stories and noticing the fear created in his group, pooh-poohed the idea and ridiculed those who believed the absurd tales. 'Don't give the stories a thought. Why worry,' flexing his little muscles, 'if there turns out to be such an animal, I'll tear him limb from limb.'

One day a group of frightened monkeys came running out of the jungle and shouted, 'Here comes the elephant—save us!' The startled litle monkey froze as he caught a glimpse of the elephant emerging from the jungle. Soon he began trembling violently and whimpered, 'I've been sick,' and thereupon 'high-tailed' it up the nearest tree, followed by his promised protectees.

Now getting back to the pamphlet 'An Atheist Manifesto,' let me quote from a portion of it, in fact the last page:

> Be brave enough to live and be brave enough to die, knowing that when the Grim Reaper comes, you did the best you could and that the world is better for your having lived.
> A God could do no more.
> I will stand between you and the hosts of heaven. I am not afraid.
> I will act as your attorney before the Bar of Judgment. I will assume all responsibility.
> My services are free.
> Put the blame on me.
> Break the chains of mental slavery to religious superstition.
> Arise and become a free and independent human being.
> Dignify yourself as a Man, and justify your living by being a Brother to All Mankind and a Citizen of the Universe.

The final paragraph we must agree is a real good blurb, except that it fails to jibe with an earlier paragraph which reads:

> The only duty you owe is to yourself and to your family.

And this paragraph would appear to be a rather poor foundation for the coming Great Society so called.

Well, that was the last atheistic literature that I have read. But, Tom, I must get back on the job. [Picking up his boards and adjusting them to his shoulders, he walked back to 42nd St.]
Tom: There goes a 'schizo' if there ever was one—or is he?

Other conversations between the two had subsequently ensued which had modified somewhat Tom's cocksure attitude. Finally one day Tom led off their discussion with the following query:

Tom: If the Christians are supposed to be such lovers of God and lovers of their fellow-men, how do you rationalize the killing of some six million Jews by a so-called Christian nation?

S.M. That to me is the sixty-four dollar question. It disturbed me considerably until I came up with an answer which partly made sense, at least to me.

Tom: Let's have it.

S.M. The answer is quite complex. First we must consider the unique mass psychology of the German people. From early school years on through graduation, the motto—"Deutschland Ueber Alles" had been drummed into the students. This served as a strong motivating force for intensive individual effort to excel. In psychological terminology, the patriotic sentiment became overpowering; the love of Deutschland became stronger and more real to them than the love of God. In his memoirs Konrad Adenauer confirms this conclusion in his statement: "For many decades the German people suffered from a wrong attitude to the State, to power, to the relationship between the individual and the State. They had made an idol of the State and set it upon an altar; the individual, his worth and his dignity had been sacrificed to this idol."

Their defeat in the first World War, which was their first attempt to dominate the world, aggravated a keen feeling of inferiority among the Germans. Then suddenly appeared a man named Hitler, with an even more intensive feeling of inferiority, but of a more intimate personal nature, and with a compensating feeling of future grandeur. He was a keen student of history and also of dynamic psychology from his own introspections. He was unencumbered with religious scruples, although it is said he had some Jewish blood in his background.

Hitler seized upon such grievances as the reported foreclosure of mortgages on German farms by Jewish bankers during the painful monetary inflation following World War I. With such grievances he held forth to the German people as their Fuehrer and suggested that the Jews were responsible for their present plight. He soon had an enthusiastic following, especially when he drummed into the Germans that they were pure Aryans, the Master Race. If they would eliminate the Jews and all the encumbrances of religious scruples, Germany would eventually dominate the entire world; the Master Race must have "lebensraum," he would scream.

There was a minority of Christians who placed the love of God and fellow-man over the love of "Deutschland Ueber Alles" and were promptly either sent to a concentration camp and shot or sent to prison.

But there is an even larger aspect which must not be overlooked. Theodor Herzl, the establisher of the Zionist movement, made an inspired prediction at the Zionist Congress in 1897, that within fifty years the State of Israel would come into being. In 1948, fifty-one years thereafter, the State of Israel did come into existence. Since it was established, its progress has been a miracle to behold. The majority of its present citizens came from the "North"; and, without the technological knowledge brought in by the European Jews, especially by those from Germany and Poland, as well as the monetary reparations paid to the State of Israel by the present German government, the miracle would have been an impossibility. Furthermore it is a reasonable conclusion that the German and Polish Jews would never have left Europe if it had not been for Hitler and his concentration camps and subsequent gas chambers.

Then did God's invisible hand have something to do with it? We naturally do not know, but we do know that the Book of Isaiah and that of Jeremiah prophesied that the Jews would be carried off into captivity to Babylon and would remain in captivity for seventy years; and furthermore that the Book of Isaiah, particularly the 13th Chapter, prophesied that the Babylonian power would be conquered and Babylon eventually wiped out; and that the Jews would be freed to return to Jerusalem to rebuild the temple and to freely worship God. Babylon was conquered by Cyrus of Persia, and the Jews freed after seventy years of captivity.

The Jews were instructed by God through his prophets Ezekiel and Daniel to flee immediately from Babylon upon their release and go directly to Palestine, their homeland. Only a small remnant did return, the remainder having established themselves as prosperous merchants in Babylon, for they had not been badly treated by the Babylonians. So,

Tom, you can see that the answer to your sixty-four-dollar question involves a rather complex and speculative answer.

Tom: Well, that was one way to get Christianity off the griddle, [smiling observed, and continued with his next question:] How do you justify war under Christianity?

S.M. That question would take a book to answer fully. However, I will venture a few basic thoughts that occur to me.

First, our Creator has apparently deemed it wise to give man freedom of choice under fixed laws, which laws he may choose either to obey or violate wilfully to attain selfish ends. God most definitely did not create puppets but wilful men. Now if man chooses to forfeit without resistance that God-given freedom to choose under law because of threats of a power group not under law, he deserves to lose that freedom.

In this connection the word "democracy" is shuttled around with two different connotations, one of which is unstated. In the normal sense democracy means basically the right to express oneself freely, or to remain silent, and to choose by secret ballot courses of action within the laws of a legally constituted government, but to abide by the will of the majority. The unstated meaning of the same word is the privilege of being freed from the burden of choice, accompanied with the further free privilege of being brainwashed; in other words, man may choose to submit to slavery under a power group.

"Liberation" is another word which requires clarification. 'Liberation' in the ordinary sense means being freed from civil oppression. The unstated definition, however, means to be freed from freedom. The minority power groups holding to the unstated connotation of both words are prone to incite aggression by infiltration and in the name of self-defense. Those holding to the original sense of the two words 'democracy' and 'liberation' have a disposition to mind their own business, except when either they or their neighbors are threatened with aggression. Aggression plus resistance results in war. If there were men who went about choking off the "freedom to breathe" among their fellow-man, the majority of men instinctively would resist the activity. However, to "choke off" the freedom of speech and the freedom of silence is something else again, the importance of which is too abstract for some men to grasp.

Now what choice should a Christian make—should he join the resisters? History reveals that the false Messiahs "chickened out" and chose being "liberated" in the unstated sense of the word, one of the more promising ones in fact abjectly changed his religion to save his own life. Christ, however, paid the price of choosing to function under the original and true meanings of the two words, and died on the cross, yet without having violated any of the established laws. Who else, we may ask, has done more to stiffen the backbone of mankind?

Tom: What is your reaction to the current phenomena of vociferous demonstrations now prevalent in the world at large, even on American college campuses?

S.M. My reaction is pretty much reflected in the cogent advice given us by a South Vietnamese student in this country, both to the shaven and the unshaven, namely—"Think—don't shout!" If we followed his advice, it would afford us all not only the opportunity of free speech but also to hear the thoughts of those in the opposite camp; thus all would have a better basis for drawing sound judgments and determining future actions.

Tom: You're in good form today, so here is another question. Doesn't this kingdom of God idea run counter to individualism?

S.M. That's a reasonable question. What you are really asking is, doesn't the subordination of our selfish instincts with that of the most encompassing instinct of all, the spirit of love and truth, result in loss of individuality? My answer based on empirical evidence, is 'No.' The effect appears to be the very reverse, for it permits the individuality more complete expression—a flowering-out so to speak. It certainly does away with the feeling of anguish and boredom of which the atheist existentialists constantly complain. Take, for instance, Jesus' apostles—did they lose their individuality? Far from it; their individuality was set free, especially from fear. Furthermore, the spirit of love and truth gives all mankind a unifying purpose and an infinite goal; it assures maintenance of its position on the continually growing "green branch" of God's creative activity.

Tom: This business about being 'born-again'—I'm like Nicodemus, I don't fathom the phenomenon. Can you cite an actual example?

S.M. [After a little hesitation, S.M. continued:] Yes, not too long ago I occupied a bed in a hospital ward next to a young man who had been brought in as a critical accident case. He had been struck down by an automobile while crossing at an intersection. I had noticed at visiting hours that in addition to his young wife and his parents, numerous individuals in Salvation Army uniforms regularly dropped in to see him. When he had sufficiently recovered, I curiously asked him whether he belonged to the Salvation Army. 'Yes I do, but my folks are members of a Protestant denomination.' 'How did you happen to join up with the Salvation Army?' 'It's a rather interesting story. At one time my brother and I went around with a tough gang who would engage in stealing cars and like activity. In other words, we were typical so-called juvenile delinquents. We gave our parents a lot of trouble and heartaches. One day I was tipped off that a man up the street gave free boxing instruction. It immediately interested me for I was of slender physical build and figured I could handle myself better with the gang if I learned something about boxing. It turned out that I became an eager regular attendant for boxing instruction. The instructor was good, not only as a boxing instructor but as a person as well, and I came to like the man. Occasionally at the close of a boxing session he would invite me and the other boys to attend a Salvation Army singing session. I was wary and always begged off. However, he never pressed me. One evening he again invited me and I again begged off. As I walked away I began having an uncomfortable feeling. Finally I stopped in my tracks; in fact I could not have gone farther if I had tried. To make a long story short I not only went to the meeting but came away as a "newborn creature"; for I had that very miraculous experience of what the Scriptures speak of as being "born-again." I cannot say that I felt any different, except that the old attraction for the gang had disappeared. One evening about a week thereafter, my brother came in and confided to me that he had smashed up my car in an accident. Ordinarily I would have "blown my top" and gone into a rage. Much to my surprise, and undoubtedly my brother's too, I did not react in the old pattern but took the incident in a matter-of-fact manner. I then knew that I was a different person inside.'

Tom: That's quite interesting, but of course that's only one

536

case, and one which psychologists could undoubtedly explain scientifically.

S.M. In psychological terminology yes, but not in fact. Do not overlook the fact that 'the prayers of a righteous man availeth much,' in this case in the person of the boxing instructor. (Resonance apparently is as necessary for the transfer of spiritual force as it is in the transference of physical energy.) To continue, the young man stated he subsequently got married, and now has a baby daughter. He also holds a good position; moreover, he is also an active volunteer worker with the Salvation Army. You, of course, appreciate that there are innumerable similar cases.

Tom: Yes, and also many 'backsliders.' How do you account for them?

S.M. First it should be kept in mind that individual and not general reasons apply here. When an individual experiences the 'new-birth' he does not necessarily surrender his R.I. nor his innate selfish tendencies, although they have lost their former driving force. He still remains responsible for his choices, if not more so because of his 'greater light.' We are 'judged by the light that is in us,' and what's more, we judge ourselves on that basis. True, there are many backsliders, but also many who again return to the 'fold.' In this connection I suggest that you re-read Jesus' parable of the sower of the seed (Mat. 13); there he explains why some 'backslide.' Incidentally, please note that Jesus uses the metaphor 'seed,' apparently implying tangible ideas specifically and not emotional appeals only. It should also be kept in mind that Jesus promised no easy going for his followers. He created no illusions but believed in instructing his disciples to face reality. He frankly pointed out to them that they must be prepared for the same opposition that he himself met up with. He did, however, assure them of ultimate victory. Darwin's principle of 'survival of the fittest' still applies. Significantly, however, the 'fittest' for the kingdom of God are those who possess a man's courage and the faith and teachable humility of a little child. Incidentally, the phenomenon of being 'born again' is actually the progressive creative technique used by the Creator all the way up the trunk of the so-called evolutionary tree. He used the prior highest form which he progressively modified up to man. And moreover it will be recalled that the prior anagenic form became extinct.

Tom: Incidentally, I picked up a paperback edition of Huxley's book "Religion Without Revelation." I've read it and have given his views some serious consideration. In fact, I believe evolutionary humanism would be easier for me to embrace.

S.M. Of course you appreciate, Tom, that humanism has had since the time of Confucius 600 B.C. to show what it can do, and so far has not given much promise as an effective solution of man's basic problem, which is his inherent instinctual nature. Humanism is not only lacking a motivating factor, but the form itself cannot be agreed upon. Confucius, the original founder, appreciated the need for the motivating factor, for he encouraged the 'worship of ancestors' when he himself did not believe in the 'hocus-pocus.' The various humanists have difficulty in getting together on its form, as each group has its own particular emphases. What the humanists appear to overlook or ignore is the necessity of a basic change in the instinctual nature of man.

Incidentally Humanism promises nothing for the individual's future but a 'dead-end street.' Keep in mind, in this connection, that the society of mankind as such has absolutely no significance apart from the significance and welfare of the individual man of which it is constituted. By the way, Huxley's chapter on 'Personalia' in that book left me with the suspicion that the Creator very much wanted to enlist Julian Huxley in the task of bridging the gap between science and religion, a task for which he was admirably fitted. However, his faith appeared to waver to go all the way. However, we should be most grateful to Professor Huxley for having gone as far as he did. Of course, certain analytic thinkers will say that biologists are really not scientists anyway, at least not pure scientists, because they delve occasionally in synthesis along with their analytic work. These thinkers give one the impression that they are averse to turning around occasionally from their analytic activities to devote a little time to synthesis for fear of seeing unity, which means facing up with the idea of a creator. For instance one such thinker is allergic to discussing the philosophic consequences resulting from the theory of the expanding universe. Why? Because it suggests a prior condensed state and hence a beginning of creation, and this idea suggests certain unpleasant metaphysical conclusions.

In defense of their apparent phobia some will assert that if they were to acknowledge the existence of God they would then be faced with the task of determining who God's father is. Yet those same individuals fail to get emotionally disturbed about Peano's "O" with his two assumptions that it is a number and furthermore that it is not the successor to any number.

So we thank God for evolutionary biologists, especially those who have called attention to the importance of a progressive forward movement.

By the way, Tom, what part of Huxley's book particularly appealed to you?

Tom: Well, [hesitating and then blurting out,] Well at least his thesis doesn't involve an implied covenant.

S.M. Oh, so that's the stumbling block. But bear in mind, Tom, you are presently considering 'the pearl of great price.' The decision is yours to make.

BIBLIOGRAPHY

Psychology

Woodworth, Robert S.: Contemporary Schools of Psychology. New York: The Ronald Press Company, 1931.

Heidbreder, Edna: Seven Psychologies. New York: D. Appleton-Century Co., Inc., 1933.

Woodworth, Robert S.: Psychology, A Study of Mental Life. New York: Henry Holt and Co., 1921.

Perrin and Klein: Psychology, Its Methods and Principles. New York: Henry Holt and Co., 1926.

Watson, John B.: Behaviorism. New York: W. W. Norton and Company, Inc., 1925.

Sidis, Boris: The Psychology of Suggestion. New York: D. Appleton and Company, 1911.

Warner-Jenkins-Warner: Introduction to Comparative Psychology. New York: The Ronald Press Co., 1934.

Stockard, Charles R.: The Physical Basis of Personality. New York: W. W. Norton & Co., Inc., 1931.

McDougall, William: Outline of Abnormal Psychology. New York: Charles Scribner's Sons, 1926.

Prince, Morton: Clinical and Experimental Studies in Personality, Revised and Enlarged by A. A. Roback. Cambridge, Mass.: Sci-Art Publishers, 1939.

Healy-Bronner-Bowers: The Structure and Meaning of Psychoanalysis. New York: Alfred A. Knopf, 1931.

Freud, Sigmund: The Basic Writings of Sigmund Freud, Translated and Edited by Dr. A. A. Brill, New York: The Modern Library, 1938.

541

Jung, Carl G.: The Integration of the Personality, Translated by Stanley M. Dell. New York: Farrar and Rinehart, Inc., 1939.

Adler, Alfred: The Practice and Theory of Individual Psychology, Translated by P. Radin. New York: Harcourt, Brace and Company, 1929.

Fisher, V. E.: An Introduction to Abnormal Psychology. New York: The Macmillan Company, 1929.

Sinclair, Upton: Mental Radio, with Introduction by William McDougall. New York: Albert & Charles Boni, 1930.

Köhler, Wolfgang: Gestalt Psychology. New York: The New American Library, 1964.

James, William: Psychology. New York: Henry Holt and Company, 1920.

James, William: Talks to Teachers on Psychology. New York: Dover Publications, Inc., 1962.

Garrett, Henry E.: Statistics in Psychology and Education. New York: Longmans, Green & Co., 1930.

Fisher, V. E., and Hanna, Jos. V.: The Dissatisfied Worker. New York: The Macmillan Company, 1931.

Hollingworth, H. L.: Vocational Psychology. New York: D. Appleton and Company, 1922.

Coghill, G. E.: Anatomy and the Problem of Behaviour. London: Cambridge at the University Press, 1929.

Kranefeldt, Dr. W. M.: Secret Ways of the Mind—A Survey of the Psychological Principles of Freud, Adler, and Jung (with an introduction by Dr. C. G. Jung and translated by Ralph M. Eaton). New York: Henry Holt & Co., 1932.

Philosophy

Weber, Alfred: History of Philosophy, New York: Charles Scribner's Sons, 1909.

Runes, Dagobert D.: Treasury of Philosophy. New York: Philosophical Library, 1955.

Russell, Bertrand: Human Knowledge, Its Scope and Limits. New York: Simon and Schuster, 1948.

Northrop, F. S. C.: The Logic of the Sciences and the Humanities. New York: Meridian Books, Inc., 1959.

Runes, Dagobert D.: Twentieth Century Philosophy. New York: Philosophical Library, 1947.

Ker, W. P.: The Dark Ages. The New American Library, New York, 1958.

Santillana, Giorgio de: The Age of Adventure, The Renaissance Philosophers. New York: The New American Library, 1956.

Hampshire, Stuart: The Age of Reason, The 17th Century Philosophers. New York: The New American Library, 1956.

Berlin, Isaiah: The Age of Enlightenment, The 18th Century Philosophers. New York: The New American Library, 1956.

Aiken, Henry D.: The Age of Ideology, The 19th Century Philosophers. New York: The New American Library, 1956.

White, Morton: The Age of Analysis, 20th Century Philosophers. New York: The New American Library, 1955.

Plato: Works of Plato. New York: Tudor Publishing Co., 1933. (The Republic and The Statesman)

Aristotle: On Man in the Universe, Metaphysics, Parts of Animals, Ethics, Politics, Poetics, Edited by Louise Ropes Loomis. New York: Walter J. Black, Inc., 1943.

Descartes, René: A Discourse on Method. New York: E. P. Dutton & Co., 1912.

Spinoza, Benedict de: Philosophy of Benedict de Spinoza. New York: Tudor Publishing Co., 1933.

Hume, David: An Enquiry Concerning Human Understanding. LaSalle, Ill.: The Open Court Publishing Co., 1949.

Kant, Immanuel: Critique of Pure Reason—(Revised Edition). New York: Willey Book Co.

Nietzsche, Friedrich: Thus Spake Zarathustra, Translated by Thomas Common. New York: Carlton House.

Voltaire: The Best Known Works of Voltaire. New York: Walter J. Black Co., 1927.

Bergson, Henri: The Creative Mind (Translated by Mabelle L. Andison). New York: The Philosophical Library, Inc., 1946.

Kierkegaard, S.: Fear and Trembling (Translated by Walter Lowrie). Garden City, New York: Doubleday & Co., Inc., 1954.

Sartre, Jean-Paul: Existentialism (Translated by Bernard Frechtman). New York: The Philosophical Library, 1947.

Whitehead, Alfred North: Adventures of Ideas. New York: The New American Library, 1955.

Whitehead, Alfred North: Science and the Modern World. New York: The New American Library, 1948.

Hayakawa, S. I.: Language in Thought and Action. New York: Harcourt, Brace and Co., 1949.

Noüy, Lecomte du: Human Destiny. New York: Longmans, Green and Co., 1947.

Maritain, Jacques: A Preface to Metaphysics. New York: The New American Library, 1962.

Whyte, Lancelot Law: The Next Development in Man. New York: The New American Library, 1962.

Huxley, Julian: Knowledge, Morality, & Destiny. New York: The New American Library, 1960.

Ware, James R.: Sayings of Mencius (A New Translation by James R. Ware). New York: The New American Library, 1960.

Croce, Benedetto: Aesthetic (3rd Revised Edition). New York: The Noonday Press, 1955.

Spaulding, Edward Gleason: A World of Chance. New York: The Macmillan Co., 1936.

Russell, Bertrand: Our Knowledge of the External World. New York: The New American Library, 1928.

Whitaker, Sir Edmund: Space and Spirit. Hinsdale, Ill.: Henry Regnery Co., 1948.

Russell, Bertrand: Human Society in Ethics and Politics. New York: The New American Library, 1962.

Price, As Recorded by Lucien: Dialogues of Alfred North Whitehead. New York: The New American Library, 1956.

Durant, Will: The Works of Schopenhauer (Abridged). New York, Garden City Publishing Co., Inc., 1928.

James, William: Pragmatism and Other Essays. New York: Washington Square Press, Inc., 1963.

Science

Dampier-Whetham, Wm. C. D.: A History of Science. New York: The Macmillan Co., 1929.

Linton, Ralph: The Tree of Culture. New York: Alfred A. Knopf, 1955.

Einstein, Albert, and Infield, Leopold: The Evolution of Physics. New York: Simon and Schuster, 1950.

Podolsky, Edward: The Thinking Machine. New York: The Beechhurst Press, 1947.

Dunlap, Knight: An Outline of Psychobiology. Baltimore: The Johns Hopkins Press, 1914.

Taylor, F. Sherwood: An Illustrated History of Science (Illustrated by A. R. Thomson). New York: Frederick A. Praeger, Inc., 1955.

Kahn, Fritz: Design of the Universe. New York: Crown Publishers, Inc., 1954.

Russell, Bertrand: The ABC of Relativity. New York: The New American Library, 1959. (Revised by F. Pirani)

Asimov, Isaac: Guide to the Physical Sciences. New York: Pocket Books, Inc., 1964.

Meyer, Jerome S.: The ABC of Physics. New York: Pyramid Publications, 1962.

Newman, James R.: What is Science? New York: Washington Square Press, Inc., 1962.

Barnett, Lincoln: The Universe and Dr. Einstein. New York: The New American Library, 1958.

Huxley, Julian: Evolution in Action. New York: The New American Library, 1957.

Gamov, George: One Two Three . . . Infinity. New York: The New American Library, 1957.

Thomson, J. Arthur: Riddles of Science. New York: Fawcett World Library, Revised 1958, by Bernard Jaffe.

Hegner, Robert W.: College Zoology. New York: The Macmillan Company, 1930.

Smith, Overton, Gilbert, Denniston, Bryan, Allen: A Textbook of General Botany. New York: The Macmillan Company, 1931.

Kendall, James: Smith's College Chemistry. New York: The Century Co., 1929.

Dull, Brooks, Metcalfe: Modern Chemistry (Revised Edition). New York: Henry Holt and Co., 1950.

Babcock and Clausen: Genetics in Relation to Agriculture. New York: McGraw-Hill Book Co., Inc., 1927.

Berrill, N. J.: You and the Universe. 1958: Dodd, Mead & Company, 1958.

Kinsey, Alfred C.: An Introduction to Biology. Philadelphia: J. B. Lippincott Company, 1926.

Moore, J. Howard: The Law of Biogenesis. Chicago: Charles H. Kerr & Company, 1914.

Montagu, Ashley: Human Heredity. New York: The New American Library, 1960.

Montagu, Ashley: Man: His First Million Years. New York: The New American Library, 1958.

Mead, Margaret: Cultural Patterns and Technical Change. New York: The New American Library, 1955.

Benedict, Ruth: Patterns of Culture. New York: The New American Library, 1948.

Kluckhohn, Clyde: Mirror for Man. New York: Fawcett World Library, 1959.

Langdon-Davies, John: On the Nature of Man. New York: The New American Library, 1961.

Warden, Carl J.: The Emergence of Human Culture. New York: The Macmillan Company, 1936.

Darwin, Charles: The Origin of Species by Means of Natural Selection. New York: The Macmillan Company, 1927.

Science Service: Atomic Bombing—How to Protect Yourself. New York: Wm. H. Wise & Co., Inc., 1950.

Religion

Smith, Huston: The Religions of Man. New York: The New American Library, 1959.

James, William: The Varieties of Religious Experience. New York: The New American Library, 1958.

Davies, A. Powell: The First Christian. New York: The New American Library, 1957.

Potter, Charles Francis: The Great Religious Leaders. New York: Washington Square Press, 1962.

Davies, A. Powell: The Ten Commandments. New York: The New American Library, 1956.

Huxley Julian: Religion Without Revelation. New York: The New American Library, 1957.

Paine, Thomas: The Age of Reason. New York: Thomas Paine Foundation, Inc., 1950.

Hill, W. Douglas P. (Translation and Commentary by): The Bhagavadgita. London: Geoffrey Cumberlege—Oxford University Press, 1927.

Swedenborg, Emanuel: Arcana Coelestia—The Heavenly Arcana, Vol. 1 New York: Swedenborg Foundation, Inc., 1949.

Watch Tower Bible & Tract Society: "Babylon the Great Has Fallen!" New York: Watchtower Bible and Tract Society of New York, Inc., 1963.

Edgar, Morton: The Great Pyramid and The Bible. Glasgow, Scotland.

Buber, Martin: Israel and the World. New York: Schocken Books, Inc., 1963. (Paperback edition).

Bickerman, Elias: From Ezra to the Last of the Maccabees. New York: Schocken Books, Inc., 1962 (Paperback).

McKelway, Alexander J.: The Systematic Theology of Paul Tillich. (A Review and Analysis). New York: Dell Publishing Co., Inc., 1966.

Loudy, Adlai: God's Eonian Purpose. Los Angeles, Calif.— Concordant Publishing Concern, 1929.

Rauschenbusch, Walter: The Social Principles of Jesus. New York: Association Press, 1927.

Roth, Cecil: History of the Jews. New York: Schocken Books, Inc., 1964.

Josephus, Flavius: The Jewish War and Other Selections from Flavius Josephus (Translated by H. St. J. Thackeray and Ralph Marcus—Edited and Abridged with an introduction by Moses I. Finley). New York: Washington Square Press, 1965.

Rowell, Earle Albert: Prophecy Speaks—Dissolving Doubts. Peekskill, N.Y.: Review and Herald Publishing Association, Washington, D.C., 1933.

Fischer, Louis: Gandhi—His Life and Message for the World. New York: The New American Library, 1954.

Sheen, Fulton J.: Lift Up Your Heart. New York: McGraw-Hill Book Co., Inc., 1953 (Permabook Edition).

Thomas à Kempis: Of the Imitation of Christ. New York: The New American Library, 1962.

Brengle, Commissioner S. L.: Helps to Holiness. London: Salvationist Publishing and Supplies, Ltd., 1948.

Gaer, Joseph: How the Great Religions Began. New York: The New American Library, 1956.

Ross and Hills: The Great Religions. New York: Fawcett World Library, 1959.

Peale, Norman Vincent: The Amazing Results of Positive Thinking. Fawcett Publications, Inc.—1959.

Frazer, Sir James George: The Golden Bough.

The Holy Bible, The Old and New Testaments—St. James Version, with Biblical Encyclopedia and Condensed Biblical Commentary, New York: The Publishers Guild, Inc.

INDEX

Leah, 309
Lebedew, 416
Lecky, Wm. E. H., 489
Leeuwenhoek, A. van, 85
Leibniz, Gottfried Wilhelm, 99, 101, 103, 111, 112, 116, 117, 134, 136, 172, 185, 414, 424
Leicester, 172
Lei Feng, 480
Lemaitre, Abbé Georges, 224, 226
Lémery, 84
Lenin (V. I. Ulianov), 239-242, 269, 277
Leo X, Pope, 80, 360
Leucippus, 47
Leverrier, 104
Lewis, 214
Leyden, 143
Liebig, Justus, 163, 166, 169, 177
Lindemann, 212
Linder, 199
Linnaeus, 107
Linton, Dr. Ralph, 33, 69, 422, 431, 498, 499, 507, 514
Lister, Lord, 168
Littré, Emil, 139
Lobatchevski, 180
Locke, John, 112-116, 121, 126, 133, 184, 424
Lockyer, Sir Norman, 158
Löffler, 168
Lorentz, 208, 216, 439
Louis XIV, 97
Ludwig, Karl, 166
Luke, 327-329, 331, 332, 337, 338, 340-346, 349-353, 355, 357, 358, 474, 475, 486, 493, 505
Lullus, 88
Luther, Martin, 360
Lyell, Sir Charles, 171, 173

McDougall, William, 16, 18, 203, 443
McLennan, 222
McTaggert, Prof., 236
Mach, Ernst, 99, 180, 181, 234, 242
Macquer, 84
Magellan, 80
Mahavira, Prince—See Vardhamana
Maimonides, 72
Majendie, 165
Malinowski, Bronislaw, 269

Malpighi, 85
Malthus, Thomas R., 173, 463
Manfredi, 84
Manson, 168
Manu, 280
Mao Tse-Tung, 480, 528
Maritain, Jacques, 228, 243
Mark, 327, 486
Marli, 143
Marsh, Adam, 77
Marx, Karl, 131, 228, 239-242, 269
Mary (Virgin), 328, 329, 355, 477, 496, 515
Mary Magdalene, 336, 355
Mathews, Dr. Albert P., 15
Matthew, Apostle, 327, 329, 330, 333, 334, 336, 353, 460, 486, 493, 510, 537
Matthias, 358
Maxwell, J. Clerk, 142, 151, 156, 159, 160, 178, 181, 208, 217, 386, 393, 396, 438, 439
Mayer, J. R., 152, 166, 383
Mayow, John, 85
Mayr, Ernst, 499
Meinong, Alexius, 236, 245, 246
Meitner, Fraulein, 210
Melissus (of Samos), 43
Melloni, 158
Mencius, 296
Mencken, H. L., 455
Mendel, Gregor J., 142, 175, 194-197
Mendeléeff, 146
Mettrie, Julien Offroy de la, 118
Meyer, Lother, 146
Michelson, 216, 393, 407
Mill, John Stuart, 139, 179, 180, 189, 234, 236, 482
Millikan, R. A., 208, 222
Millington, Sir Thomas, 106
Milne, E. A., 214, 222
Minkowski, 217
Mitscherlich, 163
Moleschott, 182
Mondino, 84
Mohl, Hugo von, 166
Montagu, Ashley, 276
Moore, George Edward, 228, 234-236, 238
Morgan, Lloyd, 10, 202
Morgan, T. H., 194

Spaulding, Edward G., 430
Spearman, Charles E., 257
Spee, Father, 95
Spencer, Herbert, 172, 175, 180, 191
Speusippus, 53
Spinoza, Baruch (Benedict), 43, 73, 89, 110-111, 125, 126, 136, 185, 366, 424
Spitama, Porushasp, 300
Spitama, Zarathustra, 299
Sreyama, King, 289
Stahl, G. E., 105, 108
Stalin, 480, 528
Starling, 200
Stas, 146
Stefan, 159
Steinach, 201
Stensen, Niels, 85, 171
Stevinus of Bruges, 87
Stoff, 182
Stokes, Sir George G., 157
Stoney, Johnstone, 208
Susanna, 336
Susruta, 40
Sylvester II, Pope, 72
Sylvius, Franciscus—See Francois Dubois

Tacitus, 63
Telesio, 88
Terah, 304, 305, 323
Thales, 41, 423
Theaetetus, 52
Thénard, 163
Theodorus, 42
Theophilus, 327, 357
Thomas, Apostle (Didymus), 356, 357
Theophrastus, 55
Thompson, G. P., 215, 414
Thomson, Sir J. J., 178, 207-209, 213, 388, 439
Thomson, William (Lord Kelvin), 153, 155, 156, 181, 182
Thoreau, Henry David, 292
Thorpe, Sir Ed., 105, 446
Titus, 71, 322
Toland, John, 117, 118
Torricelli, 94
Toscanelli, Paolo, 81
Townsend, 207

Ts'in Shih Hwang-ti (Emperor Ts'in), 297
Tylor, Dr. E. B., 189

Uexküll, 204
Uriah, 468
Ussher, Archbishop, 188

Valentine, Basil, 83
Van Allen, 409
Vardhamana, Nataputta (Mahavira), 281, 288, 289, 290, 451
Vergil, 169
Vesalius, Andreas, 84
Vespucci, Amerigo, 81
Vincent of Beauvais, 75
Vinogradsky, 169
Vincï, Leonardo da, 60, 81, 171
Virchow, Rudolf, 166
Vishnu, 280
Vishtaspa, King, 302
Vitruvius, 63
Vögt, 108, 182, 185, 395
Volta, Alessandro, 147, 148
Voltaire, 103, 105, 109, 116, 177
Vries, de, 174, 175, 193-195

Waage, 160
Wagner, Dr. Rudolph, 12
Wallace, Alfred R., 2, 3, 172, 173, 176
Waals, van der, 154
Ward, James, 190
Warden, Carl J., 268, 365
Waterston, J. J., 153
Watson, J. B., 202, 203
Watt, James, 142
Weber, Prof. Alfred, 37
Weber, E. F., 165
Weber, E. H., 165, 184
Weber, W. E., 152
Weisman, August, 175, 177
Wells, H. G., 481
Wenzel, C. F., 160
Wheatstone, Sir Charles, 184
Whewell, 179, 180
Whitehead, Alfred North, 53, 142, 228, 235, 236, 244, 248-250, 277, 378, 380, 390, 399, 404, 424, 513

Whittaker, Edmund, 220, 373, 374
Wilforth, 169
Wilhelmy, 160
William of Auvergne, 75
William of Champeaux, 74
William of Occam, 78
Williamson, A. W., 160, 164
Wilson, C. T. R., 207, 211, 530
Wislicenus, 163
Wittgenstein, Ludwig, 228, 234, 235, 238, 246
Wöhler, Friedrich, 163
Wolff, Casper F., 165
Wolff, Christian, 112
Wollaston, 148, 157
Woodward, John, 171
Woodworth, Dr. Robert S., 203, 257, 512
Wordsworth, Wm., 177, 292

Wren, 98
Wundt, Wilhelm, 184

Xenophanes, 42, 43, 423

Young, Prof., J. Z., 13
Young, Thomas, 150, 184, 386, 393, 405
Yutang, Dr. Lin, 520

Zaccheus, 346
Zacharias, 328-330, 341, 474
Zanthippe, 121
Zechariah, 348, 493
Zeeman, 208
Zeno, 43, 56, 57
Zipporah, 311
Zoroaster, 299, 300, 302, 303, 452
Zosimos, 61
Zsigmondy, 198